Mike Holt's Illustrated Guide to

UNDERSTANDING
ELECTRICAL THEORY
For NEC® Applications

Mike Holt Enterprises
MikeHolt.com • 888.NEC.CODE (632.2633)

NOTICE TO THE READER

Mike Holt's Illustrated Guide to Understanding Electrical Theory
First Printing: June 2022

Technical Illustrator: Mike Culbreath
Cover Design: Bryan Burch
Layout Design and Typesetting: Cathleen Kwas

COPYRIGHT © 2022 Charles Michael Holt
ISBN 978-1-950431-68-7

Produced and Printed in the USA

For more information, call 888.NEC.CODE (632.2633), or e-mail Info@MikeHolt.com.

This logo is a registered trademark of Mike Holt Enterprises, Inc.

If you are an instructor and would like to request an examination copy of this or other Mike Holt Publications:

Call: 888.NEC.CODE (632.2633) • Fax: 352.360.0983
E-mail: Training@MikeHolt.com • Visit: www.MikeHolt.com/Instructors

You can download a sample PDF of all our publications by visiting www.MikeHolt.com

I dedicate this book to the
Lord Jesus Christ, *my mentor and teacher.*
Proverbs 16:3

We Care...

Since the day I started my business over 40 years ago, my team and I have been working hard to produce products that get results and to help individuals learn how to be successful. I have built my business on the idea that customers come first and everyone on my team will do everything they possibly can to help you succeed. I want you to know that we value you, and are honored that you have chosen us to be your partner in training.

I believe that you are the future of this industry and that it is you who will make the difference in years to come. My goal is to share with you everything that I know and to encourage you to pursue your education on a continuous basis. I hope that not only will you learn theory, Code, calculations, or how to pass an exam, but that in the process, you will become the expert in the field and the person others know to trust.

We genuinely care about you and are dedicated to providing quality electrical training that will help you take your skills to the next level. Thanks for choosing us for electrical training.

God bless and much success,

Mike Holt

"...as for me and my house, we will serve the Lord." [Joshua 24:15]

TABLE OF CONTENTS

ABOUT THIS TEXTBOOK

Mike Holt's Illustrated Guide to Understanding Electrical Theory for NEC® Applications

For over 140 years, electricians have been installing electrical wiring in buildings to deliver power for convenience, safety, and productivity. Technology has changed a lot since Edison, Brush, and Westinghouse started installing lighting in the 19th century. Wiring systems have become more complex and every aspect of our daily life requires power to be accessible and reliable.

In the business of progress some electricians may have lost sight of the fundamental concepts that make the electrical equipment we use work. Recognizing a need to return to the basics, this book will take you on a journey that begins with the physics behind how electricity works all the way through topics and concepts that are relevant to everyone working in the electrical industry.

Whether you're a first-year apprentice still struggling to understand the difference between a volt or ampere, or a veteran journeyman trying to sharpen your troubleshooting skills, this book has something for you. Once you know the principles behind how electricity works, you will be ready to correctly apply the rules in the *National Electrical Code®* to the work you do every day. Many people in the trade don't have the information they need to be successful; it's a mix of math, science, mechanics, the *National Electrical Code*, problem solving, and electrical safety that are all required to complete a successful installation.

The installation practices of the electrical industry are controlled by the *National Electrical Code* so that people are protected from the hazards that arise from the use of electricity. The goal of this book is to bridge the gap between science, math, mechanics and *Code* to allow you to understand what you see and hear and also to read, understand and apply the *National Electrical Code* in the situations you encounter each day.

The writing style of this textbook, as with all of Mike Holt's products, is informative, practical, easy to read, and applicable for today's electrical professional. Also, just like all of Mike's textbooks, it contains hundreds of detailed graphics that support difficult concepts, facilitate

understanding, and help in applying those concepts to real-world situations. To get the most out of this book you should answer the questions at the end of each Chapter.

The Scope of This Textbook

The topics in this textbook will help you understand what electricity is, how it's produced and how it's used. You'll learn to perform basic electrical calculations necessary for everyday work, what those calculations tell you about how electricity flows in a circuit, and why it's always trying to return to its source.

This textbook explains why blinking lights, buzzing relays, hot wires and tripping breakers, all have one thing in common—they are the visible result of science and some basic math applied to an installation. If you don't understand how and why these things are happening, you're at a big disadvantage when it comes to troubleshooting and you may unintentionally place yourself or someone else in danger of injury or possibly even death. This makes it important for every electrician to learn the fundamentals of electricity to take themselves from being an installer who doesn't understand what's happening, to an electrician who can understand even the most complex situations.

In addition to the theory, *Code* topics will be introduced along the way, so that you understand why following *Codes* and standards is so important and when to apply different rules. For any references to the *National Electrical Code*, always compare what's being explained in this textbook to what the *Code* book says. This textbook is to be used along with the *NEC®*, and not as a replacement for it.

This textbook, *Mike Holt's Illustrated Guide to Understanding Electrical Theory for NEC Applications* teaches students what they need to know about how electricity behaves. Starting from basic scientific principles, it explains the following:

▶ Basics of matter and the origin of modern electricity

▶ How electricity is made

- Circuit types
- Electrical formulas and basic electrical math
- Magnetism and electromagnetism
- Practical applications of electricity (wiring systems and equipment)
- Motors, generators, and transformers
- Grounding and bonding
- How science and math apply to the *National Electrical Code* rules
- Electrical Safety

How to Use This Textbook

Each chapter of this textbook includes an introduction to the units in that chapter so you'll know what will be covered. There are also unit-based questions at the end of each chapter and a final exam.

State-of-the-art graphics illustrate the concept being taught and, where relevant, units include examples, calculations, and formulas. Author's Comments, provide additional information to help you understand the content.

To get the most out of this textbook you should answer the review questions at the end of each chapter. If you have difficulty with a question, go back in the text and reread the material to make sure you understand the topic.

As you read through this textbook, allow yourself sufficient time to review the text along with the outstanding graphics and examples, to give yourself the opportunity for a deeper understanding of electrical theory.

This is a textbook about basic electrical theory. Although it provides an introduction to the *National Electrical Code (NEC)* rules for using electricity safely, it is not a replacement for the *Code*. So be sure to have a copy of the most current *NEC* handy. Two other Mike Holt publications that explain *Code* rules in much more detail are:

- *Understanding the National Electrical Code, Volume 1 (Articles 90-480)*
- *Understanding the National Electrical Code, Volume 2 (Articles 500-820)*

Watch Videos That Accompany This Textbook

Mike, along with an expert panel, recorded accompanying videos for this *Understanding Electrical Theory for NEC Applications* book. These videos contain explanations and additional commentary that expand the topics covered in this textbook. Watching these videos will complete your learning experience.

 To watch a few video clips, scan this **QR Code** with a smartphone app or visit www.MikeHolt.com/THvideos for a sample selection. To get the complete video library that accompanies this book, call 888.632.2633 and let them know you want to add the videos.

Technical Questions

As you progress through this textbook, you might find that you don't understand every explanation, example, calculation or comment. If you find some topics difficult to understand, they are discussed in detail on the videos that correlate to this book. You may also find it helpful to discuss your questions with instructors, co-workers, other students or your supervisor—they might have a perspective that will help you understand more clearly. Don't become frustrated, and don't get down on yourself. If you have additional questions that aren't covered in this material, visit www.MikeHolt.com/forum, and post your question on the *Code* Forum for help.

Textbook Errors and Corrections

We're committed to providing you with the finest product with the fewest errors and take great care to ensure our textbooks are correct. But we're realistic and know that errors might be found after printing. If you believe that there's an error of any kind (typographical, grammatical, technical, etc.) in this textbook or in the Answer Key, send an e-mail that includes the textbook title, page number, and any other pertinent information to corrections@MikeHolt.com.

Key Features

The layout and design of this textbook incorporate special features and symbols that were designed for Mike Holt textbooks to help you easily navigate through the material, and to enhance your understanding of the content. *Note: Not all features may be included in this textbook.*

Formulas

$$P = I \times E$$

Formulas are easily identifiable in green text on a gray bar.

Caution, Warning, and Danger Icons

These icons highlight areas of concern.

CAUTION: An explanation of possible damage to property or equipment.

WARNING: An explanation of possible severe property damage or personal injury.

DANGER: An explanation of possible severe injury or death.

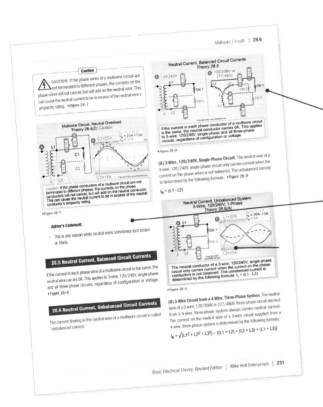

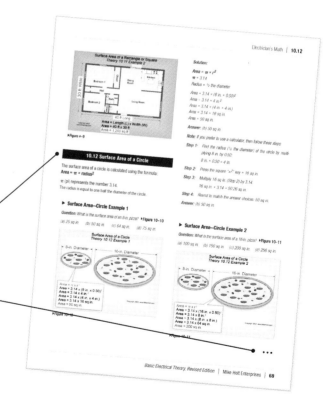

Full-Color, Detailed Educational Graphics. Industry-leading graphics help you visualize the technical topics and sometimes complex language of the *Code*, and illustrate the rule in real-world application(s). This is a great aid to reinforce learning.

Author's Comments. These comments provide additional information to help you understand the context.

Topic Headers. The topic being taught is identified with a chapter color bar and white text.

Examples. These practical application questions and answers are contained in framed yellow boxes. If you see an ellipsis (...) at the bottom of the example, it is continued on the following page.

ADDITIONAL PRODUCTS TO HELP YOU LEARN

Understanding *Electrical Theory* Videos

One of the best ways to get the most out of this textbook is to use it in conjunction with the corresponding videos. Mike Holt's videos provide a 360° view of each topic with specialized commentary from Mike and his panel of industry experts. Whether you're a visual or an auditory learner, watching the videos will enhance your knowledge and understanding, and provide additional in-depth commentary on each topic.

If you're Interested in adding the videos that accompany this textbook, call our office at 888.632.2633 or e-mail info@MikeHolt.com.

Understanding the *NEC* Complete Training Library

When you really need to understand the *National Electrical Code*, there's no better way to learn it than with Mike's *NEC* Complete Training Library. It takes you step-by-step through the *NEC*, in *Code* order with detailed illustrations, great practice questions, and in-depth video analysis.

▶ **Understanding the National Electrical Code—Volume 1** textbook and videos

▶ **Understanding the National Electrical Code—Volume 2** textbook and videos

▶ **Bonding and Grounding** textbook and videos

▶ **Understanding the National Electrical Code Workbook**, Articles 90-480

▶ Plus, digital versions of the textbooks

Electrical Calculations Video Program

Understanding how to solve electrical calculations specified in the *National Electrical Code* is essential for every electrical professional. This program is a complete system on what you need to know to correctly work out electrical calculations in the field. The textbook contains clear, easy-to-understand graphics and hundreds of examples and solutions that explain the step-by-step process of mastering calculations. The detailed videos capture Mike and his team giving an in-depth view of the application of these calculations in real world situations. The practice questions in the book let you apply that learning immediately to sample problems.

▶ *Electrical Exam Preparation* textbook

Videos on the following topics:

▶ *Raceway and Box Calculations*

▶ *Conductor Sizing and Protection Calculations*

▶ *Motor, Air-Conditioning and Transformer Calculations*

▶ *Voltage-Drop Calculations*

▶ *Dwelling Unit Calculations*

▶ *Multifamily Dwelling Calculations*

▶ *Commercial Calculations*

▶ Plus, a digital version of the textbook

To order visit www.MikeHolt.com/products, or call 888.632.2633.

Motor Controls Video Program

Why do you need to understand motor controls? Understanding how electricity flows in a motor control circuit is the key to understanding all types of switching, from lighting contacts to complex motor control centers for process equipment.

This textbook explains how to read and understand basic motor control schematics. It will help you understand the equipment represented by the symbols in the schematics, and how motor controls are used in practical applications. It's important to note that while the *Code* has little to do with how a motor control circuit runs, it contains many requirements for the disconnecting means, controllers, wiring methods used to install the control wiring, the installation of equipment, enclosures, and the overcurrent protection for the conductors, and the equipment being installed.

You'll learn:

▸ Principles of motor controls, definitions, abbreviations and drawing symbols

▸ Basic concepts, components and schematics of motor control circuits, and for reversing motor control circuits

▸ Control schemes involving more than one motor

This program includes:

▸ *Motor Controls* textbook

▸ *Motor Controls* videos

▸ Plus, a digital version of the textbook

Business Success Program

It's time to take your business skills to the next level. Whether you have recently passed an exam, recently opened a business or are just looking to understand the electrical business from a different vantage point, Mike's Business Success Program can help you in the following areas:

Estimating. You will understand estimating and make sure that all your jobs are profitable, with this step-by-step estimating training program.

Business Management. Part motivation, part business wisdom, this module will help you get where you want to go faster.

Leadership. This program distills Mike's knowledge of running a successful business for over 40 years into the primary building blocks of being a leader.

This program includes:

▸ *Leadership Skills* textbook

▸ *Business Management* workbook and videos

▸ *Estimating* textbook and videos

▸ Plus, digital versions of the textbooks

To order visit www.MikeHolt.com/products, or call 888.632.2633.

Notes

CHAPTER 1

ELECTRICAL FUNDAMENTALS

Chapter 1—Electrical Fundamentals

Unit 1—Atomic Structure

To understand electricity, you must first understand the physics that apply to electricity. The foundation of electricity begins with the structure of an atom which includes protons, neutrons, and electrons and how they interact with each other. In this unit you will learn:

▶ the atomic structure of an atom

▶ the law of electrical charges

▶ about static charge and static electricity

▶ what lightning is and how lightning protection works

Unit 2—Electron Theory and Chemical Bonding

Once atomic structure is understood, applying the concepts of electron theory and chemical bonding is next. In this unit you will learn:

▶ how the negative charge of electron movement participates in the creation of electricity

▶ the differences between conductors, semiconductors, and insulators

▶ what chemical bonding is and how it can change the electrical characteristic of an atom

Unit 3—Electrical Circuits and Power Sources

A power source must provide the energy necessary for electrons to move through a closed-loop path known as an "electrical circuit." In this unit you will learn:

▶ what an electrical circuit is

▶ what components make up an electrical circuit

▶ the two theories of electron current flow

▶ the different types of power sources that force electrons to move

• • •

Unit 4—The Electrical System

The electrical system typically begins at the utility generating plant. Knowing how electricity gets from there to a building provides a better sense of "the big picture." In this unit you will learn:

▸ how electricity is generated at the utility generating plant

▸ about step-up and step-down substation transmission voltages

▸ how electricity goes from utility distribution transformers to a customer's premises

ATOMIC STRUCTURE

1.1 Introduction

To understand electricity, you must first understand the physics that apply to electricity. The foundation of electricity begins with the structure of an atom which includes protons, neutrons, and electrons and how they interact with each other. In this unit you will learn:

▶ the atomic structure of an atom

▶ the law of electrical charges

▶ about static charge and static electricity

▶ what lightning is and how lightning protection works

1.2 Atomic Theory

An atom contains three types of subatomic particles: protons, neutrons, and electrons. The center of an atom is called the "nucleus" and it contains protons and neutrons. Electrons orbit around the nucleus of an atom. ▶Figure 1–1

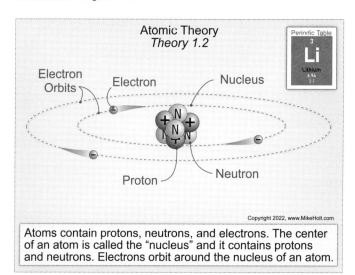

Atomic Theory
Theory 1.2

Atoms contain protons, neutrons, and electrons. The center of an atom is called the "nucleus" and it contains protons and neutrons. Electrons orbit around the nucleus of an atom.

▶Figure 1–1

(A) Protons. Protons have a positive charge with lines of force going straight out in all directions. ▶Figure 1–2

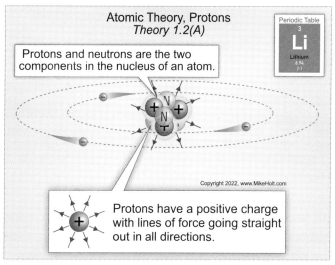

Atomic Theory, Protons
Theory 1.2(A)

Protons and neutrons are the two components in the nucleus of an atom.

Protons have a positive charge with lines of force going straight out in all directions.

▶Figure 1–2

(B) Neutrons. Neutrons have no charge and therefore no lines of force. ▶Figure 1–3

(C) Electrons. Electrons have a negative charge with lines of force going inward in all directions. Electrons are smaller than protons or neutrons and are about 1,800 times lighter. Electrons actively participate in the transfer of energy. ▶Figure 1–4

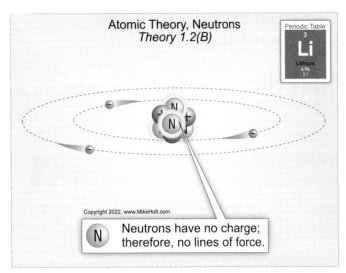

▶Figure 1–3

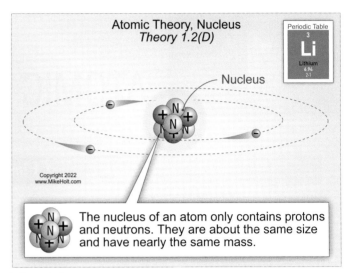

▶Figure 1–5

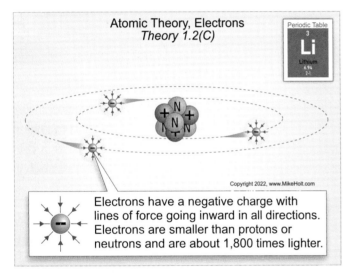

▶Figure 1–4

(D) Nucleus. The nucleus of an atom only contains protons and neutrons. They are about the same size, have nearly the same mass, and remain in the center of an atom. ▶Figure 1–5

1.3 Electrostatic Field

Subatomic particles that attract or repel other subatomic particles follow Coulomb's Law which states that, "Particles with like electrostatic charges repel each other and particles with unlike electrostatic charges attract each other."

The negative charges of electrons repel the negative charges of electrons; the positive charges of protons repel the positive charges of protons; while the negative charges of electrons and the positive charges of protons attract each other. ▶Figure 1–6, ▶Figure 1–7, and ▶Figure 1–8

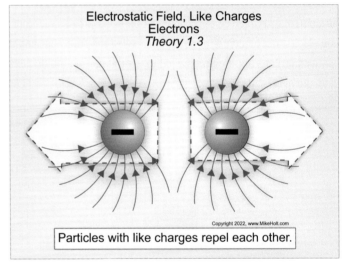

▶Figure 1–6

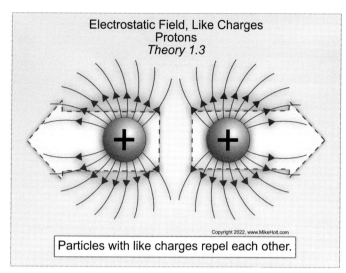

Electrostatic Field, Like Charges
Protons
Theory 1.3

Copyright 2022, www.MikeHolt.com

Particles with like charges repel each other.

▶Figure 1–7

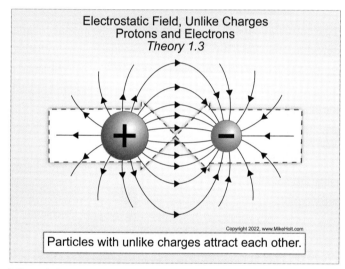

Electrostatic Field, Unlike Charges
Protons and Electrons
Theory 1.3

Copyright 2022, www.MikeHolt.com

Particles with unlike charges attract each other.

▶Figure 1–8

1.4 Atomic Charge of an Atom

The atomic electrostatic charge of an atom is either balanced, negative, or positive depending on the number of electrons compared to the number of protons.

(A) Balanced Atomic Charge. When an atom's charge is balanced, it means there are an equal number of positive and negative charges within the atom. Under this balanced atomic charge condition, the number of electrons is equal to the number of protons. ▶Figure 1–9

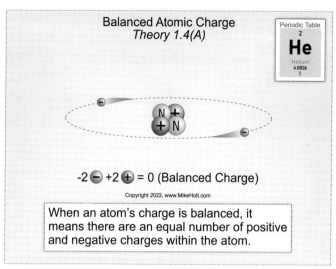

Balanced Atomic Charge
Theory 1.4(A)

Periodic Table
2
He
Helium
4.0026
2

-2 ⊖ +2 ⊕ = 0 (Balanced Charge)

Copyright 2022, www.MikeHolt.com

When an atom's charge is balanced, it means there are an equal number of positive and negative charges within the atom.

▶Figure 1–9

(B) Negative Atomic Charge. An atom that contains more electrons than protons has a negative charge. This happens when an atom gains an extra electron(s) in its electron cloud. ▶Figure 1–10

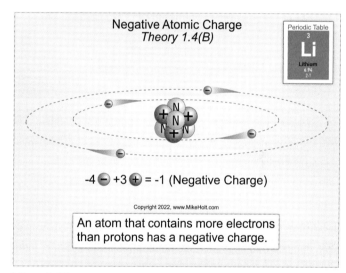

Negative Atomic Charge
Theory 1.4(B)

Periodic Table
3
Li
Lithium
6.94
2-1

-4 ⊖ +3 ⊕ = -1 (Negative Charge)

Copyright 2022, www.MikeHolt.com

An atom that contains more electrons than protons has a negative charge.

▶Figure 1–10

(C) Positive Atomic Charge. An atom that contains more protons than electrons has a positive charge. This happens when an atom loses an electron(s) from its electron cloud. ▶Figure 1–11

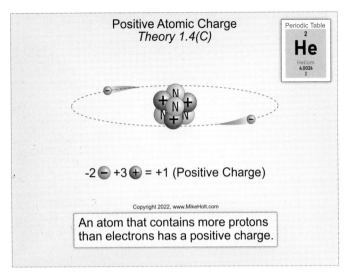

▶Figure 1–11

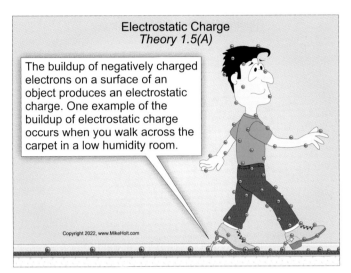

▶Figure 1–12

Author's Comment:

▶ There are a few "atomic models" that represent atomic structures; for simplicity, this material uses Bohr's model showing the electrons, protons, and neutrons.

1.5 Electrostatic Charge and Discharge

(A) Electrostatic Charge. Electrostatic charge is a condition that exists when there is an excess of, or a deficiency of, electrons between objects that have been separated. When unlike materials are in contact with each other, electrons from one material move to the surface of the other, but the protons remain on the original surface. When the objects are quickly separated, both materials display a charge because one material has an excess of electrons (negative charge), while the other has fewer electrons (positive charge).

The buildup of negatively charged electrons on a surface of an object produces an electrostatic charge. One example of this is the electrostatic charge that builds up when you walk across the carpet in a room with low humidity. ▶Figure 1–12

(B) Electrostatic Discharge. The buildup of an electrostatic charge can be so large that it can discharge to a nearby positively charged object. The human body in a low humidity area may experience a dangerous static discharge of thousands of volts. ▶Figure 1–13

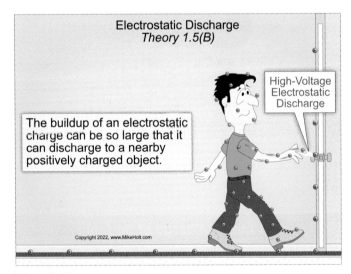

▶Figure 1–13

Danger

An electrostatic discharge can result in:

▶ ignition of flammable or explosive liquids, gases, dusts, or fibers ▶Figure 1–14

▶ damage to sensitive electronic equipment

▶ loss of electronically stored data

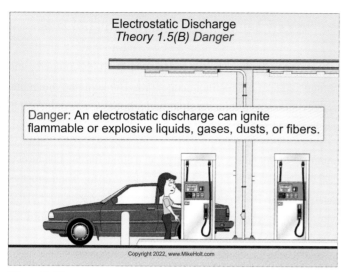

▶Figure 1–14

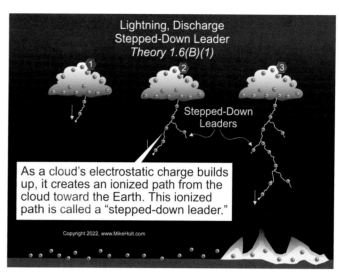

▶Figure 1–16

1.6 Lightning

(A) Electrostatic Charge. Lightning is the discharging of high-voltage cells of electrostatic charge within clouds to, and from, the Earth and sometimes to space. The electrostatic charge in a cloud is the result of friction caused by air movement within the cloud. ▶Figure 1–15

(2) Step-Up Streamer. At the same time the stepped-down leader originates, a similar ionized path called a "stepped-up streamer" rises from the Earth or other positively charged object. When the ionized path of the stepped leader and streamer connect, an electrostatic discharge or lightning strike occurs. ▶Figure 1–17

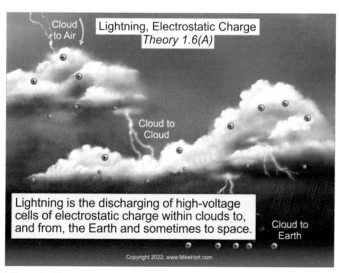

▶Figure 1–15

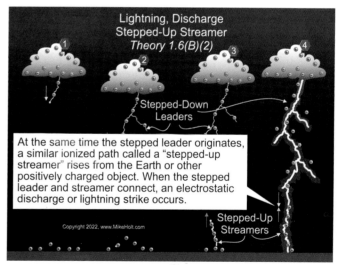

▶Figure 1–17

(3) Electrostatic Discharge. An electrostatic discharge (lightning strike) neutralizes the positive and negative electrostatic charges between the stepped-down leader and stepped-up streamer. ▶Figure 1–18

(B) Discharge. Negative electrostatic charges in clouds are attracted to positive electrostatic charges in other clouds, the Earth, or space.

(1) Step-Down Leader. As a cloud's electrostatic charge builds up, it creates an ionized path from the cloud toward the Earth; this ionized path is called a "stepped-down leader." ▶Figure 1–16

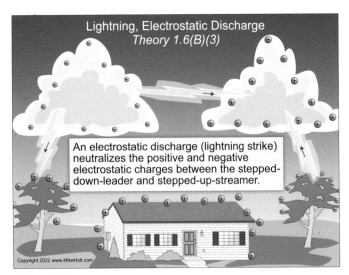

▶Figure 1–18

1.7 Lightning Protection System

A lightning protection system is designed to protect property and persons against a direct lightning strike. The lightning protection system intercepts a lightning strike and provides a safe path for it to discharge to the Earth.

Lightning protection systems consist of a strike termination device, called an "air terminal" or "lightning rod," placed on top of the structure to be protected. These strike termination devices are connected by large wires, and the wires are then connected to the Earth. ▶Figure 1–20

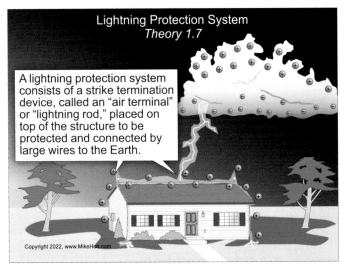

▶Figure 1–20

Caution

⚠ **CAUTION:** Lightning generally strikes a point of higher elevation such as trees, buildings, or transmission lines; however, lightning can strike an object at a lower elevation like a person in an open field.

(C) Death, Injuries, and Property Damage. Each year lightning causes deaths, injuries, and billions of dollars in property damage. When lightning strikes a nonconductive object, it will produce a high temperature at the strike point resulting in cracked concrete or the ignition of combustible materials. ▶Figure 1–19

Author's Comment:

▸ To adequately protect property from lighting, lightning protection systems should be installed in accordance with the requirements contained in NFPA 780, *Installation of Lightning Protection Systems.*

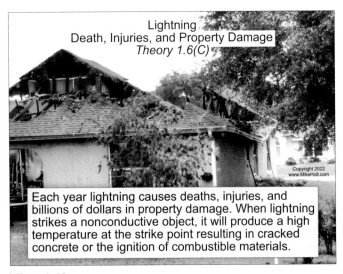

▶Figure 1–19

ELECTRON THEORY AND CHEMICAL BONDING

2.1 Introduction

Once atomic structure is understood, applying the concepts of electron theory and chemical bonding is next. In this unit you will learn:

▸ how the negative charge of electron movement participates in the creation of electricity

▸ the differences between conductors, semiconductors, and insulators

▸ what chemical bonding is and how it can change the electrical characteristic of an atom

2.2 Electron Orbitals

Electron orbitals represent the paths around the atom's nucleus that contain electrons. The negative charge of an electron is attracted to the positive charge of a proton. This attraction between electrons and protons is what keeps them together in the atom. ▸Figure 2–1

Electron Orbitals
Theory 2.2

Nucleus

Copyright 2022, www.MikeHolt.com

Electrons exist in "orbitals" that surround the nucleus of an atom. The negative charge of an electron is attracted to the positive charge of a proton. This attraction between electrons and protons keeps them together in the atom.

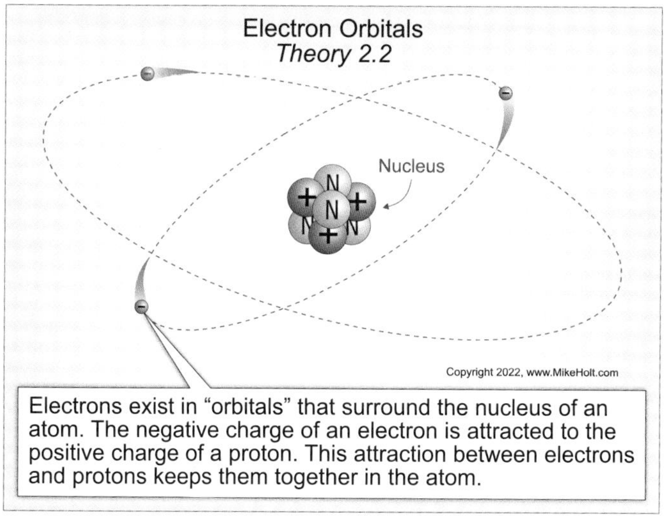

▸Figure 2–1

2.3 Valence Electrons

The outermost electron orbital of an atom is called the "valence shell"; electrons in the valence shell are called "valence electrons." ▸Figure 2–2

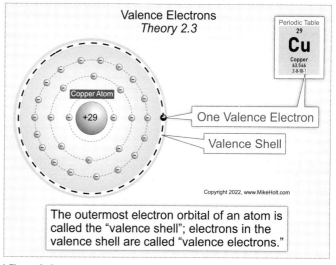

Valence Electrons
Theory 2.3

Periodic Table
29
Cu
Copper
63.546
2-8-18-1

Copper Atom

+29

One Valence Electron

Valence Shell

Copyright 2022, www.MikeHolt.com

The outermost electron orbital of an atom is called the "valence shell"; electrons in the valence shell are called "valence electrons."

▸Figure 2–2

2.4 Freeing Valence Electron(s) from an Atom

(A) Coulomb's Law. According to Coulomb's Law, the strength of the electrostatic field between protons and electrons decreases as the distance of the electrons from the nucleus increases. This means that the valence electrons farthest away from the nucleus are more easily separated from the atom. ▶Figure 2–3

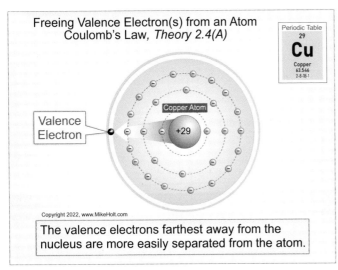

The valence electrons farthest away from the nucleus are more easily separated from the atom.

▶Figure 2–3

(B) Movement of Valence Electrons. Energy that is applied to an atom is distributed evenly among the valence electrons. If sufficient energy is applied to valence electrons, some electrons will be forced to leave their atom and move to another atom. This movement of electrons is the principle behind "electricity." ▶Figure 2–4

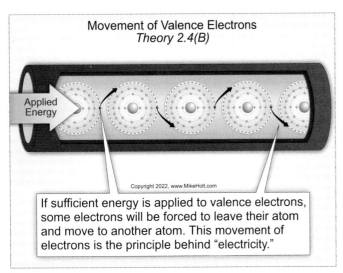

If sufficient energy is applied to valence electrons, some electrons will be forced to leave their atom and move to another atom. This movement of electrons is the principle behind "electricity."

▶Figure 2–4

2.5 Conductance

(A) General. Conductance is how easily an object permits the movement of valence electrons from their atom. Conductive elements are made of atoms that contain one, two, or three valence electrons. Copper and aluminum are the two most common conductive elements used for electrical wiring. ▶Figure 2–5 and ▶Figure 2–6

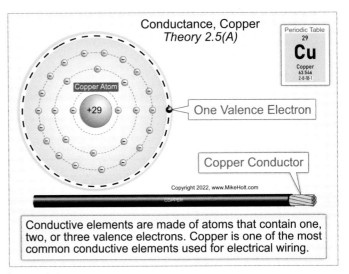

Conductive elements are made of atoms that contain one, two, or three valence electrons. Copper is one of the most common conductive elements used for electrical wiring.

▶Figure 2–5

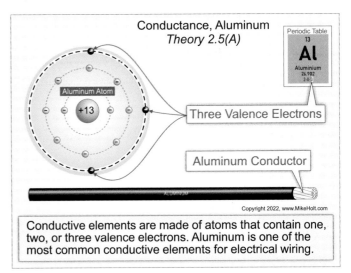

Conductive elements are made of atoms that contain one, two, or three valence electrons. Aluminum is one of the most common conductive elements for electrical wiring.

▶Figure 2–6

(B) Conductivity. The most conductive elements in order of conductivity are silver, copper, gold, and aluminum. Silver is 106 percent more conductive than copper; gold is 71 percent as conductive as copper, and aluminum is 65 percent as conductive as copper. ▶Figure 2–7

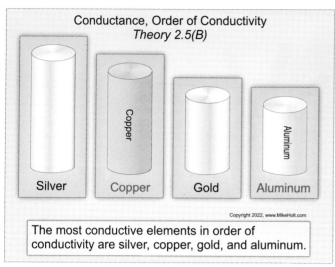

▶Figure 2–7

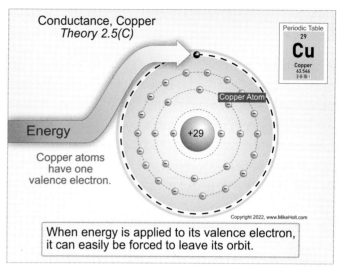

▶Figure 2–9

Author's Comment:

▶ Silver and gold are better conductors than aluminum and will not corrode, but their cost makes them impractical for electrical wiring. Connectors for electronic circuits sometimes use gold or silver plating on copper terminals to prevent corrosion and ensure a reliable connection. ▶Figure 2–8

▶Figure 2–8

(C) Copper. Copper atoms have one valence electron. When energy is applied to the atom's valence electron, the electron can easily be forced to leave its orbit. ▶Figure 2–9

(D) Aluminum. Aluminum atoms have three valence electrons. When energy is applied to the atom's valence electrons, the energy is distributed between the three electrons. This makes it more difficult for a valence electron to break free from an aluminum atom as compared to a copper atom with the same amount of energy. ▶Figure 2–10

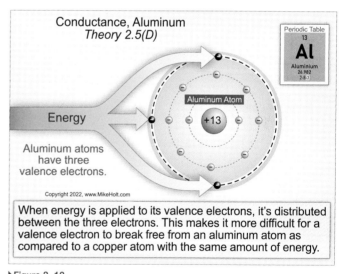

▶Figure 2–10

2.6 Insulators

Materials containing six to eight valence electrons are known as "insulators." Examples of insulators include wood, plastic, rubber, and glass. Insulators do not readily conduct electricity and are composed of atoms with one or two open spots for valence electrons. The electrostatic forces between the valence electrons and the protons actively try to fill the opening(s) in the atom's valence shell. This makes it very difficult for a valence electron to break free from an insulator. ▶Figure 2–11

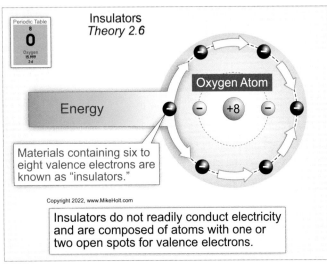

▶Figure 2–11

Author's Comment:

▶ Examples of insulators in the electrical industry include the insulation on electrical wire and cables. ▶Figure 2–12

2.7 Semiconductors

Semiconductors contain four or five valence electrons and are often made using carbon, silicon, or germanium. Semiconductors are materials with conductivity between a "conductor" and an "insulator." Semiconductors' atoms are unique because they can be made more conductive or insulative by a process known as "doping." Doping adds small quantities of an element (an impurity) to a semiconductor to change its electrical conductivity characteristics. ▶Figure 2–13

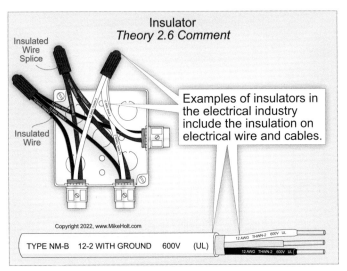

▶Figure 2–12

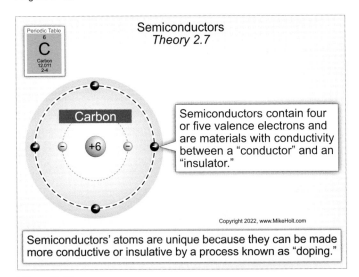

▶Figure 2–13

Author's Comment:

▶ Semiconductors are the building blocks for the electronics contained in computers, cell phones, tablets, televisions, and other electronic devices. ▶Figure 2–14

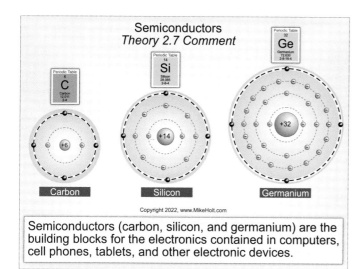

Semiconductors
Theory 2.7 Comment

Copyright 2022, www.MikeHolt.com

Semiconductors (carbon, silicon, and germanium) are the building blocks for the electronics contained in computers, cell phones, tablets, and other electronic devices.

▶Figure 2–14

2.8 Chemical Bonding

(A) Compound Molecules. Atoms strive for chemical stability where the atom's valence shell has eight valence electrons. Chemical bonding can create a compound molecule that has different electrical characteristics than the individual atoms themselves.

For example, if two copper atoms (one valence electron each) combine with one oxygen atom (six valence electrons) the compound molecule "copper oxide" (Cu_2O) is created. Copper oxide is an insulator because the valence shell of the molecule has eight valence electrons. ▶Figure 2–15

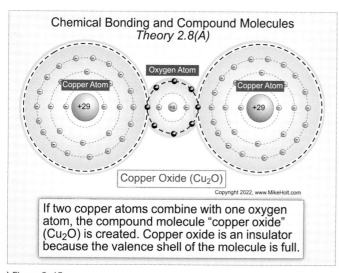

Chemical Bonding and Compound Molecules
Theory 2.8(A)

Copper Oxide (Cu_2O)

Copyright 2022, www.MikeHolt.com

If two copper atoms combine with one oxygen atom, the compound molecule "copper oxide" (Cu_2O) is created. Copper oxide is an insulator because the valence shell of the molecule is full.

▶Figure 2–15

(B) Rust. Chemical bonding can slowly break down metals by reacting with substances in their environment. This chemical reaction is called "corrosion." An example of corrosion is rust on metals which can only happen when water, iron, and oxygen are present. Only the surface of metal corrodes because the surface is exposed to the substances in the environment. ▶Figure 2–16

Chemical Bonding, Rust
Theory 2.8(B)

Copyright 2022 www.MikeHolt.com

Chemical bonding can slowly break down metals by reacting with substances in their environment. An example of corrosion is rust on metals which can only happen when water, iron, and oxygen are present.

▶Figure 2–16

(C) Corrosion.

(1) Copper Oxide. The surface of copper is bright, shiny, and very conductive. When copper is exposed to the environment, the oxygen atoms in the air will chemically bond with the copper atoms on its surface. This creates the compound molecule copper oxide (Cu_2O) (which is green or black in color) on the surface of the copper. Although copper oxide on the surface is an insulator, the pressure of an electrical connector can easily break through the insulating properties of the copper oxide to the wire. ▶Figure 2–17

(2) Aluminum Oxide. When aluminum is exposed to the environment, the oxygen atoms in the air will chemically bond with the aluminum atoms on its surface. This creates the compound molecule aluminum oxide (Al_2O_3) on the surface of the aluminum, which is an insulator. ▶Figure 2–18

▶Figure 2–17

▶Figure 2–18

UNIT

3

ELECTRICAL CIRCUITS AND POWER SOURCES

3.1 Introduction

A power source provides the energy necessary for electrons to move through a closed-loop path known as an "electrical circuit." In this unit you will learn:

▸ what an electrical circuit is

▸ what components make up an electrical circuit

▸ the two theories of electron current flow

▸ the different types of power sources that force electrons to move

3.2 The Electrical Circuit

An electrical circuit contains a power source that pushes and pulls electrons through the electrical circuit; this is known as "electricity." In an electrical circuit, the electrons leave the power source on a conductive path traveling toward a load, and then return to the power source. ▸Figure 3–1

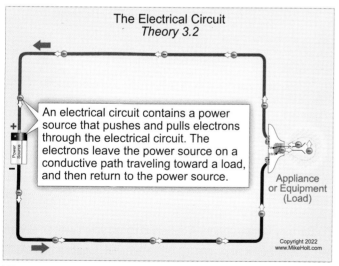

The Electrical Circuit
Theory 3.2

An electrical circuit contains a power source that pushes and pulls electrons through the electrical circuit. The electrons leave the power source on a conductive path traveling toward a load, and then return to the power source.

Appliance or Equipment (Load)

Copyright 2022
www.MikeHolt.com

▸Figure 3–1

3.3 Electric Current Flow (Electricity)

The direction of current flow (electricity) is explained by one of two theories—the "Conventional Current Flow Theory" or the "Electron Current Flow Theory."

(A) Conventional Current Flow Theory, Franklin. During an experiment in 1752, Benjamin Franklin discovered that an electric charge from static electricity could move from one object to another. He theorized that current flowed from a positive charge to a negative charge. This theory became known as the "Conventional Current Flow Theory." ▸Figure 3–2

(B) Electron Current Flow Theory, Thompson. In 1897, Joseph J. Thompson explored the properties of cathode rays and discovered that current flow (movement of electrons) was actually the movement of negatively charged particles (electrons) from the negative terminal of the source toward the positive terminal of the source. Based on his discovery Thompson developed the theory known as the "Electron Current Flow Theory." ▸Figure 3–3

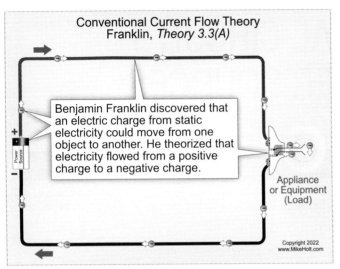

▶Figure 3–2

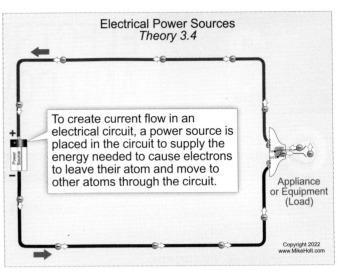

▶Figure 3–4

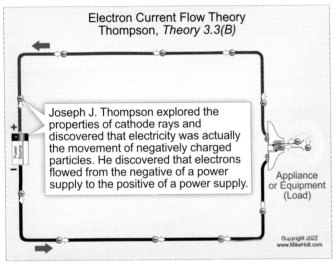

▶Figure 3–3

Author's Comment:

▶ In this material we use Thompson's Electron Current Flow Theory because it accurately represents the direction of current flow.

3.4 Electrical Power Sources

To create current flow in an electrical circuit, a power source is placed in the circuit to supply the energy needed to cause electrons to leave their atom and move to other atoms through the circuit. The energy to move electrons can come from chemical activity, electromagnetism, photovoltaics, heat, or pressure. ▶Figure 3–4

(A) Chemical Activity. A battery is a chemical energy source constructed of one or more voltaic cells. Batteries built with more than one voltaic cell have the positive side of one cell connected to the negative side of the other cell. ▶Figure 3–5

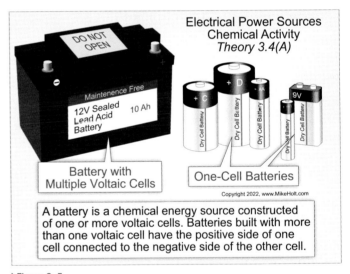

▶Figure 3–5

Author's Comment:

▶ In 1800, Alessandro Volta invented the voltaic cell.

(1) Battery Construction. A battery is constructed with an electrolyte, a negative terminal, and a positive terminal. Together they create the energy necessary to move electrons within a circuit. ▶Figure 3–6

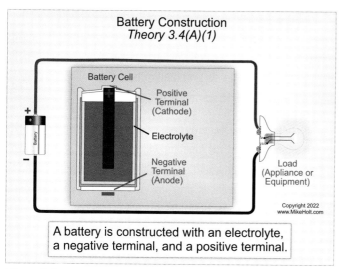

Battery Construction
Theory 3.4(A)(1)

A battery is constructed with an electrolyte, a negative terminal, and a positive terminal.

▶Figure 3–6

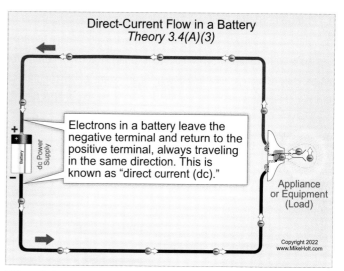

Direct-Current Flow in a Battery
Theory 3.4(A)(3)

Electrons in a battery leave the negative terminal and return to the positive terminal, always traveling in the same direction. This is known as "direct current (dc)."

▶Figure 3–8

(2) Electrical Pressure in a Battery. Chemical activity in a battery causes a buildup of electrons at the negative terminal, creating the energy necessary to move electrons within a circuit. The electron buildup creates electrical pressure between the negative and positive terminals of the battery. The negative charge on the battery's negative terminal will flow to the battery's positive terminal when there is a conductive path between the terminals. ▶Figure 3–7

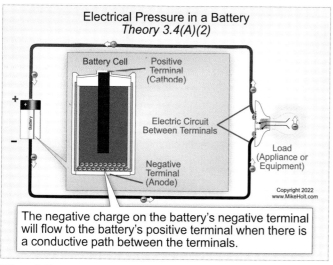

Electrical Pressure in a Battery
Theory 3.4(A)(2)

The negative charge on the battery's negative terminal will flow to the battery's positive terminal when there is a conductive path between the terminals.

▶Figure 3–7

(3) Direct-Current Flow. Electrons in a battery leave the negative terminal and return to the positive terminal, always traveling in the same direction. This is known as "direct current" (dc). ▶Figure 3–8

(B) Electromagnetism. Most electrical energy is generated using electromagnetism, which creates the power necessary to move electrons within a circuit. ▶Figure 3–9

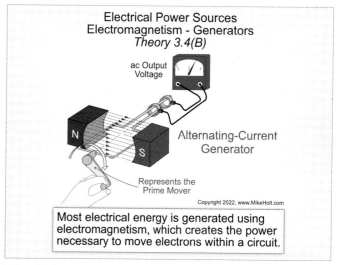

Electrical Power Sources
Electromagnetism - Generators
Theory 3.4(B)

Most electrical energy is generated using electromagnetism, which creates the power necessary to move electrons within a circuit.

▶Figure 3–9

Author's Comment:

▶ Details about electromagnetism as it relates to generators are explained later in this material.

(C) Photoelectricity. Photoelectricity is the conversion of light energy into electrical energy, which creates the power necessary to move electrons within a circuit. When photons (light) strike semiconductor plates, they cause electrons to flow from one semiconductor plate to another. ▶Figure 3–10

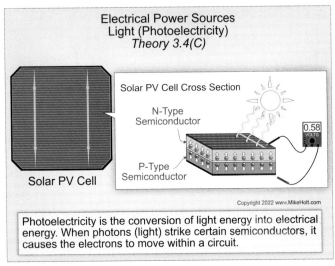

▶Figure 3–10

(D) Thermoelectricity.

(1) General. Thermoelectricity is the conversion of heat energy into electrical energy, which creates the energy necessary to move electrons within a circuit. Electrons can be forced to move in a circuit when heat is applied at a junction where two dissimilar metals or semiconductors connect. ▶Figure 3–11

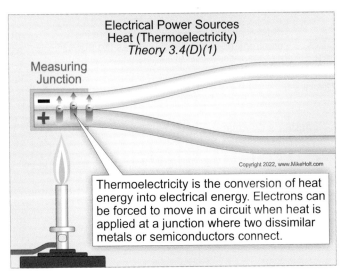

▶Figure 3–11

(2) Voltage. A common application of thermal electricity is a "thermocouple," which is a sensor that measures temperature. It consists of two different types of metals joined together at one end. When the junction of the two metals is heated or cooled, a voltage is created that can be correlated back to the temperature.

The amount of electrical energy produced by a thermocouple depends on the temperature at the junction which is typically in the millivolt (1/1,000V) range. As the temperature rises, the energy produced by the thermocouple increases, and the opposite is true if the temperature decreases. ▶Figure 3–12

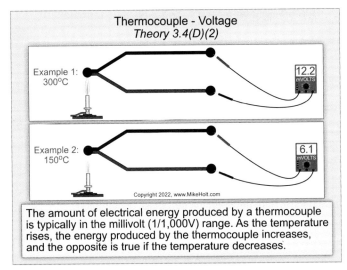

▶Figure 3–12

(E) Piezoelectricity. Piezoelectricity is the conversion of pressure or vibration into the electrical energy necessary to move electrons within a circuit. When pressure is applied to piezoelectric materials, a voltage is created. Materials such as quartz and certain ceramics exhibit piezoelectric behavior. ▶Figure 3–13

Author's Comment:

▸ Uses of piezoelectricity include:

   ▸ piezoelectric beepers in digital watches and electronics

   ▸ piezoelectric tweeters in stereo speakers

   ▸ sound generating arrays for sonar, fish finders, and ultrasound devices

   ▸ grill igniters

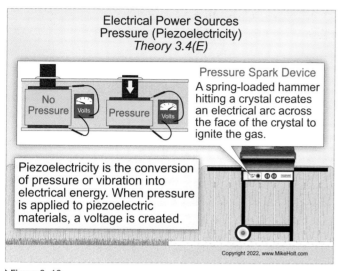

Electrical Power Sources
Pressure (Piezoelectricity)
Theory 3.4(E)

No Pressure — Volts

Pressure — Volts

Pressure Spark Device
A spring-loaded hammer hitting a crystal creates an electrical arc across the face of the crystal to ignite the gas.

Piezoelectricity is the conversion of pressure or vibration into electrical energy. When pressure is applied to piezoelectric materials, a voltage is created.

Copyright 2022, www.MikeHolt.com

▶Figure 3–13

UNIT

4

THE ELECTRICAL SYSTEM

4.1 Introduction

The electrical system typically begins at the utility generating plant. Knowing how electricity gets from there to a building provides a better sense of "the big picture." In this unit you will learn:

▸ how electricity is generated at the utility generating plant

▸ about transmission and distribution voltages

▸ how electricity gets to a customer's premises

4.2 Source of Electrical Generation

The primary energy sources used to generate electricity include fossil fuels (coal, natural gas, and petroleum), nuclear energy, and renewable energy sources. Most electricity is generated with steam turbines using fossil fuels and nuclear power. Other electricity generation sources include gas turbines, hydro turbines, wind turbines, and solar photovoltaics. ▸Figure 4–1

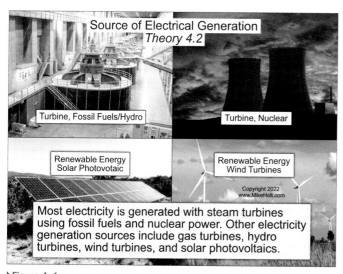

Source of Electrical Generation
Theory 4.2

Turbine, Fossil Fuels/Hydro

Turbine, Nuclear

Renewable Energy Solar Photovotaic

Renewable Energy Wind Turbines

Copyright 2022 www.MikeHolt.com

Most electricity is generated with steam turbines using fossil fuels and nuclear power. Other electricity generation sources include gas turbines, hydro turbines, wind turbines, and solar photovoltaics.

▸Figure 4–1

4.3 Step-Up Transmission Voltage

Once the utility has produced electrical energy, the voltage from the generating plant must be stepped up to be transmitted as efficiently as possible from the generating facility to where it is needed. Transformers at the utility generating facility "step-up" voltage for transmission distribution to between 69 kV and 765 kV. ▸Figure 4–2

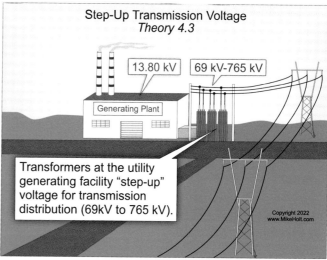

Step-Up Transmission Voltage
Theory 4.3

13.80 kV   69 kV-765 kV

Generating Plant

Transformers at the utility generating facility "step-up" voltage for transmission distribution (69kV to 765 kV).

Copyright 2022 www.MikeHolt.com

▸Figure 4–2

4.4 High-Voltage Transmission Lines

The most economical way to move electrical energy from the generating facility over long distances is to transmit the electrical energy at high voltages to distribution step-down substations. ▶Figure 4–3

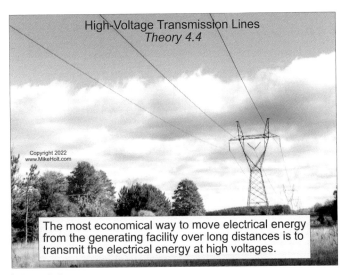

High-Voltage Transmission Lines
Theory 4.4

The most economical way to move electrical energy from the generating facility over long distances is to transmit the electrical energy at high voltages.

▶Figure 4–3

Authors Comment

▶ The most effective way to reduce voltage drop and power loss is to lower the current flowing through the transmission lines, which is accomplished by increasing the transmission voltage.

4.5 Primary Distribution Voltage

Once high-voltage transmission distribution power reaches the "step-down substation," the voltage is stepped down from transmission voltage (69 kV to 765 kV) to primary distribution voltage which is between 13 kV and 34.50 kV. ▶Figure 4–4

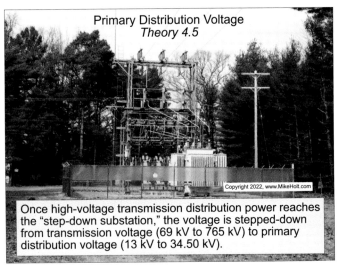

Primary Distribution Voltage
Theory 4.5

Once high-voltage transmission distribution power reaches the "step-down substation," the voltage is stepped-down from transmission voltage (69 kV to 765 kV) to primary distribution voltage (13 kV to 34.50 kV).

▶Figure 4–4

4.6 Primary Distribution Wires

"Primary distribution wires" are run from the step-down substation to "distribution transformers."

(A) Overhead Primary Distribution Wires. Overhead utility primary distribution wires provide power to "distribution transformers" mounted on poles next to the building or structure served. ▶Figure 4–5

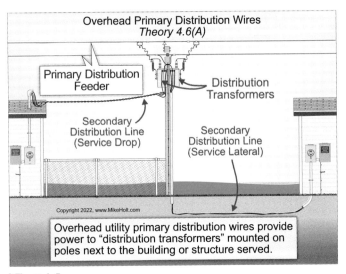

Overhead Primary Distribution Wires
Theory 4.6(A)

Primary Distribution Feeder

Distribution Transformers

Secondary Distribution Line (Service Drop)

Secondary Distribution Line (Service Lateral)

Overhead utility primary distribution wires provide power to "distribution transformers" mounted on poles next to the building or structure served.

▶Figure 4–5

(B) Underground Primary Distribution Wires. Underground utility primary distribution wires provide power to pad-mounted distribution transformers located on the ground near the building or structure served. ▶Figure 4-6

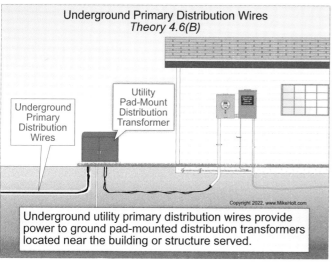

Underground Primary Distribution Wires
Theory 4.6(B)

Underground Primary Distribution Wires

Utility Pad-Mount Distribution Transformer

Copyright 2022, www.MikeHolt.com

Underground utility primary distribution wires provide power to ground pad-mounted distribution transformers located near the building or structure served.

▶Figure 4-6

4.7 Secondary Distribution Voltage

Utility distribution transformers reduce primary distribution voltage (13 kV to 34.50 kV) to secondary distribution voltage (120/240V, 120/208V, or 277/480V) for customer use. ▶Figure 4-7

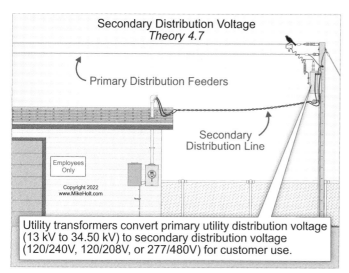

Secondary Distribution Voltage
Theory 4.7

Primary Distribution Feeders

Secondary Distribution Line

Employees Only

Copyright 2022 www.MikeHolt.com

Utility transformers convert primary utility distribution voltage (13 kV to 34.50 kV) to secondary distribution voltage (120/240V, 120/208V, or 277/480V) for customer use.

▶Figure 4-7

4.8 Service Drop and Service Lateral

Power from utility distribution transformers is delivered to the customer by utility overhead or underground wiring.

(A) Service Drop. Overhead wires from the utility primary distribution transformer to the premises are called the "utility service drop." ▶Figure 4-8

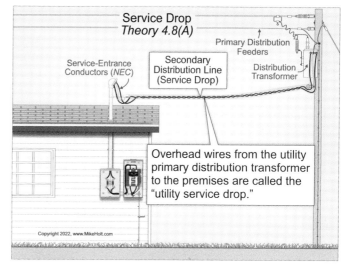

Service Drop
Theory 4.8(A)

Primary Distribution Feeders

Service-Entrance Conductors (*NEC*)

Secondary Distribution Line (Service Drop)

Distribution Transformer

Overhead wires from the utility primary distribution transformer to the premises are called the "utility service drop."

Copyright 2022, www.MikeHolt.com

▶Figure 4-8

(B) Service Lateral. Underground wires from the utility primary distribution transformer to the premises are called the "utility service lateral." ▶Figure 4-9

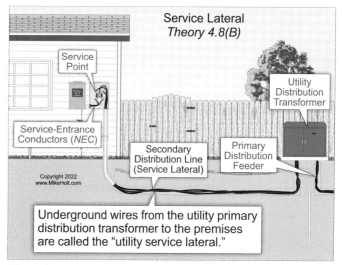

Service Lateral
Theory 4.8(B)

Service Point

Utility Distribution Transformer

Service-Entrance Conductors (*NEC*)

Secondary Distribution Line (Service Lateral)

Primary Distribution Feeder

Copyright 2022 www.MikeHolt.com

Underground wires from the utility primary distribution transformer to the premises are called the "utility service lateral."

▶Figure 4-9

CHAPTER

1

PRACTICE QUESTIONS

CHAPTER 1—PRACTICE QUESTIONS

Unit 1—Atomic Structure

1.2 Atomic Theory

1. Atoms contain three types of subatomic particles: electrons, protons, and neutrons. The _____ orbit around the nucleus of an atom.

    (a) electrons
    (b) protons
    (c) neutrons
    (d) nucleus

2. _____ do not participate in the flow of energy and they have a positive electrical charge with lines of force going straight out in all directions.

    (a) Electrons
    (b) Protons
    (c) Neutrons
    (d) Nuclei

3. _____ have no charge and therefore have no lines of force.

    (a) Electrons
    (b) Protons
    (c) Neutrons
    (d) Nuclei

4. Because of their light weight, _____ actively participate in the transfer of energy and have lines of force going inward in all directions.

    (a) electrons
    (b) protons
    (c) neutrons
    (d) nuclei

5. The _____ of an atom only contains protons and neutrons.

    (a) electrons
    (b) protons
    (c) neutrons
    (d) nucleus

1.3 Electrostatic Field

6. Coulomb's Law states that, "Particles with _____ charges repel each other."

    (a) balanced
    (b) charged
    (c) unlike
    (d) like

7. Coulomb's Law states that, "Particles with _____ charges attract each other."

    (a) balanced
    (b) charged
    (c) unlike
    (d) like

1.4 Atomic Charge of an Atom

8. The atomic charge of an atom is _____ depending on the number of electrons compared to the number of protons.

    (a) balanced
    (b) positive
    (c) negative
    (d) all of these

9. If an atom contains an equal number of electrons and protons, the atom has a _____ atomic charge.

    (a) balanced
    (b) positive
    (c) negative
    (d) none of these

10. If an atom contains more electrons than protons, the atom has a _____ atomic charge.

    (a) balanced
    (b) positive
    (c) negative
    (d) none of these

11. If an atom contains more protons than electrons, the atom has a _____ atomic charge.

    (a) balanced
    (b) positive
    (c) negative
    (d) none of these

1.5 Electrostatic Charge and Discharge

12. When unlike materials are in contact with each other, electrons from one material move to the surface of the other, but the protons remain on the _____ surface.

    (a) first
    (b) original
    (c) last
    (d) none of these

13. When objects are quickly separated, both materials display a charge because one material has an excess of electrons while the other has _____ electrons.

    (a) no
    (b) fewer
    (c) more
    (d) extra

14. The human body in a low-humidity area may have a dangerous static discharge of several _____ volts.

    (a) hundred
    (b) thousand
    (c) million
    (d) billion

1.6 Lightning

15. Lightning is the _____ of high-voltage cells within clouds to, and from, the Earth and sometimes to space.

    (a) buildup
    (b) charging
    (c) discharging
    (d) neutralizing

16. As a cloud's electrostatic charge builds up, it creates an ionized path from the cloud toward the Earth; this ionized path is called a "_____."

    (a) stepped-down leader
    (b) streamer
    (c) ray
    (d) bolt

17. At the same time the stepped leader originates, a similar ionized path called a "_____" rises from the Earth or another positively charged object.

    (a) stepped leader
    (b) stepped-up streamer
    (c) ray
    (d) bolt

18. An electrostatic discharge (lightning strike) _____ the positive and negative electrostatic charges between the stepped leader and streamer.

    (a) disrupts
    (b) interrupts
    (c) neutralizes
    (d) equalizes

19. When lightning strikes a _____ object, it will produce a high temperature at the strike point resulting in cracked concrete or the ignition of combustible materials.

    (a) conductive
    (b) nonconductive
    (c) plastic
    (d) metal

1.7 Lightning Protection System

20. The lightning protection system intercepts the lightning strike and provides a safe path for it to_____ the Earth.

    (a) discharge to
    (b) neutralize within
    (c) dissipate to
    (d) charge particles in

Unit 2—Electron Theory and Chemical Bonding

2.2 Electron Orbitals

1. The _____ between the positive charge of the protons and negative charge of electrons keeps them together in the atom.

    (a) attraction
    (b) distinction
    (c) relationship
    (d) balance

2.3 Valence Electrons

2. The outermost electron orbital of an atom is called the "valence shell" and electrons in this shell are called "_____ electrons."

    (a) negative
    (b) positive
    (c) valance
    (d) special

2.4 Freeing Valence Electron(s) from an Atom

3. According to Coulomb's Law, the strength of the electrostatic field between protons and electrons _____ as the distance of the electrons from the nucleus increases.

    (a) increases
    (b) decreases
    (c) equalizes
    (d) strengthens

4. Energy that is applied to an atom is distributed _____ among all the valence electrons.

    (a) evenly
    (b) disproportionally
    (c) unequally
    (d) unevenly

2.5 Conductance

5. Conductance is how easily an object permits the _____ of valence electrons from their atom.

    (a) resistance
    (b) water
    (c) movement
    (d) none of these

6. Conductive elements are made of one, two, or three valence electrons. Copper and aluminum are the two most common _____ elements used for electrical wiring.

    (a) insulative
    (b) conductive
    (c) expensive
    (d) light weight

7. The best conductive elements in order of their conductivity are: _____.

    (a) gold, silver, copper, and aluminum
    (b) gold, copper, silver, and aluminum
    (c) silver, gold, copper, and aluminum
    (d) silver, copper, gold, and aluminum

8. Copper atoms have _____ valence electron(s). When energy is applied to the valance electron(s), the electron(s) can easily be forced to leave the orbit.

   (a) one
   (b) two
   (c) four
   (d) six

9. Aluminum atoms have _____ valence electrons. When energy is applied to the valence electrons, the energy is distributed between the electrons.

   (a) two
   (b) three
   (c) four
   (d) eight

2.6 Insulators

10. Materials containing six to _____ valance electrons are known as "insulators."

    (a) eight
    (b) ten
    (c) twelve
    (d) fourteen

2.7 Semiconductors

11. Semiconductors contain _____ valance electrons and are often made using carbon, silicon, or germanium.

    (a) one or two
    (b) two or three
    (c) three or four
    (d) four or five

2.8 Chemical Bonding

12. Atoms strive for chemical stability where the valence shell has _____ valence electrons.

    (a) two
    (b) four
    (c) six
    (d) eight

13. Chemical bonding can create a _____ molecule that has different electrical characteristics than the individual atoms themselves.

    (a) special
    (b) compound
    (c) valance
    (d) stable

14. An example of _____ is rust on metals which can only happen when water, iron, and oxygen are present.

    (a) bonding
    (b) corrosion
    (c) chemistry
    (d) stability

15. When copper is exposed to the environment, the oxygen atoms in the air will chemically bond with the copper atoms on its surface, this creates the compound molecule _____ oxide.

    (a) aluminum
    (b) copper
    (c) silver
    (d) metal

16. When aluminum is exposed to the environment, the oxygen atoms in the air will chemically bond with the aluminum atoms on its surface, this creates the compound molecule _____ oxide.

    (a) aluminum
    (b) copper
    (c) silver
    (d) metal

Unit 3—Electrical Circuits and Power Sources

3.2 The Electrical Circuit

1. In an electrical circuit, the electrons leave the power source on a(an) _____ path traveling toward a load, and then return to the power source.

   (a) conductive
   (b) insulative
   (c) single
   (d) varying

3.3 Electric Current Flow (Electricity)

2. The direction of _____ flow is explained by one of two theories—the "Conventional Current Flow Theory" or the "Electron Current Flow Theory."

   (a) current
   (b) power
   (c) resistance
   (d) voltage

3. According to the _____ Current Flow Theory, Benjamin Franklin discovered that electricity flows from a positive charge to a negative charge.

   (a) Conventional
   (b) Electron
   (c) Maxwell
   (d) Tesla

4. According to the Conventional Current Flow Theory, Benjamin Franklin theorized that electric current flowed out of the _____ terminal, through the circuit and into the _____ terminal of the source.

   (a) positive, negative
   (b) negative, positive
   (c) negative, negative
   (d) positive, positive

5. According to the _____ Current Flow Theory, Joseph J Thompson discovered that electrons flowed from the negative terminal of the source toward the positive terminal of the source.

   (a) Conventional
   (b) Electron
   (c) Maxwell
   (d) Tesla

6. According to the Electron Current Flow Theory, Joseph J. Thompson discovered electrons flowed from the _____ terminal of the source toward the _____ terminal of the source.

   (a) positive, negative
   (b) negative, positive
   (c) negative, negative
   (d) positive, positive

3.4 Electrical Power Sources

7. To create current flow in an electrical circuit, a(an) _____ is placed in the circuit to supply the energy needed to cause electrons to leave their atom and move to other atoms through the circuit.

   (a) conductor
   (b) insulator
   (c) power source
   (d) wheel

8. A battery is a _____ energy source constructed of one or more voltaic cells.

   (a) chemical
   (b) solar
   (c) heat
   (d) magnetic

9. A _____ is constructed with an electrolyte, a negative terminal, and a positive terminal.

   (a) wind turbine
   (b) generator
   (c) solar cell
   (d) battery

10. Chemical activity in the _____ causes a buildup of electrons at the negative terminal, creating the energy necessary to move electrons within a circuit.

    (a) battery
    (b) generator
    (c) solar cell
    (d) wind turbine

11. Electrons in a battery leave the negative terminal and return to the positive terminal, always traveling in the same direction, this is known as "_____ current."

    (a) alternating
    (b) direct
    (c) straight
    (d) varying

12. Most electrical energy is generated using _____, which creates the energy necessary to move electrons within a circuit.

    (a) electromagnetism
    (b) photovoltaics
    (c) chemical activity
    (d) heat

13. Photoelectricity is the conversion of _____ energy into electrical energy, which creates the energy necessary to move electrons within a circuit.

    (a) light
    (b) magnetic
    (c) chemical
    (d) heat

14. Thermoelectricity is the conversion of _____ energy into electrical energy, which creates the energy necessary to move electrons within a circuit.

    (a) light
    (b) magnetic
    (c) chemical
    (d) heat

15. A common application of thermoelectricity is a "_____," which is a sensor that measures temperature.

    (a) thermostat
    (b) compass
    (c) heater
    (d) thermocouple

16. Piezoelectricity is the conversion of _____ or vibration into electrical energy necessary to move electrons within a circuit.

    (a) static electricity
    (b) pressure
    (c) magnetism
    (d) light

Unit 4—The Electrical System

4.2 Source of Electrical Generation

1. Most electricity is generated with steam turbines using _____.

    (a) fossil fuels
    (b) nuclear power
    (c) fossil fuels and nuclear power
    (d) none of these

4.3 Step-Up Transmission Voltage

2. Transformers at the utility generating facility "_____" voltage for transmission distribution to between 69kV and 765 kV.

    (a) transform
    (b) step-down
    (c) step-up
    (d) reduce

4.4 High-Voltage Transmission Lines

3. The most economical way to move electrical energy from the generating facility over long distances is to transmit the electrical energy at _____ voltages to distribution step-down substations.

   (a) low
   (b) high
   (c) medium
   (d) special

4.5 Primary Distribution Voltage

4. Once high-voltage transmission distribution power reaches the "step-down substation," the voltage is _____ from transmission voltage (69 kV to 765 kV) to primary distribution voltage which is between 13 kV and 34.50 kV.

   (a) stepped down
   (b) stepped up
   (c) transformed
   (d) increased

4.6 Primary Distribution Wires

5. "Primary distribution wires" are run from the step-down substation to "distribution _____."

   (a) wires
   (b) motors
   (c) generators
   (d) transformers

6. _____ utility primary distribution wires provide power to "distribution transformers" mounted on poles next to the building or structure served.

   (a) Overhead
   (b) Underground
   (c) Open
   (d) Enclosed

7. _____ utility primary distribution wires provide power to pad-mounted distribution transformers located near the building or structure served.

   (a) Overhead
   (b) Underground
   (c) Open
   (d) Enclosed

4.7 Secondary Distribution Voltage

8. Utility distribution transformers _____ the primary distribution voltage (13 kV to 34.50 kV) to secondary distribution voltage (120/240V, 120/208V, or 277/480V) for customer use.

   (a) increase
   (b) reduce
   (c) step-up
   (d) raise

4.8 Service Drop and Service Lateral

9. Power from utility distribution transformers is delivered to the customer by utility _____ wiring.

   (a) overhead
   (b) underground
   (c) overhead or underground
   (d) none of these

10. Overhead wires from the utility primary distribution transformer to the premises are called the "utility _____."

    (a) service drop
    (b) service lateral
    (c) service drop or service lateral
    (d) none of these

11. Underground wires from the utility primary distribution transformer to the premises are called the "utility _____."

    (a) service drop
    (b) service lateral
    (c) service drop or service lateral
    (d) none of these

CHAPTER 2

USES AND DANGERS OF ELECTRICITY

Chapter 2—Uses and Dangers of Electricity

Unit 5—Uses of Electricity

Electricity is used for many purposes such as lighting, cooking, and power. In this unit you will learn:

- ▸ how electricity is used for electroplating
- ▸ about the use of electromagnetism in motors, generators, relays, and transformers
- ▸ about solar PV systems
- ▸ how electricity produces heat
- ▸ about the uses of different types of lighting

Unit 6—Dangers of Electricity

People working in the electrical industry are responsible for ensuring that electrical installations are as safe as possible. In this unit you will learn:

- ▸ the purpose of the *National Electrical Code*
- ▸ how electrical fires are created
- ▸ what electric shock/electrocution are
- ▸ what arc flashes and arc blasts are

UNIT

5

USES OF ELECTRICITY

5.1 Introduction

Electricity is used for many purposes such as lighting, cooking, and power. In this unit you will learn:

▶ how electricity is used for electroplating

▶ about the use of electromagnetism in motors, generators, relays, and transformers

▶ about solar PV systems

▶ how electricity produces heat

▶ about the uses of different types of lighting systems

5.2 Uses of Electricity

Electricity has many uses, the most common include electrochemical processes, electromagnetism, solar PV systems, heat, and lighting.

5.3 Electrochemical Processes

Electricity can be used to alter or encourage the formation of new compounds. Electroplating uses electricity to transfer dissolved, positively charged metal to the surface of a negatively charged metal, such as in gold- or silver-plated jewelry. ▶Figure 5–1

5.4 Electromagnetism

Electromagnetism (an electromagnetic field) is created around a wire when electrical current flows through it (movement of electrons). It is used for many applications such as motors, generators, relays, and transformers. ▶Figure 5–2

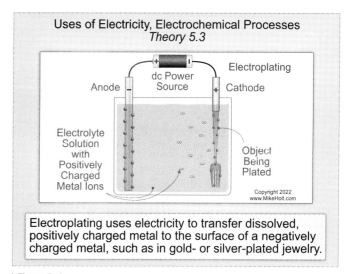

Uses of Electricity, Electrochemical Processes
Theory 5.3

Electroplating uses electricity to transfer dissolved, positively charged metal to the surface of a negatively charged metal, such as in gold- or silver-plated jewelry.

▶Figure 5–1

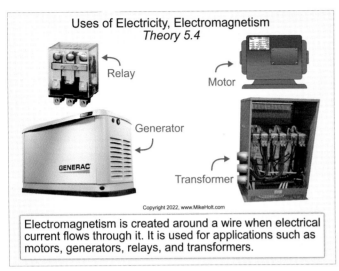

Electromagnetism is created around a wire when electrical current flows through it. It is used for applications such as motors, generators, relays, and transformers.

▶Figure 5–2

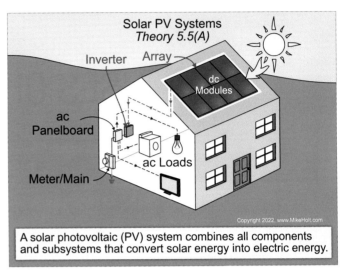

A solar photovoltaic (PV) system combines all components and subsystems that convert solar energy into electric energy.

▶Figure 5–4

5.5 Photoelectricity

Photoelectricity is the conversion of light energy into electrical energy. When photons (light) strike certain semiconductors, they cause electrons to flow from one semiconductor to another, creating the energy necessary to move electrons within a circuit. Photoelectricity is used for many purposes. ▶Figure 5–3

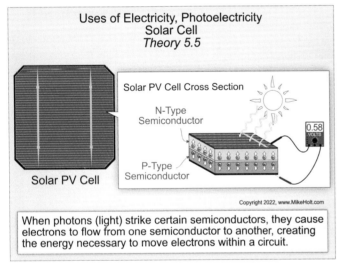

When photons (light) strike certain semiconductors, they cause electrons to flow from one semiconductor to another, creating the energy necessary to move electrons within a circuit.

▶Figure 5–3

(A) Solar Photovoltaic (PV) Systems. A solar photovoltaic (PV) system combines all components and subsystems that convert solar energy into electric energy. The primary use of solar (PV) systems is to power buildings and other structures; other uses of PV systems include: ▶Figure 5–4

(1) Billboard Signs. The billboard industry uses solar PV with storage batteries to illuminate signs in the evening and after dark.

(2) Interstate Call Boxes. Interstate highways use solar PV with storage batteries for roadside assistance devices.

(3) Navigational Markers/Buoys. Solar PV is often used to charge storage batteries connected to lights on navigational markers and buoys to aid marine craft in navigating waterways and inlets. ▶Figure 5–5

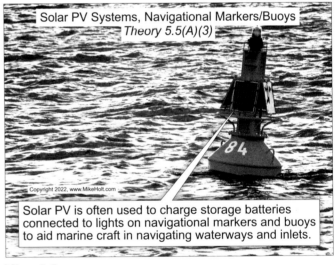

Solar PV is often used to charge storage batteries connected to lights on navigational markers and buoys to aid marine craft in navigating waterways and inlets.

▶Figure 5–5

(4) Roadside Signs. Solar PV and storage batteries are also used to illuminate highway directional, caution, and safety signs thereby eliminating dependence on local electrical utility systems.

(5) Traffic Signal Warning Signs. Small traffic signal lights or speed indicators for school zone warning signs are often solar powered. ▶Figure 5–6

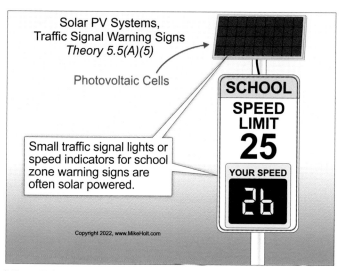

▶Figure 5–6

(6) Telecommunications. When telecommunications equipment and systems are needed in remote areas, such as on mountaintops, solar PV systems have proven economical and dependable.

(7) Weather Stations. Remote weather gathering stations for water levels, streamflow intensity, rain, and snowfall data are often powered by solar PV systems.

(8) Photocells (Light-Dependent Resistors). Photocells "sense and react" to specific light levels to open or close switch contacts to turn equipment (often lights) on at night and off at daylight. ▶Figure 5–7

5.6 Electric Heating

(A) Induction Heating. Induction heating occurs when an expanding and collapsing electromagnetic field from alternating-current flow passes through a ferrous metal (iron) object because of the hysteresis effect. ▶Figure 5–8

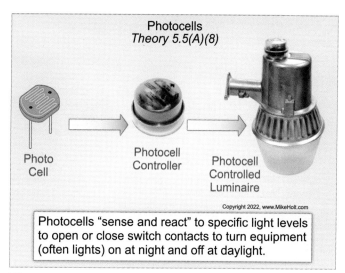

▶Figure 5–7

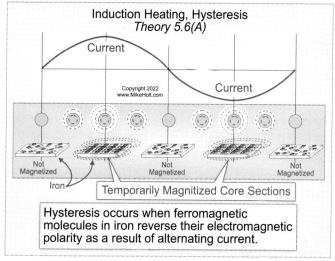

▶Figure 5–8

Heat will be created by the hysteresis effect (the back-and-forth movement of iron molecules) from an alternating electromagnetic field caused by a single wire carrying current inside a metal raceway. ▶Figure 5–9

(B) Resistance Heating. The principle of resistive heating is based on current flowing through a heating element. The movement of the electrons against the resistance within the heating element converts electrical energy into heat. ▶Figure 5–10

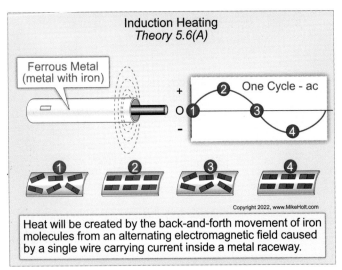

Induction Heating
Theory 5.6(A)

Heat will be created by the back-and-forth movement of iron molecules from an alternating electromagnetic field caused by a single wire carrying current inside a metal raceway.

▶Figure 5–9

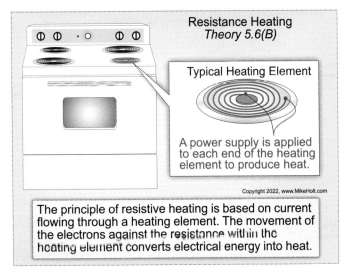

Resistance Heating
Theory 5.6(B)

The principle of resistive heating is based on current flowing through a heating element. The movement of the electrons against the resistance within the heating element converts electrical energy into heat.

▶Figure 5–10

Author's Comment:

▶ Common applications of resistance heating include toasters, ranges, ovens, water heaters, clothes dryers, clothes irons, and space heating.

(C) Thermocouple.

(1) Temperature Measuring Device. A thermocouple is a temperature measuring device that produces a voltage when the temperature of one of the junction points differs from the temperature of the other junction point. ▶Figure 5–11

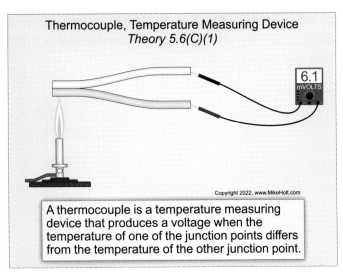

Thermocouple, Temperature Measuring Device
Theory 5.6(C)(1)

A thermocouple is a temperature measuring device that produces a voltage when the temperature of one of the junction points differs from the temperature of the other junction point.

▶Figure 5–11

(2) Safety Feature. A thermocouple can be used as an automatic safety feature by generating the energy needed to shut off valves for gas appliances. When a thermocouple is in a pilot light's flame, it generates enough power to keep the shut-off valve open. If the pilot light goes out, the thermocouple cools down, reducing the energy output to the point that the shut-off valve closes. ▶Figure 5–12

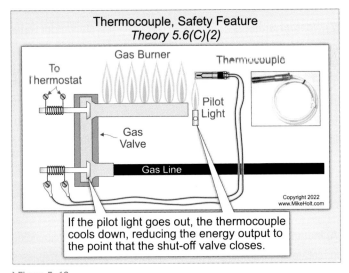

Thermocouple, Safety Feature
Theory 5.6(C)(2)

If the pilot light goes out, the thermocouple cools down, reducing the energy output to the point that the shut-off valve closes.

▶Figure 5–12

5.7 Lighting

An electric light is a device that produces illumination through the principles of incandescence, electric discharge, or a light-emitting diode (LED). ▶Figure 5–13

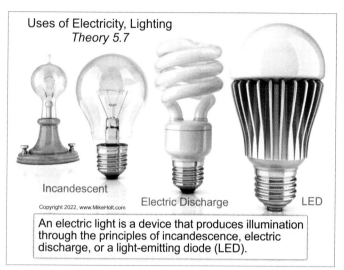

Uses of Electricity, Lighting
Theory 5.7

Incandescent
Electric Discharge
LED

Copyright 2022, www.MikeHolt.com

An electric light is a device that produces illumination through the principles of incandescence, electric discharge, or a light-emitting diode (LED).

▶Figure 5–13

(A) Incandescent Lighting. Incandescent light is produced by heating the filament within a lightbulb to a high temperature. ▶Figure 5–14

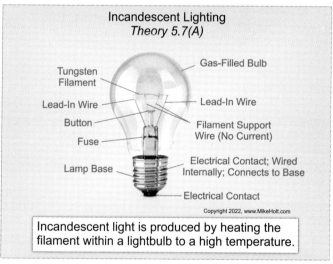

Incandescent Lighting
Theory 5.7(A)

Tungsten Filament
Gas-Filled Bulb
Lead-In Wire
Lead-In Wire
Button
Filament Support Wire (No Current)
Fuse
Electrical Contact; Wired Internally; Connects to Base
Lamp Base
Electrical Contact

Copyright 2022, www.MikeHolt.com

Incandescent light is produced by heating the filament within a lightbulb to a high temperature.

▶Figure 5–14

▸ Less than 5 percent of the energy of an incandescent bulb is converted into visible light, with the remaining 95 percent resulting in heat. Because of the poor efficiency of incandescent lighting, governments worldwide have passed measures to phase out that type of lighting in favor of more energy-efficient lighting alternatives such as electric discharge and light-emitting diodes (LEDs).

(B) Electric-Discharge Lighting. Electric-discharge lighting such as fluorescent, neon, or high-intensity discharge lighting produce light from a high-voltage arc between electrodes in a glass tube containing small amounts of a gas such as xenon or argon.

(1) Fluorescent Lighting. Fluorescent lighting uses a fluorescent bulb coated with fluorescent phosphors. The bulb is filled with mercury vapor and argon gas. When a high-voltage arc between the electrodes occurs in a fluorescent bulb, ultraviolet radiation is emitted causing the phosphor coating to glow. ▶Figure 5–15

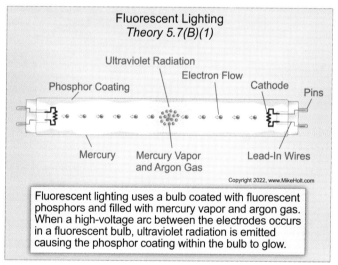

Fluorescent Lighting
Theory 5.7(B)(1)

Ultraviolet Radiation
Electron Flow
Phosphor Coating
Cathode
Pins
Mercury
Mercury Vapor and Argon Gas
Lead-In Wires

Copyright 2022, www.MikeHolt.com

Fluorescent lighting uses a bulb coated with fluorescent phosphors and filled with mercury vapor and argon gas. When a high-voltage arc between the electrodes occurs in a fluorescent bulb, ultraviolet radiation is emitted causing the phosphor coating within the bulb to glow.

▶Figure 5–15

(2) Neon Lighting. Neon lighting is the lighting of choice for exciting colors and shapes. The ability to customize the shape and size of neon bulbs has made them a favorite for attracting attention. Neon light is produced when an electric arc travels through a glass tube filled with a mixture of gases and phosphors. ▶Figure 5–16

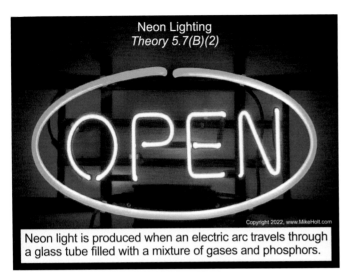

Neon light is produced when an electric arc travels through a glass tube filled with a mixture of gases and phosphors.

▶Figure 5–16

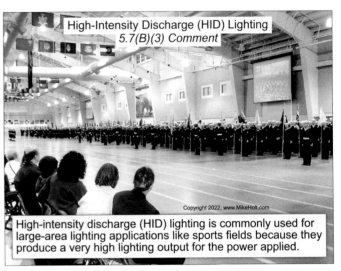

High-intensity discharge (HID) lighting is commonly used for large-area lighting applications like sports fields because they produce a very high lighting output for the power applied.

▶Figure 5–18

(3) High-Intensity Discharge (HID) Lighting. HID light is produced in high-intensity discharge lighting when an electric arc travels through a glass tube filled with argon, xenon, and gaseous metal vapors resulting in very intense light. ▶Figure 5–17

(C) Light-Emitting Diode (LED) Lighting. When direct current passes through a semiconductor device known as a "light-emitting diode," light is produced. ▶Figure 5–19

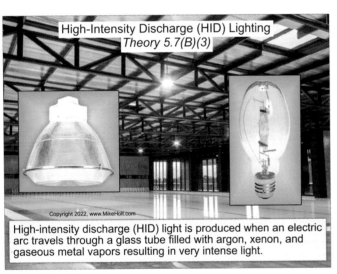

High-intensity discharge (HID) light is produced when an electric arc travels through a glass tube filled with argon, xenon, and gaseous metal vapors resulting in very intense light.

▶Figure 5–17

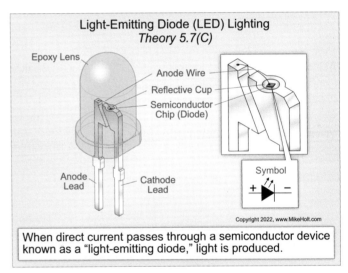

When direct current passes through a semiconductor device known as a "light-emitting diode," light is produced.

▶Figure 5–19

Author's Comment:

▶ High-intensity discharge (HID) lighting is commonly used for large-area lighting applications like sports fields because they produce a very high lighting output for the power applied. ▶Figure 5–18

Author's Comment:

▶ LED lighting surpasses the quality and efficiency of most other lighting systems. It has advantages such as providing more lumens per watt, longer bulb life, instant starting, and reduced cooling and maintenance costs. These benefits, combined with the amazing array of available colors, have positioned LEDs to replace other types of lighting systems.

UNIT

6

DANGERS OF ELECTRICITY

6.1 Introduction

People working in the electrical industry are responsible for ensuring that electrical installations are as safe as possible. In this unit you will learn:

▶ the purpose of the *National Electrical Code*

▶ how electrical fires are created

▶ what electric shock/electrocution are

▶ what arc flashes and arc blasts are

6.2 *National Electrical Code (NEC)*

To ensure the practical safeguarding of persons and property from the use of electricity, all wiring must be installed in accordance with NFPA 70, *National Electrical Code*. Installing electrical systems in accordance with the *NEC* and providing proper maintenance should result in an installation that is essentially free from fire, electric shock or electrocution, and arc flash/arc blast events.

6.3 Electrical Fire

Each year, fires from electrical failures result in the loss of lives and billions of dollars in property damage. The primary cause of an electrical fire is excessive heat when wires are not terminated correctly, not properly sized, and/or the loads exceed the circuits' rating. ▶Figure 6–1

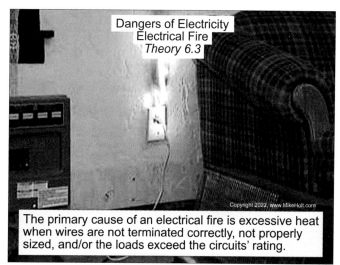

Dangers of Electricity
Electrical Fire
Theory 6.3

Copyright 2022, www.MikeHolt.com

The primary cause of an electrical fire is excessive heat when wires are not terminated correctly, not properly sized, and/or the loads exceed the circuits' rating.

▶Figure 6–1

Author's Comment:

▶ Electrical installations typically fail at the terminations. Wire terminations must be properly tightened in accordance with the manufacturers' torque values. Loose wire terminations can lead to "glowing contacts" (a high resistive point between a wire and a wire terminal), which can cause enough heat for a fire to start. ▶Figure 6–2

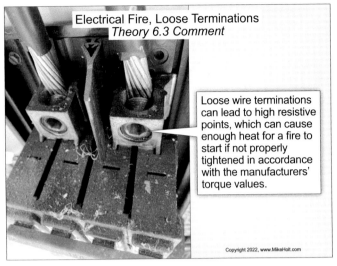

Electrical Fire, Loose Terminations
Theory 6.3 Comment

Loose wire terminations can lead to high resistive points, which can cause enough heat for a fire to start if not properly tightened in accordance with the manufacturers' torque values.

Copyright 2022, www.MikeHolt.com

▶Figure 6–2

6.4 Electric Shock

(A) General. The National Safety Council estimates that approximately 300 people in the United States die each year because of an electric shock from 120V and 277V circuits. For electrical current to flow, there must be a power source and a path for electrons to leave that power source and return to the same power source. People and animals can be shocked or electrocuted when electrons flow through their bodies, especially when those electrons flow through their hearts. ▶Figure 6–3

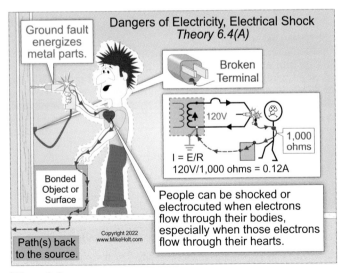

Dangers of Electricity, Electrical Shock
Theory 6.4(A)

Ground fault energizes metal parts.

Broken Terminal

120V

$I = E/R$
120V/1,000 ohms = 0.12A

1,000 ohms

Bonded Object or Surface

People can be shocked or electrocuted when electrons flow through their bodies, especially when those electrons flow through their hearts.

Copyright 2022 www.MikeHolt.com

Path(s) back to the source.

▶Figure 6–3

(B) Electric Shock or Electrocution. In less than a second, an individual can go into atrial fibrillation from electrical current when as little as 50/1,000 of an ampere connects with them. An electric shock disrupts the heart's electrical signal, and when that occurs the heart goes into a rapid, ineffective heartbeat of over 350 beats per minute. This is called "atrial fibrillation" and prevents blood from circulating through the body. Death can result in a matter of minutes (electrocution), particularly when blood circulation to the brain is hindered. Cardiopulmonary resuscitation (CPR) can provide extra time, but defibrillation is essential for surviving atrial fibrillation. ▶Figure 6–4

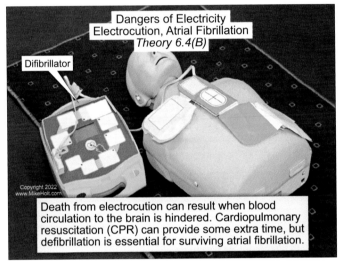

Dangers of Electricity
Electrocution, Atrial Fibrillation
Theory 6.4(B)

Difibrillator

Copyright 2022 www.MikeHolt.com

Death from electrocution can result when blood circulation to the brain is hindered. Cardiopulmonary resuscitation (CPR) can provide some extra time, but defibrillation is essential for surviving atrial fibrillation.

▶Figure 6–4

(C) Severity of Electric Shock. A shock from as little as 30V alternating current for as little as one second can disrupt the heart's electrical circuitry, causing it to go into ventricular fibrillation. The severity of an electric shock depends on the amount of current flowing through the body, which is determined by the electromotive force measured in volts and the contact resistance measured in ohms. The effects of 60 Hz alternating current on an average human include: ▶Figure 6–5

▶ *Electrical Sensation.* Tingle sensation occurs at about 0.30 mA for an adult female and 0.40 mA for an adult male.

▶ *Perception Let-Go.* Current over 0.70 mA is very uncomfortable to both genders.

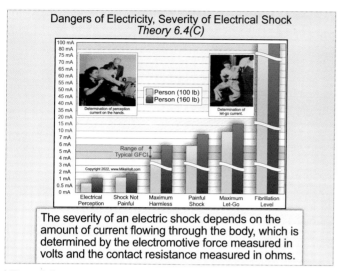

The severity of an electric shock depends on the amount of current flowing through the body, which is determined by the electromotive force measured in volts and the contact resistance measured in ohms.

▶Figure 6–5

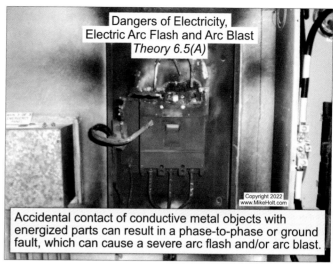

Accidental contact of conductive metal objects with energized parts can result in a phase-to-phase or ground fault, which can cause a severe arc flash and/or arc blast.

▶Figure 6–6

▶ *Maximum Let-Go Level.* The top let-go threshold level for a female is approximately 10 mA, and about 16 mA for a male. The "let-go threshold" is the current level where we lose control of our muscles, and the electricity causes muscles to contract until the current is removed. In other words, at this point we cannot let go of an energized circuit.

▶ *Fibrillation Level.* 50 mA for 0.20 seconds (female) and 75 mA for 0.50 seconds (male).

6.5 Electric Arc Flash and Arc Blast

(A) General. In addition to electric shock, accidental contact of conductive metal objects with energized parts can result in a phase-to-phase or ground fault. These faults can cause a severe arc flash and/or arc blast. ▶Figure 6–6

(B) Arc Flash. During an arcing fault, electrical energy is converted into various other forms of energy. Electrical energy can vaporize metal, which can change from a solid state to a vapor. When copper vaporizes, it expands in volume and creates a superheated plasma. Dangerous arc flashes (explosions of spewing molten metal) are possible when equipment and safeguards are not properly installed and used. An arc flash can cause temperatures approaching 35,000°F to vaporize anything within its immediate vicinity. ▶Figure 6–7

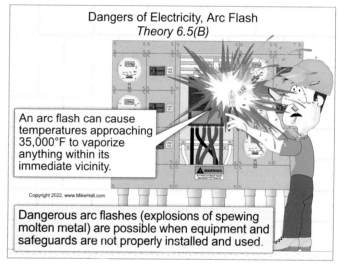

An arc flash can cause temperatures approaching 35,000°F to vaporize anything within its immediate vicinity.

Dangerous arc flashes (explosions of spewing molten metal) are possible when equipment and safeguards are not properly installed and used.

▶Figure 6–7

Author's Comment:

▶ As an electrician it, is important for you to understand the information on an arc flash label to determine what level of personal protective equipment (PPE) to wear. ▶Figure 6–8

(C) Arc Blast. In addition to an arc flash, an arcing fault can generate an arc blast. The strength of an arc blast creates an explosive pressure wave that can eject shrapnel, molten metal, plastic, and paint across a room and cause severe injuries or death to those who are close to the blast. There is no protection against an arc blast! ▶Figure 6–9

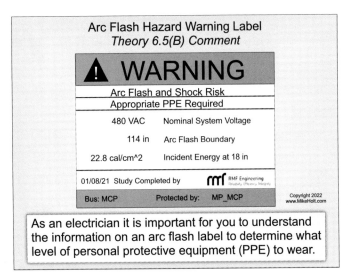

▶Figure 6–8

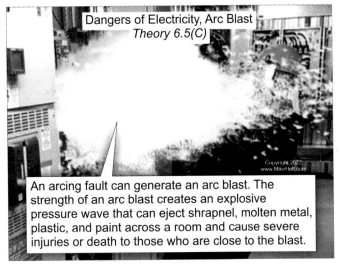

▶Figure 6–9

6.6 Arc Flash Incident Energy

(A) General. Incident energy is the amount of thermal energy measured in cal/cm^2 at a given working distance from an arc flash. Thermal energy of 1.20 cal/cm^2 is sufficient to cause second-degree burns to exposed skin. ▶Figure 6–10

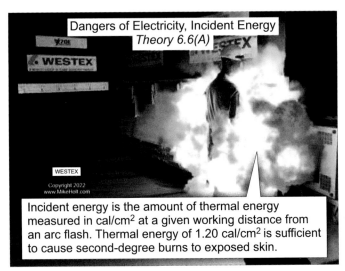

▶Figure 6–10

(1) Incident Energy Analysis. Predicting the amount of available incident energy is crucial when selecting the appropriate personal protective equipment (PPE) to prevent injury from clothing melting or burning due to the use of incorrectly rated PPE. Arc-rated clothing and other PPE associated with exposure to an arc flash must be selected in accordance with NFPA 70E, *Standard for Electrical Safety in the Workplace.* ▶Figure 6–11

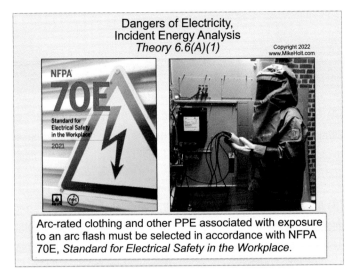

▶Figure 6–11

(B) Incident Energy Calculation. Determining the incident energy at a given point in the electrical system requires software that utilizes the values of short-circuit current and the time it takes for the circuit overcurrent protective device to clear. ▶Figure 6–12

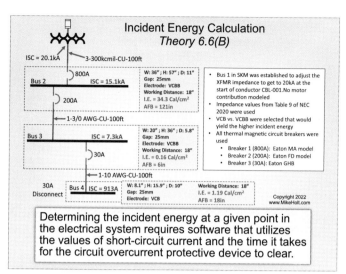

▶Figure 6–12

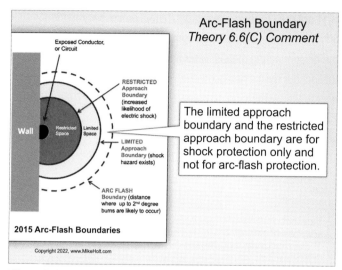

▶Figure 6–14

(C) Arc-Flash Boundary. The arc-flash boundary separates an area in which a person is likely to be exposed to second-degree burns. Where a body part is within the arc-flash boundary, the selected PPE must be rated for the anticipated available incident energy. ▶Figure 6–13

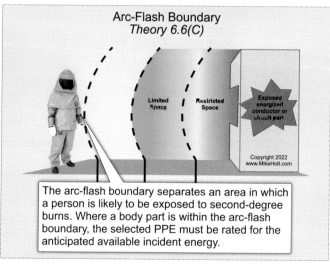

▶Figure 6–13

Author's Comment:

▶ The limited approach boundary and the restricted approach boundary are for shock protection only and not for arc-flash protection. ▶Figure 6–14

6.7 Electrically Safe Work Condition

(A) General. Electrical work should never be performed while electrical equipment is energized. An electrically safe work condition is where electrical circuits have been de-energized, locked out/tagged out, and verification that the circuit is de-energized was completed.

(B) Absence of Voltage Test. In order to de-energize electrical equipment, an absence of voltage test must be performed wearing adequate PPE as required by NFPA 70E, *Standard for Electrical Safety in the Workplace*. ▶Figure 6–15

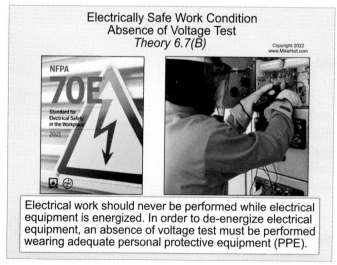

▶Figure 6–15

(C) Lockout/Tagout. The lockout/tagout process is intended to shut off all sources of energy to equipment by preventing the operation of the disconnecting means. After a disconnect has been opened and the lockout device has been attached, a tag is placed on the disconnect to warn others not to operate the disconnect. ▶Figure 6–16

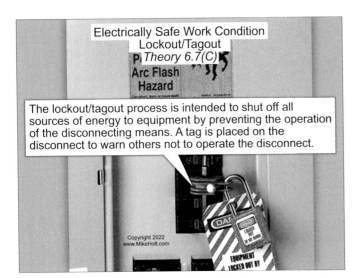

Electrically Safe Work Condition
Lockout/Tagout
Theory 6.7(C)
Arc Flash
Hazard

The lockout/tagout process is intended to shut off all sources of energy to equipment by preventing the operation of the disconnecting means. A tag is placed on the disconnect to warn others not to operate the disconnect.

Copyright 2022
www.MikeHolt.com

▶Figure 6–16

6.8 Personal Protective Equipment

(A) General. PPE is intended to minimize the severity of an injury so it is survivable. Personal protective equipment is designed to protect the body from a particular electrical hazard. Properly selected PPE for an application can protect against other electrical hazards. For example, rubber insulated gloves and leather protectors provide shock protection for hands and forearms and provides arc-flash protection. ▶Figure 6–17

(B) PPE Selection. When selecting the proper PPE for shock and arc-flash protection, the areas of the body to take into consideration include the head, face, neck, chin, eyes, ears, body, hands, arms, and feet. In addition, the protective clothing or gear must allow for movement and visibility. ▶Figure 6–18

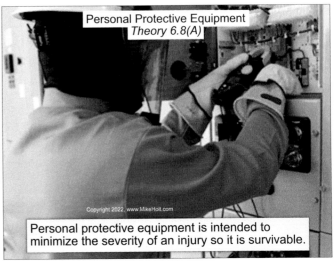

Personal Protective Equipment
Theory 6.8(A)

Copyright 2022. www.MikeHolt.com

Personal protective equipment is intended to minimize the severity of an injury so it is survivable.

▶Figure 6–17

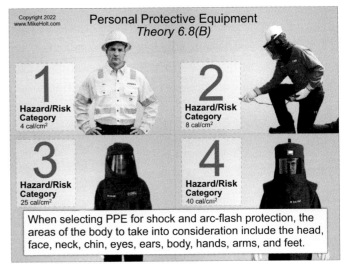

Copyright 2022
www.MikeHolt.com

Personal Protective Equipment
Theory 6.8(B)

1
Hazard/Risk Category
4 cal/cm²

2
Hazard/Risk Category
8 cal/cm²

3
Hazard/Risk Category
25 cal/cm²

4
Hazard/Risk Category
40 cal/cm²

When selecting PPE for shock and arc-flash protection, the areas of the body to take into consideration include the head, face, neck, chin, eyes, ears, body, hands, arms, and feet.

▶Figure 6–18

(C) Arc-Flash PPE Category Method. The Arc-Flash PPE Category Table is used to determine the need for an appropriate level of arc flash PPE and the arc-flash boundary if the following is known.

▶ nominal system voltage

▶ calculated short-circuit current

▶ overcurrent protective device clearing time (0.03 seconds or 2 cycles)

▶ minimum working distance (18 in.)

▶ Arc-Flash PPE Category Method Example

Question: *What level of PPE category and arc-flash boundary is required for a 480V, three-phase panelboard with a short-circuit current of 7,000A, a working distance of 18 in., and a 200A circuit breaker with a clearing time of 0.03 seconds (2 cycles)?* ▶Figure 6–19

(a) Category 1, 19 in.

(b) Category 2, 36 in.

(c) Category 3, 60 in.

(d) Category 4, 240 in.

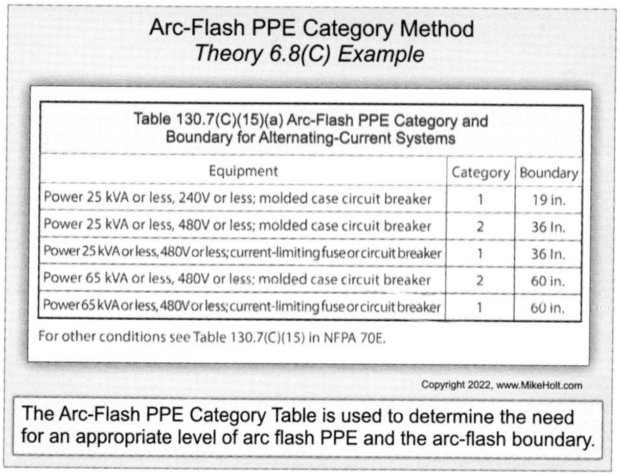

Arc-Flash PPE Category Method
Theory 6.8(C) Example

Table 130.7(C)(15)(a) Arc-Flash PPE Category and Boundary for Alternating-Current Systems		
Equipment	Category	Boundary
Power 25 kVA or less, 240V or less; molded case circuit breaker	1	19 in.
Power 25 kVA or less, 480V or less; molded case circuit breaker	2	36 In.
Power 25 kVA or less, 480V or less; current-limiting fuse or circuit breaker	1	36 In.
Power 65 kVA or less, 480V or less; molded case circuit breaker	2	60 in.
Power 65 kVA or less, 480V or less; current-limiting fuse or circuit breaker	1	60 in.

For other conditions see Table 130.7(C)(15) in NFPA 70E.

Copyright 2022, www.MikeHolt.com

The Arc-Flash PPE Category Table is used to determine the need for an appropriate level of arc flash PPE and the arc-flash boundary.

▶Figure 6–19

Answer: *(b) Category 2, 36 in.*

CHAPTER 2

PRACTICE QUESTIONS

CHAPTER 2—PRACTICE QUESTIONS

Unit 5—Uses of Electricity

5.2 Uses of Electricity

1. _____ has many uses, the most common include electrochemical processes, electromagnetism, solar PV systems, heat, and lighting.

    (a) Electricity
    (b) Magnetism
    (c) Static electricity
    (d) None of these

5.3 Electrochemical Processes

2. "_____" uses electricity to transfer dissolved, positively charged metal to the surface of a negatively charged metal.

    (a) Electroplating
    (b) Electromagnetism
    (c) Electric heating
    (d) Electric discharge lighting

5.4 Electromagnetism

3. _____ from current flow is used for many applications such as motors, generators, relays, and transformers.

    (a) Electroplating
    (b) Electromagnetism
    (c) Electric heating
    (d) Electric discharge lighting

5.5 Photoelectricity

4. _____ is the conversion of light energy into electrical energy.

    (a) Photoelectricity
    (b) Electromagnetism
    (c) Electric heating
    (d) Chemical activity

5. A solar _____ system combines all components and subsystems that convert solar energy into electric energy.

    (a) pluton
    (b) photovoltaic (PV)
    (c) electron
    (d) none of these

5.6 Electric Heating

6. _____ heating occurs when an expanding and collapsing electromagnetic field from current flow passes through ferrous metal (iron).

    (a) Capacitance
    (b) Induction
    (c) Resistive
    (d) Reactance

7. When the electromagnetic field changes polarity from positive to negative and then negative to positive, the ferromagnetic molecules in the iron reverse their electromagnetic polarity. This is known as "_____."

    (a) capacitance
    (b) induction
    (c) resistance
    (d) hysteresis

8. The principle of _____ heating is that when current flows through a heating element, the movement of the electrons against the resistance within the heating element converts electrical energy into heat.

   (a) capacitance
   (b) induction
   (c) resistive
   (d) hysteresis

9. A typical application of thermoelectricity is the _____, a temperature measuring device that produces a voltage when the temperature of one of the junction points differs from the temperature of the other junction point.

   (a) thermostat
   (b) magnetic coupler
   (c) thermocouple
   (d) thermometer

10. If the pilot light goes out, the thermocouple cools down, reducing the energy output to the point that the shut-off valve _____.

   (a) activates
   (b) opens
   (c) closes
   (d) activates and opens

5.7 Lighting

11. An electric light is a device that produces _____ through the principles of incandescence, electric discharge, or a light-emitting diode (LED).

   (a) heat
   (b) illumination
   (c) gas
   (d) sunshine

12. _____ light is produced by heating the filament within a light-bulb to a high temperature.

   (a) Incandescent
   (b) Fluorescent
   (c) LED
   (d) HID

13. _____ lighting such as fluorescent, neon, or high-intensity discharge lighting produce light from a high-voltage arc between electrodes in a glass tube containing small amounts of a gas such as xenon or argon.

   (a) Electric-discharge
   (b) Electric heat
   (c) Arc
   (d) none of these

14. When a high-voltage arc between the electrodes occurs in a _____ bulb, ultraviolet radiation is emitted causing the phosphor coating to glow.

   (a) incandescent
   (b) fluorescent
   (c) LED
   (d) none of these

15. _____ light is produced when an electric arc travels through a glass tube filled with a mixture of gases and phosphors.

   (a) Incandescent
   (b) Neon
   (c) Solar
   (d) none of these

16. _____ light is produced in high-intensity discharge lighting when an electric arc travels through a glass tube filled with argon, xenon, and gaseous metal vapors resulting in very intense light.

   (a) Incandescent
   (b) HID
   (c) Solar
   (d) none of these

17. When direct current passes through a semiconductor device known as a(an) "_____," light is produced.

    (a) incandescent circuit
    (b) light-emitting diode
    (c) fluorescent tube
    (d) none of these

Unit 6—Dangers of Electricity

6.2 National Electrical Code (NEC)

1. To ensure the minimum practical safeguarding of persons and property from the use of _____, all wiring must be installed in accordance with the *National Electrical Code* (*NEC*).

    (a) magnetism
    (b) electricity
    (c) heating
    (d) welding

6.3 Electrical Fire

2. The primary causes of an electrical _____ is excessive heat when wires are not terminated correctly, not properly sized, and the loads exceed the circuit wires' ampacity rating.

    (a) fire
    (b) overload
    (c) short circuit
    (d) fault

6.4 Electric Shock

3. The National Safety Council estimates that approximately _____ people in the United States die each year because of an electric shock from 120V and 277V circuits.

    (a) 100
    (b) 200
    (c) 300
    (d) 400

4. People and animals can be _____ or electrocuted when electrons flow through their bodies, especially when those electrons flow through their hearts.

    (a) knocked out
    (b) shocked
    (c) startled
    (d) injured

5. An electric shock disrupts the heart's electrical signal, and when that occurs, the heart goes into a rapid, ineffective heartbeat of over 350 beats per minute. This is called "_____ fibrillation" and prevents blood from circulating through the body.

    (a) atrial
    (b) ventricular
    (c) pressure
    (d) none of these

6. The severity of an electric shock is dependent on the amount of current flowing through the body, which is impacted by circuit voltage and _____ resistance.

    (a) contact
    (b) the Earth's
    (c) the body's
    (d) circuit

6.5 Electric Arc Flash and Arc Blast

7. In addition to electric shock, accidental contact of conductive metal objects with energized parts can result in a phase-to-phase or ground fault. These faults can cause a severe _____.

    (a) arc flash
    (b) arc blast
    (c) arc flash and/or arc blast
    (d) none of these

8. An electric arc flash can cause temperatures approaching _____ to vaporize anything within its immediate vicinity.

   (a) 10,000°F
   (b) 15,000°F
   (c) 25,000°F
   (d) 35,000°F

9. The strength of an arc _____ creates an explosive pressure wave that can eject shrapnel, molten metal, plastic, and paint across a room and cause severe injuries or death.

   (a) flash
   (b) blast
   (c) fault
   (d) fire

6.6 Arc Flash Incident Energy

10. _____ energy is the amount of thermal energy measured in cal/cm^2 at a given working distance during an electric arc flash event.

    (a) Flash
    (b) Blast
    (c) Fault
    (d) Incident

11. Predicting the amount of available incident energy is crucial when selecting the appropriate _____ to prevent injury from clothing melting or burning.

    (a) personal protective equipment
    (b) long-sleeved shirt
    (c) helmet
    (d) gloves

12. Determining the incident energy at a given point in the electrical system requires _____ that utilizes the values of short-circuit current and the time it takes for the circuit overcurrent protective device to open.

    (a) PPE
    (b) software
    (c) an app
    (d) a calculator

13. The arc-flash _____ separates an area in which a person is likely to be exposed to second-degree burns.

    (a) zone
    (b) perimeter
    (c) boundary
    (d) area

6.7 Electrically Safe Work Condition

14. A(An) _____ safe work condition is where electrical circuits have been de-energized, locked out/tagged out, and tested to verify that the circuit is de-energized.

    (a) arc
    (b) PPE
    (c) mechanically
    (d) clectrically

15. In order to de-energize electrical equipment, a(an) _____ of voltage test must be performed wearing the adequate personal protective equipment (PPE) as required by NFPA 70E, *Standard for Electrical Safety in the Workplace*.

    (a) absence
    (b) missing
    (c) confirmation
    (d) diagnosis

16. The intent of the _____ is to shut off all sources of energy by operating the applicable disconnecting means.

    (a) lockout/tagout process
    (b) safety program
    (c) employee handbook
    (d) safety meeting

6.8 Personal Protective Equipment

17. Personal protective equipment (PPE) is intended to _____ the severity of an injury so it is survivable.

    (a) eliminate
    (b) maximize
    (c) minimize
    (d) deflect

18. The protective clothing or gear must allow for _____.

    (a) movement
    (b) visibility
    (c) movement and visibility
    (d) none of these

CHAPTER 3

MAGNETISM AND ELECTROMAGNETISM

Chapter 3—Magnetism and Electromagnetism

Unit 7—Basics of Magnetism

Studying magnetism provides the background necessary to understand electromagnetism. In this unit you will learn:

- ▸ the law of attraction and repulsion of magnets
- ▸ why some metals are easily magnetized and how to demagnetize metals
- ▸ the difference between permanent and temporary magnets
- ▸ about the magnetic field around a magnet

Unit 8—Electromagnetism

Electromagnetism is used in electrical applications such as motors, transformers, generators, doorbells, telephones, and many other types of electrical equipment. In this unit you will learn:

- ▸ how electromagnetism in a wire is produced
- ▸ about electromagnetic field intensity
- ▸ how an electromagnetic field is influenced by the shape of the wire

Unit 9—Uses of Electromagnetism

In this unit you will learn of the common uses of electromagnetism for motors, generators, relays, and transformers.

1st Printing

BASICS OF MAGNETISM

7.1 Introduction

Studying magnetism provides the background necessary to understand electromagnetism. In this unit you will learn:

▶ the law of attraction and repulsion of magnets

▶ why some metals are easily magnetized and how to demagnetize metals

▶ the difference between permanent and temporary magnets

▶ about the magnetic field around a magnet

7.2 The Natural Magnet

Over 2,000 years ago, the ancient Greeks in Magnesia, Greece discovered that certain stones could magically attract small pieces of iron. The magic stones were used for compasses and became known as "lodestoncs" meaning "leading stone." ▶Figure 7–1

The Natural Magnet
Theory 7.2

Over 2,000 years ago, the ancient Greeks in Magnesia, Greece discovered that certain stones could magically attract small pieces of iron.

Copyright 2022, www.MikeHolt.com

▶Figure 7–1

7.3 Magnetic Polarities

When a magnet is allowed to swing freely, it will align itself with the Earth's magnetic field. The end of the magnet that points to the Earth's north pole is called the "north-seeking pole," and the opposite end of the magnet is called the "south-seeking pole." ▶Figure 7–2

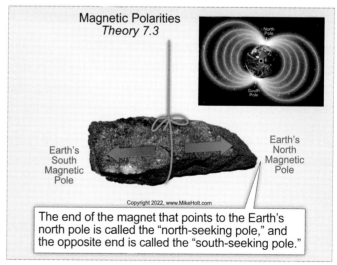

Magnetic Polarities
Theory 7.3

Earth's South Magnetic Pole

Earth's North Magnetic Pole

The end of the magnet that points to the Earth's north pole is called the "north-seeking pole," and the opposite end is called the "south-seeking pole."

Copyright 2022, www.MikeHolt.com

▶Figure 7–2

7.4 Theory of Magnetism

There are different theories that explain magnetism, one is Ewing's Molecular Theory of magnets which states, "Molecules of magnetic materials such as iron have a north and south pole." The magnetic molecules in iron can align themselves so their magnetic poles point in the same direction. The iron is magnetized when the magnetic forces of the molecules combine. ▶Figure 7–3

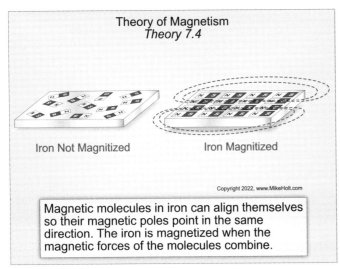

Theory of Magnetism
Theory 7.4

Iron Not Magnitized   Iron Magnitized

Copyright 2022, www.MikeHolt.com

Magnetic molecules in iron can align themselves so their magnetic poles point in the same direction. The iron is magnetized when the magnetic forces of the molecules combine.

▶Figure 7–3

7.5 Permanent and Temporary Magnets

When a magnet keeps its magnetic field for a long time, it is called a "permanent magnet." If it loses its magnetism quickly, it is called a "temporary magnet." Hard iron and steel are used to make permanent magnets and soft iron is used to make temporary magnets.

(A) Permanent Magnets. Permanent magnets are used to stick a note on your refrigerator and in equipment such as electric measuring instruments and compasses.

Authors Comment:

▶ A compass is made with a tiny permanent magnet that pivots freely to easily align the north-seeking pole of the compass needle to the north magnetic pole of the Earth. ▶Figure 7–4

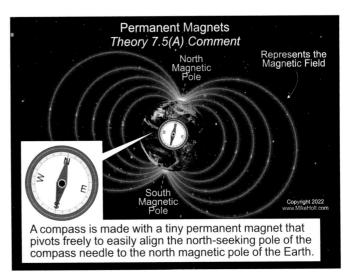

Permanent Magnets
Theory 7.5(A) Comment

North Magnetic Pole

Represents the Magnetic Field

South Magnetic Pole

Copyright 2022 www.MikeHolt.com

A compass is made with a tiny permanent magnet that pivots freely to easily align the north-seeking pole of the compass needle to the north magnetic pole of the Earth.

▶Figure 7–4

(B) Temporary Magnets. Temporary magnets (electromagnets) are used in motors, generators, transformers, and relays. ▶Figure 7–5

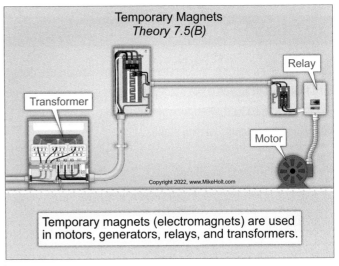

Temporary Magnets
Theory 7.5(B)

Relay

Transformer

Motor

Copyright 2022, www.MikeHolt.com

Temporary magnets (electromagnets) are used in motors, generators, relays, and transformers.

▶Figure 7–5

7.6 Magnetizing and Demagnetizing Magnets

(A) Magnetizing. To magnetize iron, a magnetic force must be applied to the metal with a magnet, or an electromagnetic field must be applied to the metal. For example, a compass needle can be magnetized by stroking the material with a magnet and then floating it on water. ▶Figure 7–6

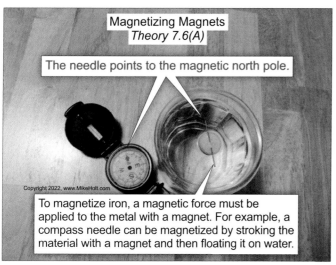

▶Figure 7–6

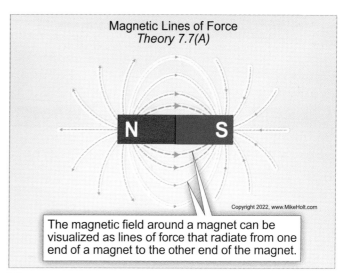

▶Figure 7–7

(B) Demagnetizing. To demagnetize iron, its magnetic fields must be disarranged so the molecules return to random positions. Iron can be demagnetized as follows:

(1) Striking the iron with a hard impact will cause the magnet to lose some magnetism. Each subsequent hard impact will return more molecules to random positions.

(2) Heat the iron to excite the molecules out of magnetic alignment.

(3) Place the iron in a reversing electromagnetic field.

7.7 Magnetic Lines of Force

(A) General. The magnetic field around a magnet can be visualized as lines of force that radiate from one end of a magnet to the other end of the magnet. Magnetic lines of force cannot cross each other ▶Figure 7–7

(B) Intensity. The intensity of the magnetic lines of force are stronger near the magnet's poles and become weaker as they move away from the magnet. Magnetic lines of force cannot cross other magnetic lines of force. ▶Figure 7–8

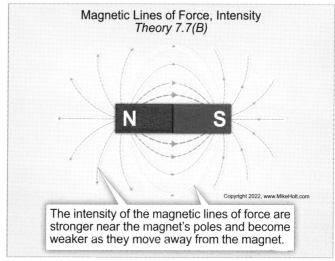

▶Figure 7–8

7.8 Law of Attraction and Repulsion of Magnets

The magnetic field of a magnet can attract or repel the magnetic field of another magnet. The Law of Attraction and Repulsion states, "Like magnetic poles repel each other and unlike magnetic poles attract each other." ▶Figure 7–9

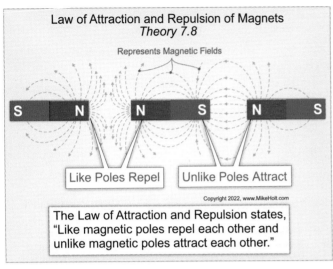

UNIT 8

ELECTROMAGNETISM

8.2 Electromagnetism in a Wire

(A) General. In 1820, Hans Oersted discovered that when he applied power from a battery to a section of wire, the electrons flowing in the wire produced an electromagnetic field that influenced the direction in which a nearby compass pointed. ▸Figure 8–1

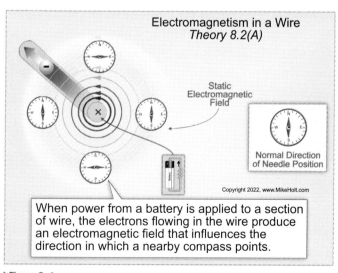

When power from a battery is applied to a section of wire, the electrons flowing in the wire produce an electromagnetic field that influences the direction in which a nearby compass points.

▸Figure 8–1

(B) Reversing Electromagnetic Field. Oersted also discovered that reversing the direction of electrons flowing in the wire would reverse the orientation of a nearby compass. ▸Figure 8–2

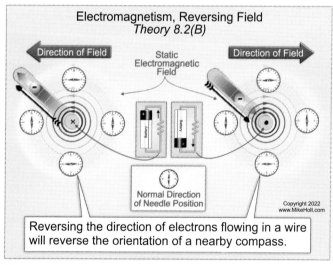

Reversing the direction of electrons flowing in a wire will reverse the orientation of a nearby compass.

▸Figure 8–2

(C) Electromagnetic Field Intensity. The lines of force from electromagnetism increase with increased electron current flow. The lines of force from electromagnetism will decrease as their distance from the wire increases. ▸Figure 8–3

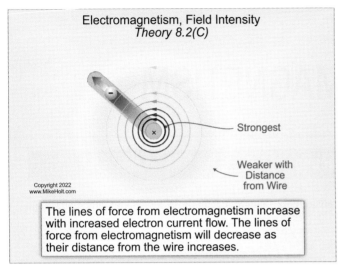

Electromagnetism, Field Intensity
Theory 8.2(C)

— Strongest

← Weaker with Distance from Wire

Copyright 2022
www.MikeHolt.com

The lines of force from electromagnetism increase with increased electron current flow. The lines of force from electromagnetism will decrease as their distance from the wire increases.

▶Figure 8–3

8.3 Electromagnet Field Interaction

(A) Current in Opposite Directions. When two wires with current flowing in opposite directions are next to each other, the electromagnetic fields generated by the current flowing in each wire will repel each other. Since electromagnetic fields cannot cross one another, the repelling electromagnetic fields attempt to push the wires apart. ▶Figure 8–4

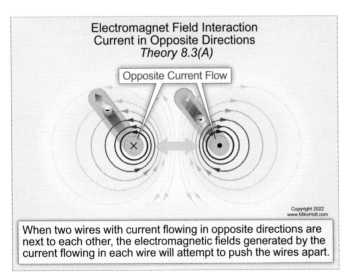

Electromagnet Field Interaction
Current in Opposite Directions
Theory 8.3(A)

Opposite Current Flow

Copyright 2022
www.MikeHolt.com

When two wires with current flowing in opposite directions are next to each other, the electromagnetic fields generated by the current flowing in each wire will attempt to push the wires apart.

▶Figure 8–4

(B) Current in the Same Direction. When two wires with current flowing in the same direction are next to each other, the electromagnetic fields of the wires will combine. The combined electromagnetic fields of the wires will have greater intensity and pull the wires together. ▶Figure 8–5

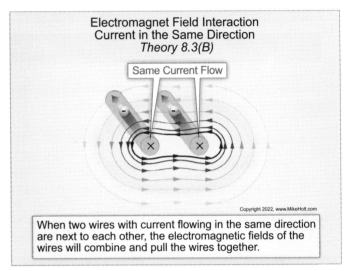

Electromagnet Field Interaction
Current in the Same Direction
Theory 8.3(B)

Same Current Flow

Copyright 2022, www.MikeHolt.com

When two wires with current flowing in the same direction are next to each other, the electromagnetic fields of the wires will combine and pull the wires together.

▶Figure 8–5

8.4 Electromagnetic Field Interaction of Wire Loops

(A) General. When a wire is formed into a loop, the electromagnetic fields around the wire will flow into the wire loop on one side and out of the other side. When this occurs, the electromagnetic fields in the center of the wire loop will be compressed. ▶Figure 8–6

Author's Comment:

▶ The direction of the electromagnetic field around a wire, based on electron current flow theory follows the "left-hand rule," where the thumb represents the direction of current flow, and the four fingers represent the direction of the magnetic field. ▶Figure 8–7

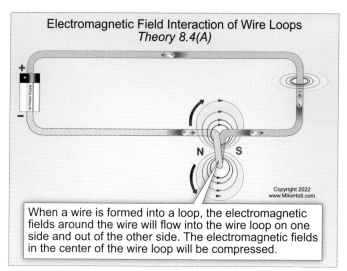

Electromagnetic Field Interaction of Wire Loops
Theory 8.4(A)

When a wire is formed into a loop, the electromagnetic fields around the wire will flow into the wire loop on one side and out of the other side. The electromagnetic fields in the center of the wire loop will be compressed.

▶Figure 8–6

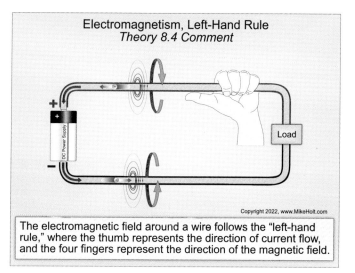

Electromagnetism, Left-Hand Rule
Theory 8.4 Comment

The electromagnetic field around a wire follows the "left-hand rule," where the thumb represents the direction of current flow, and the four fingers represent the direction of the magnetic field.

▶Figure 8–7

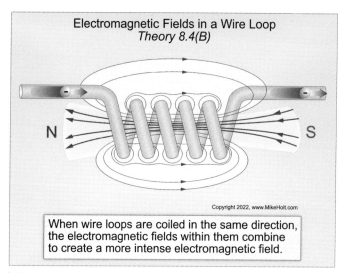

Electromagnetic Fields in a Wire Loop
Theory 8.4(B)

When wire loops are coiled in the same direction, the electromagnetic fields within them combine to create a more intense electromagnetic field.

▶Figure 8–8

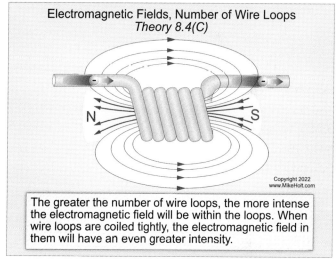

Electromagnetic Fields, Number of Wire Loops
Theory 8.4(C)

The greater the number of wire loops, the more intense the electromagnetic field will be within the loops. When wire loops are coiled tightly, the electromagnetic field in them will have an even greater intensity.

▶Figure 8–9

(B) Electromagnetic Fields in a Wire Loop. When wire loops are coiled in the same direction, the electromagnetic fields within them combine to create a more intense electromagnetic field. ▶**Figure 8–8**

(C) Number of Wire Loops. The greater the number of wire loops, the more intense the electromagnetic field will be within the loops. When wire loops are coiled tightly, the electromagnetic field in them will have an even greater intensity. ▶**Figure 8–9**

8.5 Electromagnetic Core

The electromagnetic field in wire loops can be made more intense by placing a soft iron core inside the coil winding. The iron core inside the wire loops permits a higher concentration of electromagnetic lines of force than does air alone. ▶**Figure 8–10**

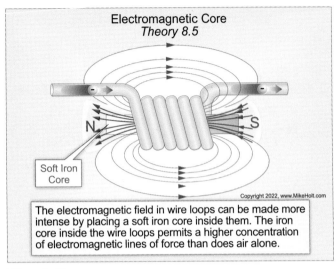

The electromagnetic field in wire loops can be made more intense by placing a soft iron core inside them. The iron core inside the wire loops permits a higher concentration of electromagnetic lines of force than does air alone.

▶Figure 8–10

UNIT
9

USES OF ELECTROMAGNETISM

9.1 Introduction

In this unit you will learn of the common uses of electromagnetism for motors, generators, relays, and transformers. ▶Figure 9–1

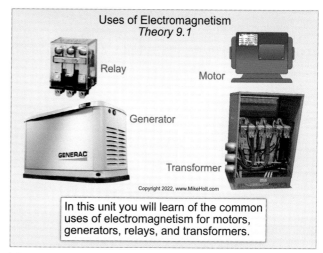

Uses of Electromagnetism
Theory 9.1

Relay

Motor

Generator

GENERAC

Transformer

Copyright 2022, www.MikeHolt.com

In this unit you will learn of the common uses of electromagnetism for motors, generators, relays, and transformers.

▶Figure 9–1

9.2 Motors

Motors convert electrical energy into mechanical work and operate on the principle of attracting and repelling electromagnetic fields to turn the shaft of a motor. Motors are used in many applications such as fans, conveyors, water pumps, appliances, compressors, and so on. ▶Figure 9–2

Author's Comment:

▶ Details about electromagnetism as it relates to motors are explained later in this material.

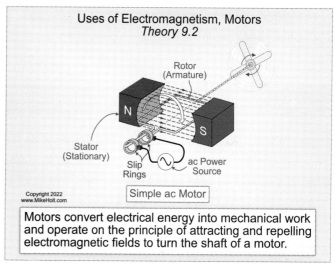

Uses of Electromagnetism, Motors
Theory 9.2

Rotor
(Armature)

N

S

Stator
(Stationary)

Slip
Rings

ac Power
Source

Copyright 2022
www.MikeHolt.com

Simple ac Motor

Motors convert electrical energy into mechanical work and operate on the principle of attracting and repelling electromagnetic fields to turn the shaft of a motor.

▶Figure 9–2

9.3 Generators

The operation of an electrical generator is opposite that of a motor in that a generator converts mechanical work into electrical energy using the principle of electromagnetism. Generators are used for many applications such as utility power plants, and for temporary and permanent power. ▶Figure 9–3

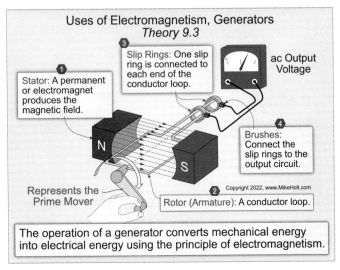

▶Figure 9–3

Author's Comment:

▸ Details about electromagnetism as it relates to generators are explained later in this material.

9.4 Relays

A relay is a switch which uses electromagnetism to open or close a contact(s). One part of the relay contact is fixed, and the other part of the relay contact is moved by an electromagnetic field to either open or close the relay contact. ▶Figure 9–4

Author's Comment:

▸ Details about electromagnetism as it relates to relays are explained later in this material.

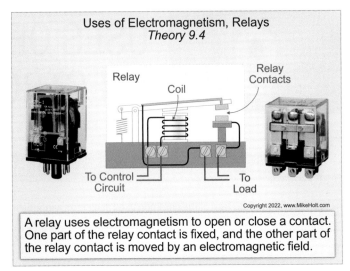

A relay uses electromagnetism to open or close a contact. One part of the relay contact is fixed, and the other part of the relay contact is moved by an electromagnetic field.

▶Figure 9–4

9.5 Transformers

A transformer uses electromagnetism to convert input voltage to an output voltage. Transformers are used for many applications from utility transmission and distribution to simple power supplies for home appliances and computers. ▶Figure 9–5

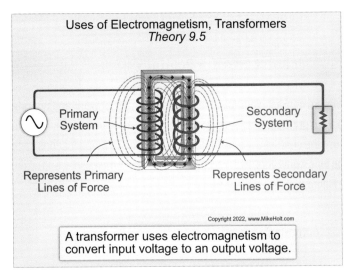

A transformer uses electromagnetism to convert input voltage to an output voltage.

▶Figure 9–5

Author's Comment:

▸ Details about electromagnetism as it relates to transformers are explained later in this material.

CHAPTER 3

PRACTICE QUESTIONS

CHAPTER 3—PRACTICE QUESTIONS

Unit 7—Basics of Magnetism

7.2 The Natural Magnet

1. The Greeks discovered that certain stones could magically attract small pieces of iron. The magic stones were used for compasses and became known as "_____" meaning "leading stone."

    (a) iron core
    (b) lodestones
    (c) Earth
    (d) compass crystals

7.3 Magnetic Polarities

2. When a magnet is allowed to swing freely, it will align itself with the _____ magnetic field(s).

    (a) Earth's
    (b) magnet's
    (c) crystal's
    (d) rock's

3. The end of the magnet that points to the north is called the "_____-seeking pole."

    (a) south
    (b) north
    (c) Earth
    (d) none of these

7.4 Theory of Magnetism

4. The magnetic molecules in iron can align themselves so their magnetic poles point in the _____ direction.

    (a) same
    (b) opposite
    (c) Earth's
    (d) magnet's

7.5 Permanent and Temporary Magnets

5. When magnetized material keeps its magnetic field for a long time, it is a _____ magnet.

    (a) plastic
    (b) temporary
    (c) permanent
    (d) crystal

6. If a metal loses its magnetism quickly, it is a _____ magnet.

    (a) plastic
    (b) temporary
    (c) permanent
    (d) crystal

7. _____ magnets are used to stick a note on your refrigerator, and in equipment such as electric measuring instruments.

    (a) Plastic
    (b) Temporary
    (c) Permanent
    (d) Crystal

8. _____ magnets (electromagnets) are used in motors, generators, transformers, and relays.

   (a) Plastic
   (b) Temporary
   (c) Permanent
   (d) Crystal

7.6 Magnetizing and Demagnetizing Magnets

9. To _____ iron, a magnetic force must be applied to the metal with a magnet, or an electromagnetic field must be applied to the metal.

   (a) magnetize
   (b) demagnetize
   (c) destroy
   (d) heat

10. To _____ iron, its magnetic fields must be disarranged so the molecules return to a random position.

    (a) magnetize
    (b) demagnetize
    (c) destroy
    (d) heat

7.7 Magnetic Lines of Force

11. Magnetic lines of force _____ cross each other.

    (a) can
    (b) cannot
    (c) do
    (d) do not

12. The _____ of the magnetic lines of force are stronger near a magnet's poles and become weaker as they move away from the magnet.

    (a) intensity
    (b) force
    (c) power
    (d) volume

7.8 Law of Attraction and Repulsion of Magnets

13. The Law of Attraction and Repulsion of magnets states, "Like poles _____ each other and unlike poles _____ each other."

    (a) repel, attract
    (b) attract, repel
    (c) oppose, oppose
    (d) none of these

Unit 8—Electromagnetism

8.2 Electromagnetism in a Wire

1. Hans Oersted discovered that when he applied power from a battery to a section of wire, the electrons flowing in the wire produced a(an) _____ field that influenced the direction in which a nearby compass pointed.

   (a) magnetic
   (b) electromagnetic
   (c) current
   (d) voltage

2. Reversing the direction of electrons flowing in a wire will _____ the orientation of a nearby compass.

   (a) reverse
   (b) oppose
   (c) attract
   (d) repel

3. The lines of force from electromagnetism will _____ as their distance from a wire increases.

   (a) increase
   (b) decrease
   (c) stay the same
   (d) none of these

8.3 Electromagnet Field Interaction

4. When two wires with current flowing in opposite directions are next to each other, the electromagnetic fields generated by the current flowing in each wire will _____ each other.

    (a) repel
    (b) attract
    (c) combine with
    (d) none of these

5. When two wires with current flowing in the same direction are next to each other, the electromagnetic fields of the wires will _____.

    (a) repel each other
    (b) oppose each other
    (c) combine
    (d) none of these

8.4 Electromagnetic Field Interaction of Wire Loops

6. If a wire is formed into a loop, the electromagnetic fields around the wire will be _____.

    (a) twisted
    (b) compressed
    (c) weaker
    (d) expanded

7. If the wire loops are coiled in the same direction, the electro-magnetic fields within the wire loops combine to create a _____ electromagnetic field.

    (a) more intense
    (b) softer
    (c) more capable
    (d) smaller

8. The _____ the number of wire loops, the more intense the elec-tromagnetic field will be within the loops.

    (a) greater
    (b) fewer
    (c) closer together
    (d) further apart

8.5 Electromagnetic Core

9. The electromagnetic field in wire loops can be made more intense by placing a soft _____ core inside the coil windings.

    (a) silver
    (b) plastic
    (c) metal
    (d) iron

Unit 9—Uses of Electromagnetism

9.2 Motors

1. Motors convert electrical energy into _____ work and operate on the principle of attracting and repelling electromagnetic fields to turn the shaft of a motor.

    (a) voltage
    (b) electrical
    (c) mechanical
    (d) magnetic

9.3 Generators

2. The operation of an electrical generator is opposite that of a motor in that a generator converts mechanical energy into _____ energy using the principle of electromagnetism.

    (a) voltage
    (b) electrical
    (c) horsepower
    (d) magnetic

9.4 Relays

3. A relay is a switch that uses _____ to open or close its contacts.

    (a) resistance
    (b) electromagnetism
    (c) springs
    (d) power

9.5 Transformers

4.   A _____ uses electromagnetism to convert input voltage to a
      different output voltage.

      (a) motor
      (b) generator
      (c) transformer
      (d) relay

CHAPTER 4

MATHEMATICS

Chapter 4—Mathematics

Unit 10—Basic Math

Understanding math is the foundation to becoming a successful electrician. Many people fear math, but as you work through this material you will see there is nothing to fear. In this unit you will learn:

▸ the difference between whole numbers and fractional numbers

▸ how to convert a percentage into a decimal to use as a multiplier

▸ the differences between a reciprocal, a square root, and squaring a number

Unit 11—Trigonometry

Trigonometry is the mathematical study of triangles, particularly right triangles. Trigonometry is used to determine three-phase voltage systems, size power factor correction capacitors, and determine alternating-current wire impedance. In this unit you will learn:

▸ what right triangles are

▸ what the Pythagorean Theorem is

▸ what sines, cosines, and tangents are

BASIC MATH

10.1 Introduction

Understanding mathematics is the foundation to becoming a successful electrical professional. As you work through this material you will see how easy math is. In this unit you will learn:

▶ the difference between whole numbers and fractional numbers

▶ how to convert a percentage into a decimal to use as a multiplier

▶ the differences between a reciprocal, a square root, and squaring a number

10.2 Whole Numbers

Whole numbers are exactly what the term implies; these numbers do not contain any fractions, decimals, or percentages.

10.3 Fractional Numbers

Parts of a whole number are called "fractions" from the Latin word "fractus," meaning broken into parts. ▶Figure 10–1

10.4 Decimal Numbers

(A) General. A decimal number is a number that is a fractional part of a number separated by a decimal point.

(B) Fractions Converted to Decimal Numbers. A fraction represents part of a whole number. If you use a calculator for adding, dividing, subtracting, or multiplying fractions, you need to convert the fraction to a decimal or whole number. To change a fraction to a decimal or whole number, divide the top number of the fraction by its bottom number. ▶Figure 10–2

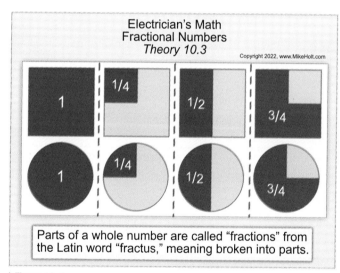

Electrician's Math
Fractional Numbers
Theory 10.3
Copyright 2022, www.MikeHolt.com

Parts of a whole number are called "fractions" from the Latin word "fractus," meaning broken into parts.

▶Figure 10–1

(C) Number of Decimal Places. The decimal system places numbers to the right of a decimal point to indicate values that are a fraction of "one." For example, the first digit on the right of the decimal is one-tenth of a whole number, the second is one-hundredth of a whole number, and the third digit is one-thousandth of a whole number. ▶Figure 10–3

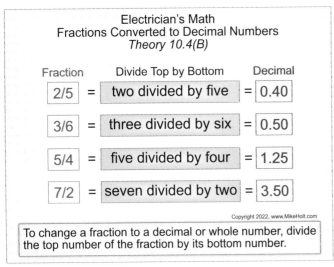

Electrician's Math
Fractions Converted to Decimal Numbers
Theory 10.4(B)

Fraction	Divide Top by Bottom	Decimal
2/5 =	two divided by five =	0.40
3/6 =	three divided by six =	0.50
5/4 =	five divided by four =	1.25
7/2 =	seven divided by two =	3.50

Copyright 2022, www.MikeHolt.com

To change a fraction to a decimal or whole number, divide the top number of the fraction by its bottom number.

▶Figure 10–2

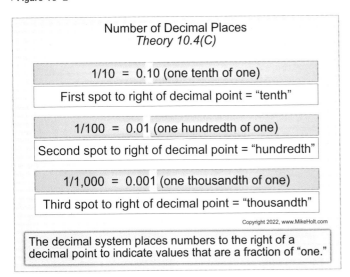

Number of Decimal Places
Theory 10.4(C)

1/10 = 0.10 (one tenth of one)
First spot to right of decimal point = "tenth"

1/100 = 0.01 (one hundredth of one)
Second spot to right of decimal point = "hundredth"

1/1,000 = 0.001 (one thousandth of one)
Third spot to right of decimal point = "thousandth"

Copyright 2022, www.MikeHolt.com

The decimal system places numbers to the right of a decimal point to indicate values that are a fraction of "one."

▶Figure 10–3

If the decimal number is greater than "one," the whole number will be to the left of the decimal point such as 1.25, 1.732, and 2.50.

10.5 Percentages

(A) General. A percentage is another method used to display the value of a number. One hundred percent means the entire value; 50 percent means one-half of a value, and 25 percent means one-fourth of a value. ▶Figure 10–4

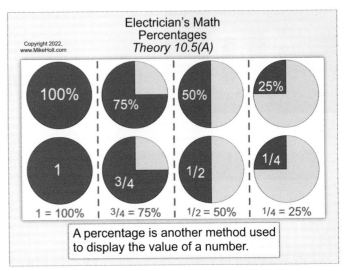

Electrician's Math
Percentages
Theory 10.5(A)

Copyright 2022, www.MikeHolt.com

100% | 75% | 50% | 25%
1 | 3/4 | 1/2 | 1/4

1 = 100% | 3/4 = 75% | 1/2 = 50% | 1/4 = 25%

A percentage is another method used to display the value of a number.

▶Figure 10–4

(B) Convert a Percentage to a Decimal. For convenience in multiplying or dividing by a percentage, convert the percentage value to a whole number or whole number with a decimal, and then use that value for the calculation.

When changing a percent value to a decimal or whole number with a decimal, drop the percentage symbol and move the decimal point two places to the left. ▶Figure 10–5

Convert Percentage to a Decimal
Theory 10.5(B)

Copyright 2022, www.MikeHolt.com

Percentage	Drop "%"	Decimal
32.50%	0.325 ✗	0.325
80%	0.80 ✗	0.80
125%	1.25 ✗	1.25
250%	2.50 ✗	2.50

Move the decimal point two places to the left.

▶Figure 10–5

10.6 Parentheses

In a math problem, parentheses are used to group steps of mathematical functions together. Whenever numbers are in parentheses, complete the mathematical function within the parentheses before proceeding with the remaining math functions.

▶ Parentheses Example

Question: *What is the sum of 3 and 15 added to the product of 4 and 2?*

Note: *A "sum" is the result of adding numbers, and a "product" is the result of multiplying numbers.*

(a) 6   (b) 12   (c) 16   (d) 26

Solution:

$(3 + 15) + (4 \times 2)$
$18 + 8 = 26$

Answer: *(d) 26*

10.7 Squaring a Number

Squaring (^{2}) a number is the process of multiplying a number by itself.

▶ Squaring a Number Example 1

$8^2 = 8 \times 8$
$8^2 = 64$

▶ Squaring a Number Example 2

$12^2 = 12 \times 12$
$12^2 = 144$

10.8 Square Root

The square root ($\sqrt{}$) of a number is the number that, if squared (multiplied by itself), would equal the original number. You must use the square root key ($\sqrt{}$) on your calculator to perform this function.

▶ Square Root Example 1

Question: *What is the square root of 100?* ▶Figure 10–6

(a) 1   (b) 10   (c) 21.52   (d) 31.62

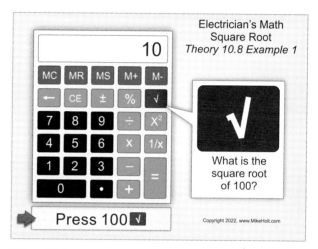

▶Figure 10–6

Answer: *(b) 10*

▶ Square Root Example 2

Question: *What is the square root of 3?*

(a) 1.255   (b) 1.55   (c) 1.732   (d) 1.935

Answer: *(c) 1.732*

10.9 Kilo

The letter "k" is the abbreviation for "kilo" which means "1,000." To convert a number that includes the "k," multiply the number by 1,000. To convert a number to a "k" value, divide the number by 1,000 and add "k" after the number.

▶ **Kilo Conversion Example 1**

Question: What is the value of 8k?

(a) 8   *(b) 800*   *(c) 4,000*   *(d) 8,000*

Solution:

8 × 1,000 = 8,000

Answer: (d) 8,000

▶ **Kilo Conversion Example 2**

Question: What is the "k" value of 3,000?

(a) 0.30k   *(b) 3k*   *(c) 30k*   *(d) 300k*

Solution:

k = 3,000/1,000
k = 3k

Answer: (b) 3k

10.10 Rounding

(A) General. There is no specific rule for rounding numbers, but; rounding to two or three "significant digits" should be sufficient for most electrical calculations. When rounding is desired, numbers below five are rounded down, while numbers five and above are rounded up. ▶Figure 10–7

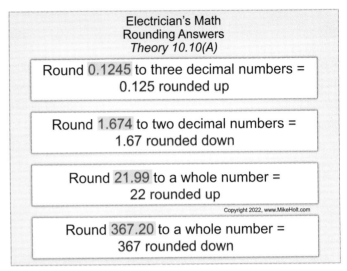

Electrician's Math
Rounding Answers
Theory 10.10(A)

Round 0.1245 to three decimal numbers =
0.125 rounded up

Round 1.674 to two decimal numbers =
1.67 rounded down

Round 21.99 to a whole number =
22 rounded up

Copyright 2022, www.MikeHolt.com

Round 367.20 to a whole number =
367 rounded down

▶Figure 10–7

(B) Rounding Answers for Multiple-Choice Questions. When selecting an answer for a multiple-choice question, you need to round your answers in the same manner as the multiple-choice selections are given.

▶ **Rounding Answers for Multiple-Choice Questions Example**

Question: The sum of 12, 17, 28, and 40 is approximately equal to _____.

(a) 70   *(b) 80*   *(c) 90*   *(d) 100*

Solution:

12 + 17 + 28 + 40 = 97

The multiple-choice selections in this case are rounded off to the nearest "tens," so the answer is 100.

Answer: (d) 100

10.11 Surface Area of a Rectangle or Square

The surface area for a rectangle or square is calculated using the formula: **Area = Length (L) × Width (W)**

▶ Surface Area—Rectangle or Square Example 1

Question: What is the surface area of a bedroom that is 10 ft wide and 12 ft long? ▶**Figure 10–8**

(a) 10 sq ft   (b) 50 sq ft   (c) 80 sq ft   (d) 120 sq ft

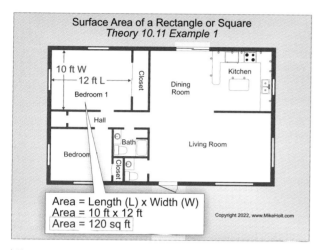

▶Figure 10–8

Solution:

Area = L × W

Area = 12 ft × 10 ft

Area = 120 sq ft

Answer: (d) 120 sq ft

▶ Surface Area—Rectangle or Square Example 2

Question: What is the surface area of a house that is 30 ft wide and 40 ft long? ▶**Figure 10–9**

(a) 1,000 sq ft   (b) 1,200 sq ft   (c) 1,800 sq ft   (d) 2,000 sq ft

Solution:

Area = L × W

Area = 40 ft × 30 ft

Area = 1,200 sq ft

Answer: (b) 1,200 sq ft

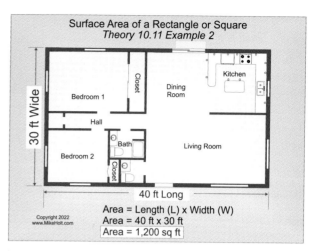

▶Figure 10–9

10.12 Surface Area of a Circle

The surface area of a circle is calculated using the formula:

Area of a Circle = $\pi \times r^2$

Use 3.14 for π (pi).

The radius (r^2) is equal to one half the diameter of the circle.

▶ Surface Area—Circle Example 1

Question: What is the surface area of an 8-in. pizza? ▶**Figure 10–10**

(a) 25 sq in.   (b) 50 sq in.   (c) 64 sq in.   (d) 75 sq in.

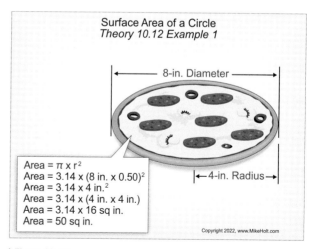

▶Figure 10–10

Solution:

Area of a Circle = $\pi \times r^2$

π = 3.14

Radius = ½ the diameter

Area = 3.14 × (8 in. × 0.50)²
Area = 3.14 × 4 in.²
Area = 3.14 × (4 in. × 4 in.)
Area = 3.14 × 16 sq in.
Area = 50 sq in.

Answer: *(b) 50 sq in.*

Note: *If you prefer to use a calculator, then follow these steps:*

Step 1: *Find the radius (½ the diameter) of the circle by multiplying 8 in. by 0.50:*

8 in. × 0.50 = 4 in.

Step 2: *Press the square "×²" key = 16 sq in.*

Step 3: *Multiply 16 sq in. (Step 2) by 3.14.*

16 sq in. × 3.14 = 50.26 sq in.

Step 4: *Round to match the answer choices: 50 sq in.*

Answer: *(b) 50 sq in.*

▶ **Surface Area—Circle Example 2**

Question: *What is the surface area of a 16-in. pizza?* ▶**Figure 10–11**

(a) 100 sq in.   (b) 150 sq in.   (c) 200 sq in.   (d) 256 sq in.

Solution:

Area of a Circle = $\pi \times r^2$

π = 3.14

Radius = ½ the diameter

Area = 3.14 × (16 in. × 0.50)²
Area = 3.14 × 8 in.²
Area = 3.14 × (8 in. × 8 in.)
Area = 3.14 × 64 sq in.
Area = 200 sq in.

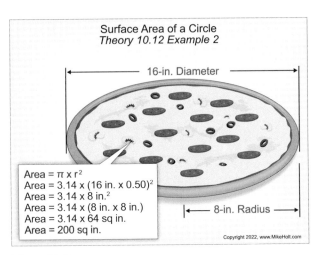

Surface Area of a Circle
Theory 10.12 Example 2

16-in. Diameter

Area = π x r²
Area = 3.14 x (16 in. x 0.50)²
Area = 3.14 x 8 in.²
Area = 3.14 x (8 in. x 8 in.)
Area = 3.14 x 64 sq in.
Area = 200 sq in.

8-in. Radius

Copyright 2022, www.MikeHolt.com

▶Figure 10–11

Answer: *(c) 200 sq in.*

Author's Comment:

▶ As you can see, if you double the circle's diameter (an 8-in. pizza versus a 16-in. pizza), its area is increased by a factor of four. By the way, a large (or extra-large) pizza is always cheaper per square inch than a small one! ▶**Figure 10–12**

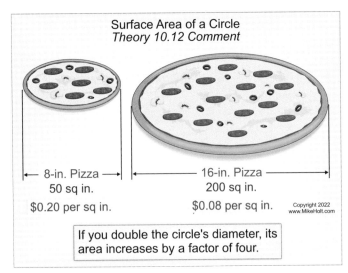

Surface Area of a Circle
Theory 10.12 Comment

8-in. Pizza
50 sq in.
$0.20 per sq in.

16-in. Pizza
200 sq in.
$0.08 per sq in.

Copyright 2022
www.MikeHolt.com

If you double the circle's diameter, its area increases by a factor of four.

▶Figure 10–12

10.13 Volume

The volume of an enclosure is expressed in cubic inches (cu in. or in^3), and is determined by multiplying the enclosure's length, width, and depth together: **Volume = Length (L) × Width (W) × Depth**.

▶ **Volume Example**

Question: *What is the volume of a 6 in. × 6 in. × 4 in. box?* ▶**Figure 10–13**

(a) 134 cu in.   *(b) 144 cu in.*   *(c) 154 cu in.*   *(d) 164 cu in.*

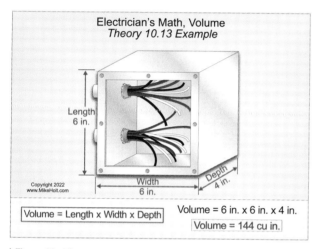

Electrician's Math, Volume
Theory 10.13 Example

Length 6 in.

Width 6 in.

Depth 4 in.

Copyright 2022
www.MikeHolt.com

Volume = Length x Width x Depth

Volume = 6 in. x 6 in. x 4 in.
Volume = 144 cu in.

▶Figure 10–13

Solution:

Volume = Length (L) × Width (W) × Depth
Volume = 6 in. × 6 in. × 4 in.
Volume = 144 cu in.

Answer: *(b) 144 cu in.*

10.14 Reciprocal

A reciprocal is the value of 1 divided by the number. All whole numbers shown as a fraction are over 1, a reciprocal flips the top number and puts it on the bottom for the mathematical function.

▶ **Reciprocal Example**

Question: *What is the reciprocal of 0.80?*

(a) 0.80   *(b) 1.10*   *(c) 1.25*   *(d) 1.50*

Solution:

1/0.80 = 1.25

Answer: *(c) 1.25*

10.15 Testing Your Answer

Never assume a mathematical calculation you have done is correct. Always do a "reality check" to be sure your answer makes sense. Even the best of us makes mistakes. You may have part of the problem jotted down incorrectly, or perhaps you pressed the wrong key on the calculator. Always examine your answer to see if it makes sense.

UNIT 11

TRIGONOMETRY

11.1 Introduction

Trigonometry is the mathematical study of triangles. Trigonometry is used to determine three-phase voltage systems, size power factor correction capacitors, and determine alternating-current wire impedance. In this unit you will learn:

▸ what right triangles are

▸ what the Pythagorean Theorem is

▸ what signs, cosines, and tangents are

11.2 Triangles

The basic things to remember when dealing with trigonometry, and specifically with math problems involving triangles, are that: ▶Figure 11–1

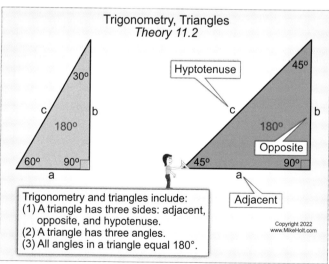

▶Figure 11–1

(1) A triangle has three sides: a = adjacent, b = opposite, and c = hypotenuse.

(2) A triangle has three angles.

(3) The total degrees of all angles in a triangle equals 180°.

11.3 Right Triangle

A right triangle is a triangle that contains a right angle. Important concepts concerning right triangles include: ▶Figure 11–2

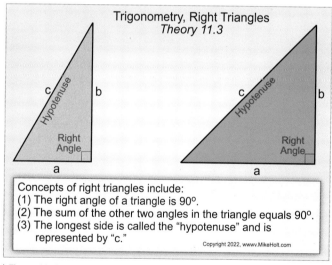

▶Figure 11–2

(1) One angle of the triangle is 90° and is called the right angle.

(2) The sum of the other two angles in the triangle equals 90°.

(3) The side of a right triangle that is opposite the right angle is called the "hypotenuse," which is the longest side of a right triangle and is represented by "c."

11.4 Pythagorean Theorem

The Pythagorean Theorem describes the mathematical relationship between the sides and angles of right triangles.

(1) You can calculate the length of the Hypotenuse side using:

$$c = \sqrt{(a^2 + b^2)}$$

▶ Example 1

Question: What is the length of the hypotenuse (c) of a right triangle where the opposite side (b) has a height of 32 ft, and the adjacent side (a) has a length of 24 ft? ▶Figure 11–3

(a) 20 ft   *(b) 24 ft*   *(c) 32 ft*   *(d) 40 ft*

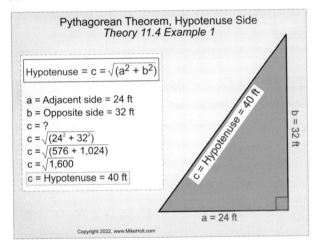

▶Figure 11–3

Solution:

$$c = \sqrt{(a^2 + b^2)}$$

a = Adjacent side = 24 ft
b = Opposite Side = 32 ft
c = Hypotenuse?

Hypotenuse = $\sqrt{(24^2 + 32^2)}$
Hypotenuse = $\sqrt{(576 + 1,024)}$
Hypotenuse = $\sqrt{1,600}$
Hypotenuse = 40 ft

Note: *To solve for the square root of a number, use the square root key on your calculator.*

Answer: *(d) 40 ft*

(2) You can calculate the length of the Opposite side using:

$$b = \sqrt{(c^2 - a^2)}$$

▶ Example 2

Question: What is the length of the opposite (b) side of a right triangle where the adjacent side (a) has a length of 24 ft, and the hypotenuse (c) has a length of 40 ft? ▶Figure 11–4

(a) 20 ft   *(b) 24 ft*   *(c) 32 ft*   *(d) 40 ft*

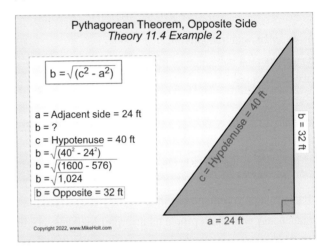

▶Figure 11–4

Solution:

$$b = \sqrt{(c^2 - a^2)}$$

a = Adjacent Side = 24 ft
b = Opposite Side?
c = Hypotenuse = 40 ft

Opposite Side = $\sqrt{(40^2 - 24^2)}$
Opposite Side = $\sqrt{(1,600 - 576)}$
Opposite Side = $\sqrt{1,024}$
Opposite Side = 32 ft

Note: *To solve for the square root of a number, use the square root key on your calculator.*

Answer: *(c) 32 ft*

(3) You can calculate the length of the Adjacent side using:

$$a = \sqrt{(c^2 - b^2)}$$

▶ **Example 3**

Question: What is the length of the adjacent side (a) of a right triangle where the opposite side (b) has a height of 32 ft, and the hypotenuse (c) has a length of 40 ft? ▶**Figure 11–5**

(a) 20 ft   *(b) 24 ft*   *(c) 32 ft*   *(d) 40 ft*

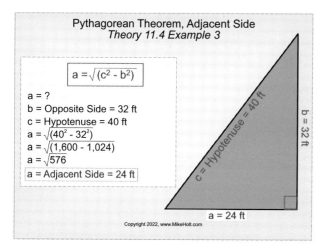

▶Figure 11–5

Solution:

$$a = \sqrt{(c^2 - b^2)}$$

a = Adjacent Side?

b = Opposite Side = 32 ft

c = Hypotenuse = 40 ft

Adjacent Side = $\sqrt{(40^2 - 32^2)}$

Adjacent Side = $\sqrt{(1,600 - 1,024)}$

Adjacent Side = $\sqrt{576}$

Adjacent Side = 24 ft

Note: *To solve for the square root of a number, use the square root key on your calculator.*

Answer: *(b) 24 ft*

11.5 Practical Use of Trigonometry

Trigonometry can be used to find the height of a structure with just a carpenter's speed square and a calculator.

Speed Square Method of Measuring Height

Step 1: Walk away from the structure until you can see the top without titling your head up.

Step 2: Hold a speed square at eye level in your line of sight with the bottom of the speed square level with the ground.

Step 3: Note the angle mark on the speed square that lines up with the top of the structure.

Step 4: Measure (in feet) the distance you are standing away from the structure.

Step 5: Find the approximate height of the structure using the formula:

Height = [Distance from Structure × (Tan of the Angle)] + Eye Height

▶ **Example**

Question: What is the height of a structure if you are standing 52 ft away from the structure, the angle on the speed square is 30°, and your eyes are 5 ft above the ground? ▶**Figure 11–6**

(a) 25 ft   *(b) 35 ft*   *(c) 45 ft*   *(d) 55 ft*

Solution:

Height = [Distance from Structure × (Tan of the Angle)] + Eye Height

Distance = 52 ft (given)

Tan of 30° is equal to 0.58 (from calculator)

Eye Height = 5 ft (given)

Height of Structure = [52 ft × (Tan of 30°)] + 5 ft

Height of Structure = (52 ft × 0.58) + 5 ft

Height of Structure = 30 ft + 5 ft

Height of Structure = 35 ft

• • •

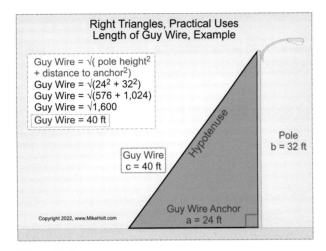

The figure shows:

Right Triangles, Practical Uses
Length of Guy Wire, Example

Guy Wire = √(pole height² + distance to anchor²)
Guy Wire = √(24² + 32²)
Guy Wire = √(576 + 1,024)
Guy Wire = √1,600
Guy Wire = 40 ft

Guy Wire
c = 40 ft

Hypotenuse

Pole
b = 32 ft

Guy Wire Anchor
a = 24 ft

Copyright 2022, www.MikeHolt.com

▶Figure 11–6

Answer: (b) 35 ft

CHAPTER 4

PRACTICE QUESTIONS

CHAPTER 4—PRACTICE QUESTIONS

Unit 10—Basic Math

10.2 Whole Numbers

1. _____ numbers do not contain any fractions, decimals, or percentages.

   (a) Decimal
   (b) Fractional
   (c) Real
   (d) Whole

10.3 Fractional Numbers

2. Parts of a whole number are called "_____" from the Latin word "fractus," meaning broken into parts.

   (a) decimals
   (b) fractions
   (c) percentages
   (d) integers

10.4 Decimal Numbers

3. A(An) _____ number is a number that is a fractional part of a number separated by a decimal point.

   (a) decimal
   (b) fractional
   (c) percentage
   (d) integer

4. To change a fraction to a decimal or whole number, _____ the top number of the fraction by its bottom number.

   (a) divide
   (b) multiply
   (c) add
   (d) subtract

5. The decimal equivalent for the fraction "½" is _____.

   (a) 0.20
   (b) 0.50
   (c) 2
   (d) 5

6. The approximate decimal equivalent for the fraction "4/18" is _____.

   (a) 0.22
   (b) 2.52
   (c) 3.52
   (d) 4.52

7. The decimal system places numbers to the _____ of a decimal point to indicate values that are a fraction of "one."

   (a) left
   (b) right
   (c) left or right
   (d) none of these

10.5 Percentages

8. To change a percent value to a decimal or whole number, drop the percentage sign and move the decimal point two places to the _____.

    (a) right
    (b) left
    (c) right or left
    (d) none of these

9. The decimal equivalent for "75 percent" is _____.

    (a) 0.075
    (b) 0.75
    (c) 7.50
    (d) 75

10. The decimal equivalent for "225 percent" is _____.

    (a) 0.225
    (b) 2.25
    (c) 22.50
    (d) 225

11. The decimal equivalent for "300 percent" is _____.

    (a) 0.03
    (b) 0.30
    (c) 3
    (d) 30.00

10.6 Parentheses

12. Whenever numbers are _____, complete the mathematical function within the parentheses before proceeding with the remaining math functions.

    (a) in brackets
    (b) in parentheses
    (c) underlined
    (d) none of these

13. What is the sum of 5 and 10 added to the product of 5 and 10?

    (a) 26
    (b) 32
    (c) 46
    (d) 65

10.7 Squaring a Number

14. Squaring a number means multiplying the number by _____.

    (a) itself
    (b) two
    (c) four
    (d) none of these

15. The numeric equivalent of 4^2 is _____.

    (a) 2
    (b) 8
    (c) 16
    (d) 32

16. The numeric equivalent of 12^2 is _____.

    (a) 3.46
    (b) 24
    (c) 144
    (d) 1,728

10.8 Square Root

17. Deriving the _____ of a number is the number that, if squared, would equal the number requested to be square rooted.

    (a) square root
    (b) square
    (c) multiplier
    (d) area

18. What is the approximate square root ($\sqrt{}$) of 1,000?

    (a) 3
    (b) 32
    (c) 100
    (d) 500

10.9 Kilo

19. What is the "k" value of 75,000?

   (a) 0.07k
   (b) 0.75k
   (c) 7.50k
   (d) 75k

10.10 Rounding

20. The total value of 2, 7, 8, and 9 is approximately _____.

   (a) 20
   (b) 25
   (c) 30
   (d) 35

10.11 Surface Area of a Rectangle or Square

21. What is the surface area of a bedroom that is 10 ft by 20 ft?

   (a) 100 sq ft
   (b) 150 sq ft
   (c) 200 sq ft
   (d) 250 sq ft

10.12 Surface Area of a Circle

22. What is the surface area of a 10-in. pizza?

   (a) 25.50 sq in.
   (b) 55.50 sq in.
   (c) 64.50 sq in.
   (d) 78.50 sq in.

23. What trade size ENT is required for three fiber optic cables, where each cable has a diameter of 0.22 in.?

   (a) Trade Size ½
   (b) Trade Size ¾
   (c) Trade Size 1
   (d) Trade Size 1¼

10.13 Volume

24. The volume of an enclosure is expressed in _____, and it is calculated by multiplying the length, by the width, by the depth of the enclosure.

   (a) cubic inches
   (b) weight
   (c) inch-pounds
   (d) none of these

25. What is the volume (in cubic inches) of a 4 in. × 4 in. × 1.50 in. box?

   (a) 20 cu in.
   (b) 24 cu in.
   (c) 30 cu in.
   (d) 33 cu in.

10.14 Reciprocal

26. What is the reciprocal of 1.25?

   (a) 0.80
   (b) 1.10
   (c) 1.25
   (d) 1.50

10.15 Testing Your Answer

27. Never assume a mathematical calculation you have done is correct. Always do a "_____" to be sure your answer makes sense.

   (a) reality check
   (b) quick scan
   (c) fast review
   (d) none of these

Unit 11—Trigonometry

11.2 Triangles

1. The basic things to remember when dealing with trigonometry and triangles, are that:

   (a) a triangle has three sides
   (b) a triangle has three angles
   (c) the total degrees of all angles in a triangle equals 180°
   (d) all of these

11.3 Right Triangle

2. Important concepts concerning right triangles include: _____.

   (a) one angle of the triangle is 90°
   (b) the sum of the other two angles equals 90°
   (c) the side of the triangle opposite the right angle is called the "hypotenuse"
   (d) all of these

11.4 Pythagorean Theorem

3. The _____ Theorem describes the mathematical relationship between the sides and angles of right triangles.

   (a) Edison
   (b) Pythagorean
   (c) Tesla
   (d) Maxwell

4. The length of the hypotenuse (c) side of a right triangle where the opposite side (b) has a height of 32 ft and the adjacent side (a) has a length of 24 ft is _____.

   (a) 20 ft
   (b) 24 ft
   (c) 32 ft
   (d) 40 ft

5. The length of the opposite (b) side of a right triangle where the adjacent side (a) has a length of 24 ft and the hypotenuse side (c) has a length of 40 ft is _____.

   (a) 20 ft
   (b) 24 ft
   (c) 32 ft
   (d) 40 ft

6. The length of the adjacent side (a) of a right triangle where the opposite side (b) has a height of 32 ft and the hypotenuse side (c) has a length of 40 ft is _____.

   (a) 20 ft
   (b) 24 ft
   (c) 32 ft
   (d) 40 ft

11.5 Practical Use of Trigonometry

7. What is the height of a structure if you are standing 52 ft away from the structure, the angle on the speed square is 30°, and your eyes are 5 ft above the ground?

   (a) 25 ft
   (b) 35 ft
   (c) 45 ft
   (d) 55 ft

[52 x tan 3] + 5

(52 + .58) + 5

30 + 5 = 35 ft

5

OHM'S LAW AND WATT'S LAW

Chapter 5—Ohm's Law and Watt's Law

Unit 12—Ohm's Law

To understand electrical circuits, you must understand electrical terminology. In this unit you will learn:

▸ what electromotive force, intensity, and resistance are

▸ what voltmeters, ammeters, and ohmmeters are

▸ how to use the Ohm's Law formula

Unit 13—Watt's Law

Wattage is a measure of the amount of power that is being used in a circuit. In this unit you will learn:

▸ what Watt's Law is

▸ how to use Watt's Law

▸ what a wattmeter is

UNIT

12

OHM'S LAW

12.1 Introduction

To understand electrical circuits, you must understand electrical terminology. In this unit you will learn:

▸ what electromotive force, intensity, and resistance are

▸ what voltmeters, ammeters, and ohmmeters are

▸ how to use the Ohm's Law formula

12.2 The Electrical Circuit

All electrical circuits contain a power source necessary to produce the pressure to move electrons through the circuit wires to supply the load. ▸Figure 12–1

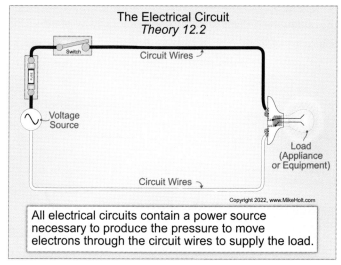

▸Figure 12–1

12.3 Electromotive Force (Pressure)

(A) General. In a circuit, the electrical pressure necessary for current flow is called "electromotive force" and is measured in the unit called a "volt" (V). Electromotive force is abbreviated as "EMF."

(1) Residential Voltage. In the United States, circuits for residential lights and receptacles operate at 120V, while large demanding loads like ranges, dryers, and air-conditioning equipment operate at 120/240V or 240V. ▸Figure 12–2

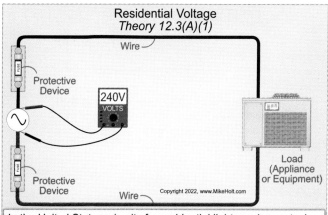

▸Figure 12–2

Understanding Electrical Theory | www.MikeHolt.com | **93**

(2) Commercial Voltage. In commercial and industrial occupancies, the voltage is often 277V for lighting and 480V for commercial loads like motors, air-conditioning units, and other equipment. ▶Figure 12–3

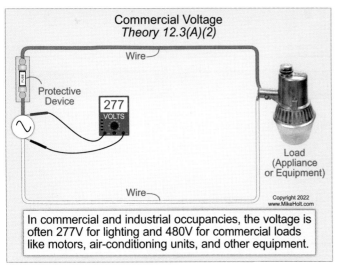

Commercial Voltage
Theory 12.3(A)(2)

In commercial and industrial occupancies, the voltage is often 277V for lighting and 480V for commercial loads like motors, air-conditioning units, and other equipment.

▶Figure 12–3

(B) Voltmeter. Voltmeters are connected in parallel with the load and are used to measure the difference of potential between the two test leads. ▶Figure 12–4

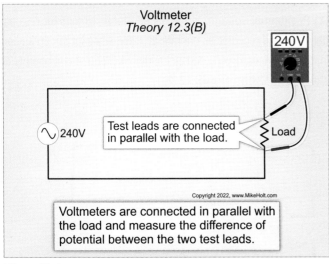

Voltmeter
Theory 12.3(B)

Test leads are connected in parallel with the load.

Voltmeters are connected in parallel with the load and measure the difference of potential between the two test leads.

▶Figure 12–4

12.4 Circuit Resistance

(A) General. In a circuit, resistance is the opposition to current flow. Every component of an electrical circuit contains resistance, which includes the power source, the circuit wiring, and the load. Resistance is represented by the letter "R" or "Ω," which is the ancient Greek letter Omega capitalized as "O," in honor of Georg Simon Ohm (1787–1854). ▶Figure 12–5

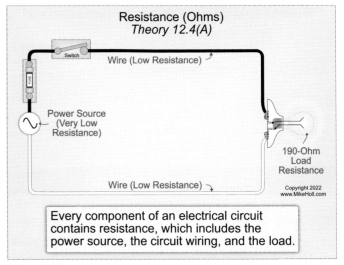

Resistance (Ohms)
Theory 12.4(A)

Every component of an electrical circuit contains resistance, which includes the power source, the circuit wiring, and the load.

▶Figure 12–5

(B) Ohmmeters. Ohmmeters are used to measure resistance in the unit called an "ohm" (Ω). ▶Figure 12–6

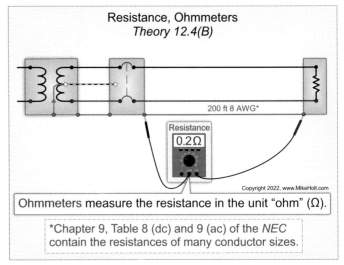

Resistance, Ohmmeters
Theory 12.4(B)

Ohmmeters measure the resistance in the unit "ohm" (Ω).

*Chapter 9, Table 8 (dc) and 9 (ac) of the *NEC* contain the resistances of many conductor sizes.

▶Figure 12–6

12.5 Circuit Intensity

(A) General. In an electrical circuit, the intensity of the current flow is measured in the unit called an "ampere," which is represented by the letter "I" for intensity. ▶Figure 12–7

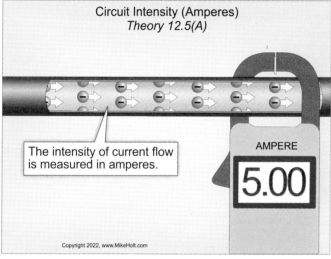

Circuit Intensity (Amperes)
Theory 12.5(A)

The intensity of current flow is measured in amperes.

AMPERE
5.00

Copyright 2022, www.MikeHolt.com

▶Figure 12–7

(B) Current Measurement.

(1) Series-Connected Ammeters. Series-connected ammeters measure current in amperes and are connected in series with the circuit. Handheld series-connected ammeters are typically limited to a maximum current of 10 amperes. ▶Figure 12–8

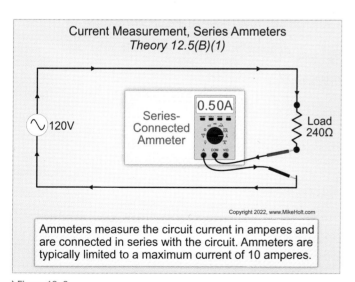

Current Measurement, Series Ammeters
Theory 12.5(B)(1)

120V

Series-Connected Ammeter
0.50A

Load
240Ω

Copyright 2022, www.MikeHolt.com

Ammeters measure the circuit current in amperes and are connected in series with the circuit. Ammeters are typically limited to a maximum current of 10 amperes.

▶Figure 12–8

(2) Clamp-On Ammeter. Clamp-on ammeters measure the circuit current without opening the circuit wires as is required for a series-connected ammeter. In addition, these meters can measure current in the thousands of amperes.

A clamp-on ammeter has a sensor that is clamped around the wire and detects the rising and falling electromagnetic field being produced due to the ac flow through the wire. ▶Figure 12–9

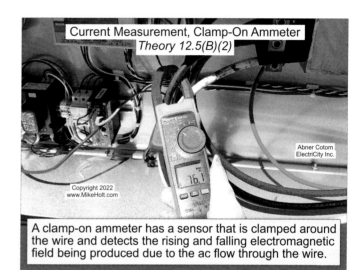

Current Measurement, Clamp-On Ammeter
Theory 12.5(B)(2)

Abner Cotom
ElectriCity Inc.

Copyright 2022
www.MikeHolt.com

A clamp-on ammeter has a sensor that is clamped around the wire and detects the rising and falling electromagnetic field being produced due to the ac flow through the wire.

▶Figure 12–9

12.6 Ohm's Law

(A) General. The German physicist Georg Simon Ohm (1787–1854) discovered that current is directly proportional to voltage and inversely proportional to resistance.

(1) Directly Proportional. Ohm's Law states that current is directly proportional to voltage. This means that current will increase in direct proportion to the voltage increase if the resistance of the circuit remains the same. If the voltage decreases and the circuit resistance remains the same, the circuit amperes will decrease in direct proportion to the voltage change. ▶Figure 12–10

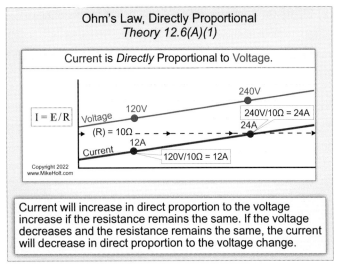

▶Figure 12–10

(2) Inversely Proportional. Ohm's Law also states that current is inversely proportional to resistance. This means that current will decrease in direct proportion to the increase in resistance if the voltage remains the same. If the resistance decreases and the voltage remains the same, then the circuit amperes will increase in direct proportion to the change in resistance. ▶Figure 12–11

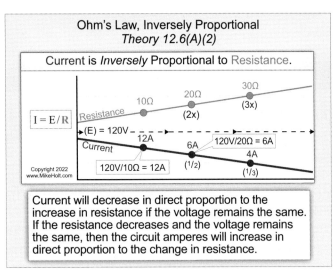

▶Figure 12–11

(B) Ohm's Law Formula. The Ohm's Law formula demonstrates the relationship between the circuit intensity (I) or current measured in amperes, the electromotive force (E) or pressure measured in volts, and the resistance (R) measured in ohms as expressed in the formula: $I = E/R$.

The Ohm's Law formula can be transposed as follows:

$I = E/R$, Intensity = Electromotive Force/Resistance, Measured in Amperes

$E = I \times R$, Electromotive Force = Intensity × Resistance, Measured in Volts

$R = E/I$, Resistance = Electromotive Force/Intensity, Measured in Ohms

12.7 Ohm's Law Formula Circle

To determine which formula in the Ohm's Law Formula Circle to use, place your finger on the unknown value for which you are looking. The two remaining variables "show" you the formula to be used. ▶Figure 12–12

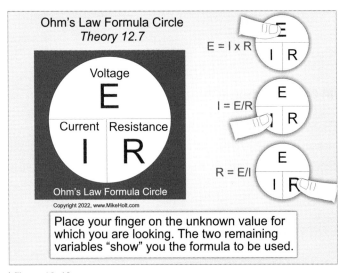

▶Figure 12–12

▶ Electromotive Force E = I × R Example

Question: *The voltage to a 192Ω resistor carrying 0.625A is _____.* ▶Figure 12–13

(a) 1V   (b) 110V   (c) 120V   (d) 125V

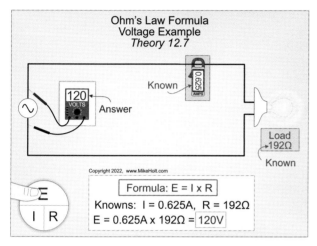

▶Figure 12–13

Solution:

The voltage of this circuit is determined by the formula ***E = I × R.***

E = I × R

I = 0.625A
R = 192Ω
E = 0.625A × 192Ω

Answer: *(c) 120V*

▶ Intensity I = E/R Example

Question: *If a 120V source supplies a 192Ω light bulb, the current flow in the circuit will be _____.* ▶Figure 12–14

(a) 0.525A   (b) 0.625A   (c) 1.30A   (d) 2.50A

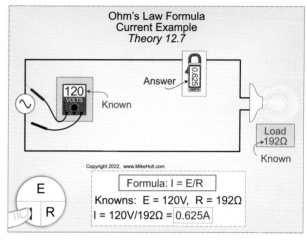

▶Figure 12–14

Solution:

Step 1: *What is the question? What is "I"?*

Step 2: *What do you know?*

Voltage (E) = 120V
Resistance (R) = 192Ω

Step 3: *The formula to use is* ***I = E/R.***

Step 4: *The answer is I = 120V/192Ω.*

Step 5: *The answer is I = 0.625A.*

Answer: *(b) 0.625A*

▶ **Resistance R = E/I Example**

Question: *The resistance of an incandescent light bulb rated 120V drawing 0.625A is _____.* ▶Figure 12–15

(a) 100Ω   (b) 175Ω   (c) 192Ω   (d) 200Ω

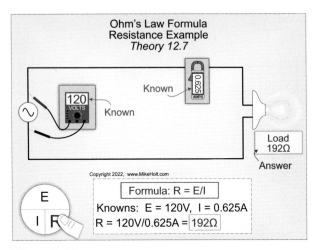

▶Figure 12–15

Solution:

Step 1: *What is the question? What is "R"?*

Step 2: *What do you know?*

    Voltage (E) = 120V

    Current (I) = 0.625A

Step 3: *The formula to use is **R = E/I**.*

Step 4: *The answer is R = 120V/0.625A.*

Step 5: *The answer is R = 192Ω.*

Answer: *(c) 192Ω*

WATT'S LAW

13.1 Introduction

Wattage is a measure of the amount of power that is being used in a circuit. In this unit you will learn:

▸ what Watt's Law is

▸ how to use Watt's Law

▸ what a wattmeter is

13.2 Watt's Law

Power is defined as the rate of work measured by the unit called the "watt."

(A) Watt's Law Formula. Watt's Law states that power (P) in watts is equal to intensity (I) in amperes, times the electromotive force (E) in volts. ▸Figure 13–1

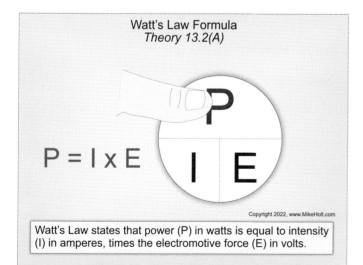

Watt's Law Formula
Theory 13.2(A)

$P = I \times E$

Copyright 2022, www.MikeHolt.com

Watt's Law states that power (P) in watts is equal to intensity (I) in amperes, times the electromotive force (E) in volts.

▸Figure 13–1

The formula for Watt's Law can be transposed as follows:

$P = I \times E$, Power = Intensity × Electromotive Force, Measured in Watts

$I = P/E$, Intensity = Power/Electromotive Force, Measured in Amperes

$E = P/I$, Electromotive Force = Power/Intensity, Measured in Volts

(B) Wattmeter. A wattmeter measures power by connecting it in parallel with the circuit to measure voltage, and in series with the circuit to measure amperes to calculate watts. ▸Figure 13–2

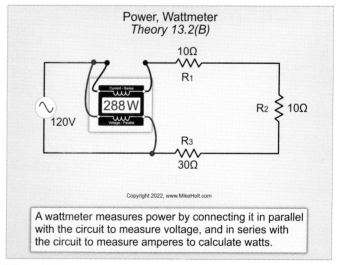

Power, Wattmeter
Theory 13.2(B)

Current - Series
288 W
Voltage - Parallel

120V

10Ω R1

R2 10Ω

R3 30Ω

Copyright 2022, www.MikeHolt.com

A wattmeter measures power by connecting it in parallel with the circuit to measure voltage, and in series with the circuit to measure amperes to calculate watts.

▸Figure 13–2

▶ **Example**

Question: A(An) _____ is used to measure power.

(a) wattmeter   (b) voltmeter   (c) ohmmeter   (d) megger

Answer: (a) wattmeter

13.3 Power Formula Circle

The Power Formula Circle demonstrates the relationship between power, current, and voltage. To apply Watt's Law using the Power Formula Circle, place your finger on the unknown value for which you are looking and the two remaining variables "show" you the formula to be used. ▶Figure 13–3

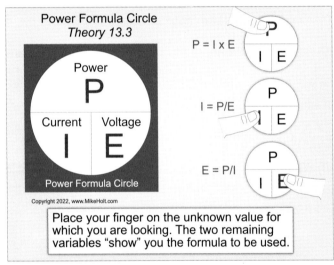

▶Figure 13–3

▶ **Power (P) Example**

Question: What is the power consumed by a circuit carrying 24A having a voltage drop of 7.20V? ▶Figure 13–4

(a) 125W   (b) 175W   (c) 235W   (d) 350W

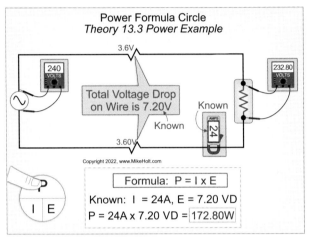

▶Figure 13–4

Solution:

Step 1:   What is the question asking you to find? What is the wire power loss? "P."

Step 2:   What do you know about the wires?

    $I = 24A$

    $E = 7.20 VD$

Step 3:   The formula is $P = I \times E$.

Step 4:   Calculate the answer.

    $P = 24A \times 7.20 VD$

    $P = 172.80W$

Answer: (b) 175W

▶ Intensity (I) Example

Question: *What is the current through a 7.50 kW heat strip rated 230V?*
▶Figure 13–5

(a) 25A   (b) 33A   (c) 39A   (d) 230A

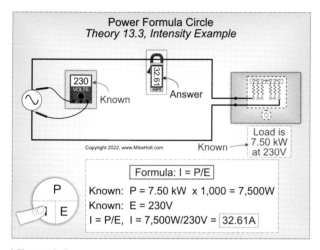

▶Figure 13–5

Solution:

Step 1: *What is the question? What is "I"?*

Step 2: *What do you know?*

Heat Strip Power Rating, P = 7.50 kW × 1,000

Heat Strip Power Rating, P = 7,500W

Heat Strip Voltage Rating, E = 230V

Step 3: *The formula is **I = P/E**.*

Step 4: *The answer is I = 7,500W/230V.*

Step 5: *The answer is 32.61A.*

Answer: (b) 33A

13.4 Power Changes with the Square of the Voltage

The voltage applied to a load affects the power consumed by that load. The voltage can dramatically affect the power consumed by a load because power is a function of the square of the voltage. This

means that if the voltage is doubled, the power will be four times the original value. If the voltage is decreased to 50 percent, the power will be 25 percent of its original value. ▶Figure 13–6

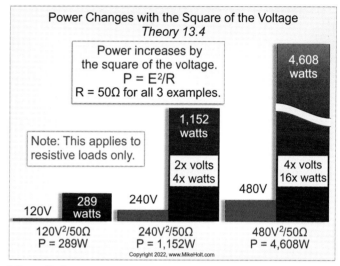

▶Figure 13–6

▶ Power Equals the Square (^{2}) of the Voltage Example 1

Question: *What is the power consumed by a 10Ω load operating at 120V?*

(a) 1,040W   (b) 1,400W   (c) 1,440W   (d) 1,444W

Solution:

$P = E^2/R$

E = 120V (given)
R = 10Ω (given)

P = (120V × 120V)/10Ω
P = 14,400/10Ω
P = 1,440W

Answer: (c) 1,440W

▶ **Power Equals the Square (^{2}) of the Voltage**
Example 2

Question: What is the power consumed by a 10Ω load operating at 240V?

(a) 5,600W   (b) 5,660W   (c) 5,700W   (d) 5,760W

Solution:

$P = E^2/R$

E = 240V (given)
R = 10Ω (given)

P = (240V × 240V)/10Ω
P = 57,600/10Ω
P = 5,760W

Answer: (d) 5,760W

Note: At 240V, the 10Ω resistor consumes four times the power as compared to the 120V circuit power.

CHAPTER 5

PRACTICE QUESTIONS

CHAPTER 5—PRACTICE QUESTIONS

Unit 12—Ohm's Law

12.2 The Electrical Circuit

1. All electrical circuits contain a _____ necessary to produce pressure to move electrons through the circuit wire to supply the load.

   (a) power source
   (b) wire
   (c) load
   (d) all of these

12.3 Electromotive Force (Pressure)

2. Electrical pressure is called "_____," and it is measured in volts.

   (a) EMF
   (b) potential
   (c) EMF or potential
   (d) none of these

3. In the United States, circuits for residential lights and receptacles operate at _____, while large demanding loads like ranges, dryers, and air-conditioning equipment operate at 120/240V or 240V.

   (a) 120V
   (b) 208V
   (c) 277V
   (d) 480V

4. In commercial and industrial occupancies, the voltage is often _____ for lighting and 480V for commercial loads like motors, air-conditioning units, and other equipment.

   (a) 100V
   (b) 200V
   (c) 240V
   (d) 277V

5. Voltmeters are connected in _____ with the circuit and measure the difference of potential between the two test leads.

   (a) series
   (b) parallel
   (c) series-parallel
   (d) none of these

12.4 Circuit Resistance

6. Every component of an electrical circuit contains _____, which includes the power source, the circuit wiring, and the load.

   (a) resistance
   (b) voltage
   (c) current
   (d) power

7. The circuit resistance includes the resistance of the _____.

   (a) power source
   (b) circuit wring
   (c) load
   (d) all of these

8. Ohmmeters measure the _____ of the circuit in the unit "ohm."

    (a) voltage
    (b) current
    (c) power
    (d) resistance

12.5 Circuit Intensity

9. In an electrical circuit, the volume of the current flow is measured in the unit "amperes" which is represented by the letter "I" for _____.

    (a) resistance
    (b) power
    (c) pressure
    (d) intensity

10. The intensity of the circuit is measured in _____.

    (a) voltage
    (b) ohms
    (c) watts
    (d) amperes

11. Ammeters measure the current in amperes and are connected in _____ with the circuit.

    (a) series
    (b) parallel
    (c) series-parallel
    (d) none of these

12. A clamp-on ac ammeter has a coil that is clamped around the wire and detects the rising and falling _____ field being produced due to the ac flow through the wire.

    (a) static
    (b) current
    (c) power
    (d) electromagnetic

12.6 Ohm's Law

13. Ohm's Law states that current is _____ proportional to the voltage, this means that current will increase in direct proportion to the voltage increase if the resistance of the circuit remains the same.

    (a) indirectly
    (b) inversely
    (c) aversely
    (d) directly

14. Ohm's Law states that current is _____ proportional to the resistance, this means that current will decrease in direct proportion to the increase in resistance if the voltage remains the same.

    (a) indirectly
    (b) inversely
    (c) aversely
    (d) directly

15. The Ohm's Law formula demonstrates the relationship between circuit _____.

    (a) intensity
    (b) EMF
    (c) resistance
    (d) all of these

16. The symbol "I" in Ohm's Law represents the circuit _____.

    (a) coulomb
    (b) in-rush
    (c) intensity
    (d) impedance

12.7 Ohm's Law Formula Circle

17. The voltage to a 12Ω resistor carrying 10A is _____.

    (a) 1V
    (b) 110V
    (c) 120V
    (d) 125V

18. If a 120V source supplies a 12Ω resistor, the current flow in the circuit will be _____.

    (a) 5A
    (b) 10A
    (c) 13A
    (d) 25A

19. The resistance of circuit rated 120V drawing 10A is _____.

    (a) 12Ω
    (b) 17Ω
    (c) 19Ω
    (d) 20Ω

Unit 13—Watt's Law

13.2 Watt's Law

1. _____ is defined as the rate of work measured by the unit called the "watt."

    (a) Resistance
    (b) Power
    (c) Pressure
    (d) Intensity

2. _____ Law states that power (P) in watts is equal to intensity (I) in amperes, times the electromotive force (E) in volts.

    (a) Ohm's
    (b) Watt's
    (c) Kirchhoff's
    (d) Circle

3. A(An) _____ measures power by connecting it in parallel with the circuit to measure the voltage, and in series with the circuit to measure the amperes to calculate watts.

    (a) ammeter
    (b) ohmmeter
    (c) voltmeter
    (d) wattmeter

13.3 Power Formula Circle

4. The _____ Formula Circle demonstrates the relationship between power, current, and voltage.

    (a) Amp
    (b) Ohm
    (c) Voltage
    (d) Power

5. What is the power loss for a circuit carrying 20A having a voltage drop of 10.20V?

    (a) 122W
    (b) 174W
    (c) 204W
    (d) 354W

6. What is the current through a 9.50 kW heat strip rated 240V?

    (a) 25.40A
    (b) 33.50A
    (c) 39.60A
    (d) 42.70A

13.4 Power Changes with the Square of the Voltage

7. The voltage can dramatically affect the power consumed by a load because power is a function of the _____ of the voltage.

    (a) square
    (b) mean
    (c) volume
    (d) multiplier

8. What is the approximate power consumed by a 4.32Ω heat strip rated 208V?

    (a) 8 kW
    (b) 9 kW
    (c) 10 kW
    (d) 11 kW

CHAPTER 6

ELECTRICAL CIRCUIT TYPES

Chapter 6—Electrical Circuit Types

Unit 14—Series Circuits

A series circuit is a circuit in which a certain amount of current leaves the power source and flows through every electrical device in a single path before it returns to the power source. In this unit you will learn:

- ▸ the relationship between resistance, current, and voltage in series circuits
- ▸ about the voltage of series-connected power supplies
- ▸ about common applications of series circuits

Unit 15—Parallel Circuits

"Parallel" is a term used to describe a method of connecting an electrical circuit so there are two or more paths through which current can flow simultaneously. A parallel circuit has different characteristics and calculations than a series circuit. In this unit you will learn:

- ▸ the relationship between resistance, current, and voltage in parallel circuits
- ▸ about the voltage of parallel-connected power supplies
- ▸ about common applications of parallel circuits

UNIT 16—Series-Parallel Circuits

In this unit you will learn how to calculate total circuit resistance for series-parallel circuits.

UNIT 14

SERIES CIRCUITS

14.1 Introduction

A series circuit is a circuit in which a current leaves the power source and flows through every electrical device in a single path before it returns to the power source. In this unit you will learn:

▸ the relationship between resistance, current, and voltage in series circuits

▸ about the voltage of series-connected power supplies

▸ about common applications of series circuits

14.2 Series Circuits

(A) General. A series circuit can be envisioned as a circle where current leaves the power source, flows through every load in a single path, and then returns to the power source. ▸Figure 14–1

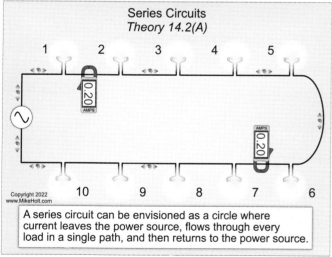

Series Circuits
Theory 14.2(A)

A series circuit can be envisioned as a circle where current leaves the power source, flows through every load in a single path, and then returns to the power source.

▸Figure 14–1

(B) Open Circuit. If there is a break in a series circuit, the current in the circuit will stop flowing. ▸Figure 14–2

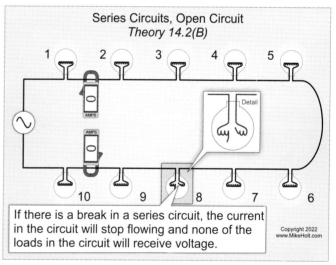

Series Circuits, Open Circuit
Theory 14.2(B)

If there is a break in a series circuit, the current in the circuit will stop flowing and none of the loads in the circuit will receive voltage.

▸Figure 14–2

14.3 Understanding Series Circuits

It is important to understand the relationship between resistance, current, and voltage in a series circuit.

(A) Resistance. In a series circuit, the total circuit resistance is equal to the sum of the resistance of all the resistors. It is calculated according to the total resistance formula: $R_T = R_1 + R_2 + R_3$... ▸Figure 14–3

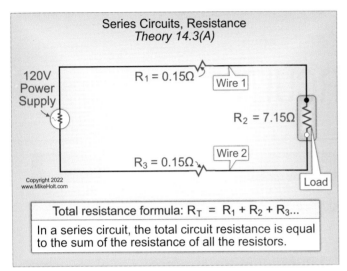

▶Figure 14–3

▶ Series Circuit Resistance Example

Question: *What is the total resistance of three resistors where R_1 is 16Ω, R_2 is 13Ω, and R_3 is 36Ω?* ▶**Figure 14–4**

(a) 50Ω   (b) 65Ω   (c) 100Ω   (d) 150Ω

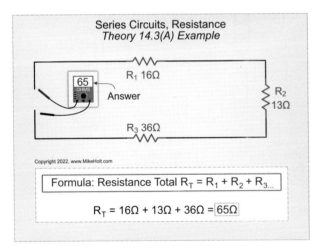

▶Figure 14–4

Solution:

$R_T = R_1 + R_2 + R_3$
$R_T = 16Ω + 13Ω + 36Ω$
$R_T = 65Ω$

Answer: (b) 65Ω

(B) Current.

(1) Current Remains the Same. Kirchhoff's Current Law states that the current flowing through each resistor of a series circuit will be the same value as the current leaving and returning to the power source. ▶Figure 14–5

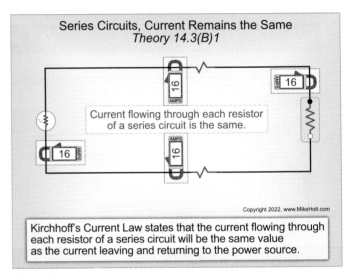

▶Figure 14–5

(2) Current Formula. To calculate the current in a series circuit, you need to know the circuit voltage and the circuit's total resistance as expressed by the formula: **I = E/R**.

▶ Circuit Current Formula Example

Question: *The current for a 240V circuit that has three resistors in series where R_1 is 5Ω, R_2 is 10Ω, and R_3 is 5Ω is _____.* ▶**Figure 14–6**

(a) 5A   (b) 7A   (c) 9A   (d) 12A

Solution:

I = E/R

E = 240V, voltage source

$R_T = R_1 + R_2 + R_3$
$R_T = 5Ω + 10Ω + 5Ω$
$R_T = 20Ω$

I = 240V/20Ω
I = 12A, current of the circuit

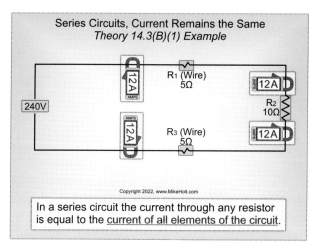

▶Figure 14–6

Answer: (d) 12A

(C) Voltage.

(1) Voltage across Each Resistor. The voltage across each resistor is determined using the formula: $E = I \times R$.

▶ **Voltage of Each Resistor Example 1**

Question: A 120V circuit has three resistors in series where R_1 is 10Ω, R_2 is 5Ω, and R_3 is 5Ω. The voltage across R_1 is _____.
▶Figure 14–7

(a) 30V   (b) 60V   (c) 90V   (d) 120V

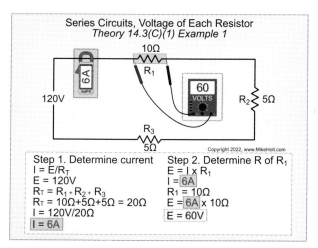

▶Figure 14–7

Solution:

Step 1: Determine the current of the series circuit:

$$I = E/R$$

E = 120V, voltage source

$R_T = R_1 + R_2 + R_3$

$R_T = 10Ω + 5Ω + 5Ω$

$R_T = 20Ω$, resistance total

$I = 120V/20Ω$

$I = 6A$, current of the circuit

Step 2: Determine the voltage across R_1:

$$E = I \times R_1$$

I = 6A, current of the circuit

$R_1 = 10Ω$

$E = 6A \times 10Ω$

Answer: (b) 60V

▶ **Voltage of Each Resistor Example 2**

Question: A 120V circuit has three resistors in series where R_1 is 10Ω, R_2 is 5Ω, and R_3 is 5Ω. The voltage across R_2 or R_3 is _____. ▶Figure 14–8

(a) 30V   (b) 60V   (c) 90V   (d) 120V

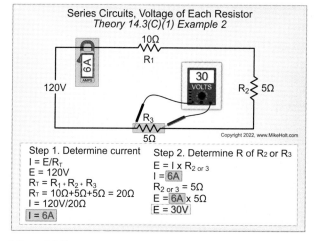

▶Figure 14–8

Solution:

Step 1: *Determine the current of the series circuit:*

$I = E/R_T$

$E = 120V$, *voltage source*

$R_T = R_1 + R_2 + R_3$

$R_T = 10\Omega + 5\Omega + 5\Omega$

$R_T = 20\Omega$, *resistance total*

$I = 120V/20\Omega$

$I = 6A$, *current of the circuit*

Step 2: *Determine the voltage across R_2 or R_3:*

$E = I \times R_1$

$I = 6A$, *current of the circuit*

R_2 or $R_3 = 5\Omega$

$E = 6A \times 5\Omega$

Answer: (a) 30V

(2) Voltage Source. Kirchhoff's Voltage Law states that the source voltage of a series circuit is equal to the sum of the voltages across all circuit resistors as expressed by the formula: $E_S = E_1 + E_2 + E_3...$

▶ **Voltage Source Example**

Question: A 20Ω circuit has three resistors in series where R_1 is 60V, R_2 is 30V, and R_3 is 30V. The voltage source is equal to _____. ▶Figure 14–9

(a) 30V   (b) 60V   (c) 90V   (d) 120V

Solution:

Determine the voltage source of the series circuit:

$E_S = E_1 + E_2 + E_3$

$E_S = 60V + 30V + 30V$

$E_S = 120V$

Answer: (d) 120V

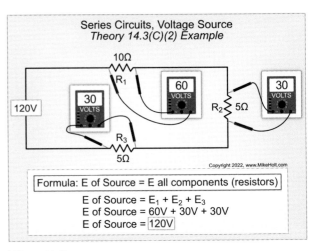

▶Figure 14–9

(3) Voltage Law of Proportion. The voltage of a power source is distributed among all the resistors in a series circuit according to the Law of Proportion. The Law of Proportion states that the voltage across each resistor is relative to the resistance of that resistor as compared to the total circuit resistance. ▶Figure 14–10

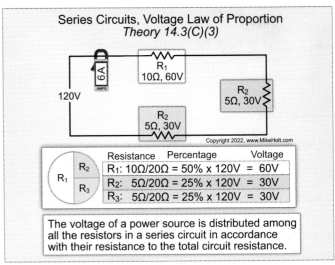

▶Figure 14–10

14.4 Series Circuit Summary

A series circuit has the following characteristics: ▶**Figure 14–11**

Note 1: Circuit resistance is equal to the sum of the resistances.

Note 2: Current is the same through all the resistors.

Note 3: Total voltage across all resistors is equal to the voltage of the source.

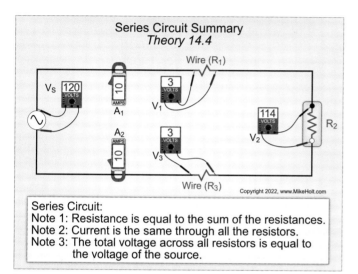

▶Figure 14–11

14.5 Series-Connected Power Supplies

(A) Additive Voltage. When power supplies are connected in series, the voltage of the series-connected power supplies is equal to the sum of the power supply voltages as expressed by the formula: $E_S = E_1 + E_2 + E_3...$ ▶**Figure 14–12**

(B) Subtractive Voltage. If series-connected power supplies are not arranged positive (+) to negative (-), the circuit voltage will not equal the sum of the power supply voltages. ▶**Figure 14–13**

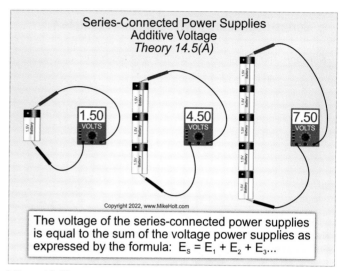

▶Figure 14–12

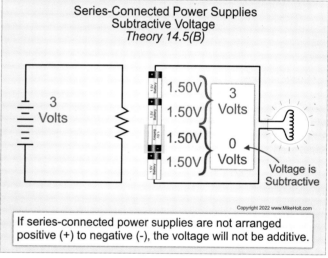

▶Figure 14–13

▶ **Series-Connected Power Supplies Example 1**

Question: *The voltage across two 12V batteries connected in series is _____.* ▶Figure 14–14

(a) 12V   *(b) 24V*   *(c) 120V*   *(d) 240V*

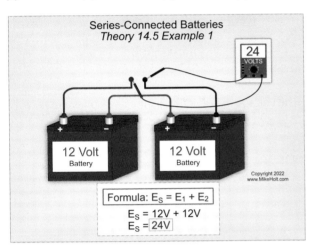

▶Figure 14–14

Solution:

$E_S = E_1 + E_2$

$E_S = 12V + 12V$

$E_S = 24V$, *two series-connected power sources*

Answer: *(b) 24V*

▶ **Series-Connected Power Supplies Example 2**

Question: *The voltage of ten 42.70V solar panels in series is _____.* ▶Figure 14–15

(a) 120V   *(b) 240V*   *(c) 427V*   *(d) 480V*

▶Figure 14–15

Solution:

$E_S = E_1 + E_2 + E_3 \dots E_{10}$

$E_S = 42.70V \times 10$ *solar panels*

$E_S = 427V$, *ten series-connected power sources*

Answer: *(c) 427V*

14.6 Applications of Series Circuits

Series circuits are used for equipment control, signaling, and (at times) the internal wiring of equipment.

(A) Control Circuits. Series circuits are often used for control applications (starting and stopping) for electrical equipment. ▶Figure 14–16

(B) Signaling Circuits. Series circuits are used to give a signal that something has occurred. They can indicate that a door is open, a process is operating, or there is fire or smoke. ▶Figure 14–17

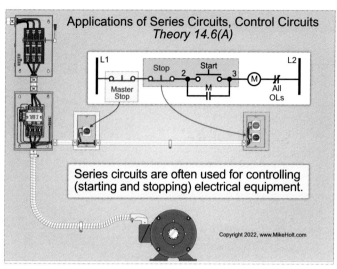

Applications of Series Circuits, Control Circuits
Theory 14.6(A)

Series circuits are often used for controlling (starting and stopping) electrical equipment.

▶Figure 14–16

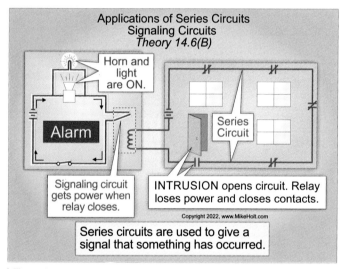

Applications of Series Circuits
Signaling Circuits
Theory 14.6(B)

Horn and light are ON.

Alarm

Series Circuit

Signaling circuit gets power when relay closes.

INTRUSION opens circuit. Relay loses power and closes contacts.

Series circuits are used to give a signal that something has occurred.

▶Figure 14–17

(C) Internal Equipment Wiring. The internal wiring of many types of equipment, such as motor windings, can be connected in series. ▶Figure 14–18

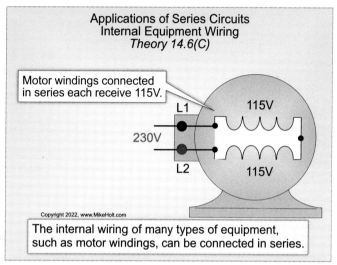

Applications of Series Circuits
Internal Equipment Wiring
Theory 14.6(C)

Motor windings connected in series each receive 115V.

L1   115V
230V
L2   115V

The internal wiring of many types of equipment, such as motor windings, can be connected in series.

▶Figure 14–18

UNIT 15

PARALLEL CIRCUITS

15.1 Introduction

"Parallel" is a term used to describe a method of connecting an electrical circuit so there are two or more paths through which current can flow simultaneously. A parallel circuit has different characteristics and calculations than a series circuit. In this unit you will learn: ▶Figure 15-1

- ▶ the relationship between resistance, current, and voltage in parallel circuits
- ▶ about the voltage of parallel-connected power supplies
- ▶ about common applications of parallel circuits

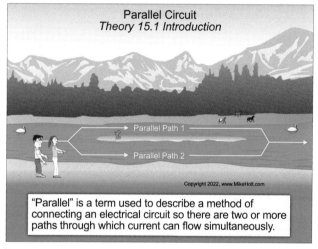

Parallel Circuit
Theory 15.1 Introduction

Parallel Path 1

Parallel Path 2

Copyright 2022, www.MikeHolt.com

"Parallel" is a term used to describe a method of connecting an electrical circuit so there are two or more paths through which current can flow simultaneously.

▶Figure 15–1

15.2 Understanding Parallel Circuits

(A) Voltage. In a parallel circuit, the voltage across each component of the circuit is equal to the voltage source. ▶Figure 15–2

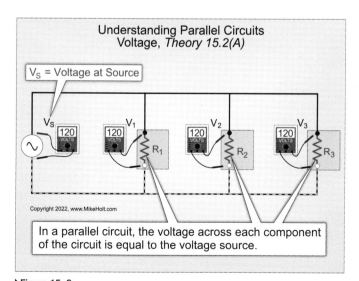

Understanding Parallel Circuits
Voltage, Theory 15.2(A)

V_S = Voltage at Source

V_S 120 VOLTS V_1 120 VOLTS R_1 V_2 120 VOLTS R_2 V_3 120 VOLTS R_3

Copyright 2022, www.MikeHolt.com

In a parallel circuit, the voltage across each component of the circuit is equal to the voltage source.

▶Figure 15–2

▶ Voltage in Parallel Circuits Example 1

Question: A 240V circuit has three 15Ω resistors connected in parallel. The voltage across any one of these resistors is _____. ▶Figure 15–3

(a) 60V   (b) 90V   (c) 120V   (d) 240V

Answer: (d) 240V

• • •

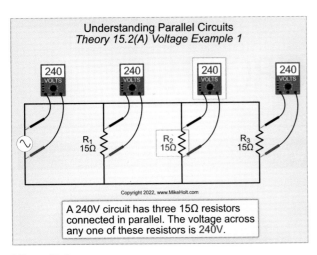

▶Figure 15-3

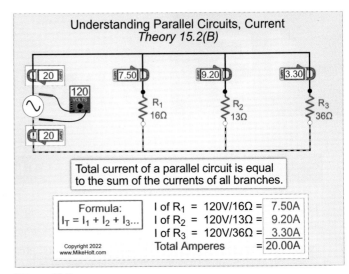

▶Figure 15-5

▶ Voltage in Parallel Circuits Example 2

Question: *A 24V circuit has two 5Ω resistors connected in parallel. The voltage across any one of these resistors is _____.* ▶**Figure 15-4**

(a) 12V   (b) 24V   (c) 48V   (d) 120V

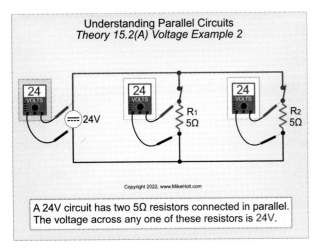

▶Figure 15-4

Answer: (b) 24V

(B) Circuit Current. A parallel circuit has two or more paths through which current can flow simultaneously. Kirchhoff's Current Law states that the total current of a parallel circuit is equal to the sum of the currents of all the parallel branches. In other words, current in a parallel circuit is additive as expressed by the formula:

$I_T = I_1 + I_2 + I_3...$ ▶**Figure 15-5**

▶ Current in Parallel Circuits Example

Question: *A circuit has three 15A resistors connected in parallel. The current of this circuit is _____.* ▶**Figure 15-6**

(a) 15A   (b) 25A   (c) 35A   (d) 45A

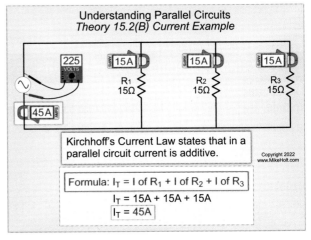

▶Figure 15-6

Solution:

$I_T = I$ of $R_1 + I$ of $R_2 + I$ of R_3

$I_T = 15A + 15A + 15A$

$I_T = 45A$, circuit current

Answer: (d) 45A

15.3 Parallel Circuit Resistance Calculations

There are three methods for calculating the total resistance of a parallel circuit:

▶ the Equal Resistance method

▶ the Product-Over-Sum method

▶ the Reciprocal method

Author's Comment

▷ The total resistance of a parallel circuit is always less than the smallest individual branch's resistance. ▶Figure 15-7

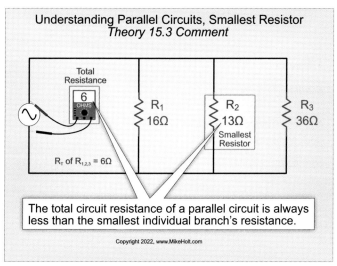

▶Figure 15-7

(A) Equal Resistance Method. When all components of a parallel circuit have the same value, the resistance can be determined by the formula: **R_T = Resistance of One Resistor/Number of Resistors**.

▶ Equal Resistance Method Example 1

Question: *The total resistance of three 10Ω resistors connected in parallel is _____.* ▶Figure 15-8

(a) 3.33Ω   *(b) 10Ω*   *(c) 20Ω*   *(d) 30Ω*

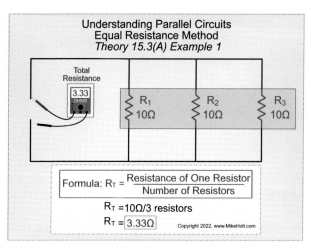

▶Figure 15-8

Solution:

R_T = *Resistance of One Resistor/Number of Resistors*

R_T = *10Ω/3 resistors*

R_T = *3.33Ω*

Answer: (a) 3.33Ω

Note: The total resistance is always smaller than the smallest resistor.

▶ Equal Resistance Method Example 2

Question: *The total resistance of ten 10Ω resistors connected in parallel is _____.* ▶Figure 15-9

(a) 1Ω   *(b) 10Ω*   *(c) 50Ω*   *(d) 100Ω*

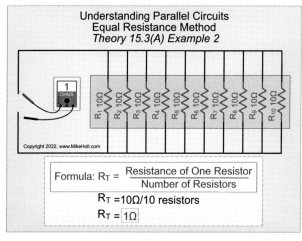

▶Figure 15-9

● ● ●

Solution:

R_T = *Resistance of One Resistor/Number of Resistors*

R_T = *10Ω/10 resistors*

R_T = *1 ohm*

Answer: *(a) 1Ω*

Note: *The total resistance is always smaller than the smallest resistor.*

▶ **Equal Resistance Method Example 3**

Question: *A 240V circuit has three resistors in parallel where R_1 is 15Ω, R_2 is 15Ω, and R_3 is 15Ω. The resistance of this parallel circuit is _____.* ▶**Figure 15–10**

(a) 5Ω   (b) 15Ω   (c) 30Ω   (d) 45Ω

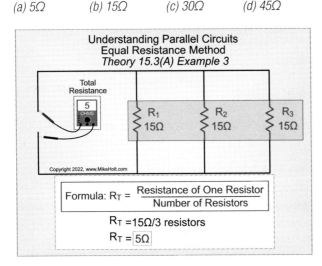

Understanding Parallel Circuits
Equal Resistance Method
Theory 15.3(A) Example 3

Total Resistance

5 OHMS

R₁ 15Ω   R₂ 15Ω   R₃ 15Ω

Copyright 2022, www.MikeHolt.com

Formula: R_T = $\dfrac{\text{Resistance of One Resistor}}{\text{Number of Resistors}}$

R_T =15Ω/3 resistors

R_T = 5Ω

▶Figure 15–10

Solution:

R_T = *Resistance of One Resistor/Number of Resistors*

R_T = *15Ω/3 resistors*

R_T = *5Ω*

Answer: *(a) 5Ω*

Note: *The total resistance is always smaller than the smallest resistor.*

▶ **Equal Resistance Method Example 4**

Question: *A circuit has three 20Ω resistors connected in parallel. The resistance of this circuit is _____.* ▶**Figure 15–11**

(a) 3.20Ω   (b) 4.20Ω   (c) 5.70Ω   (d) 6.70Ω

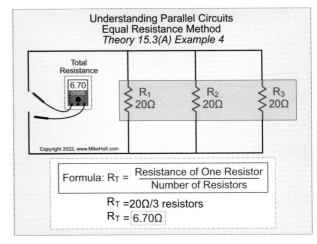

Understanding Parallel Circuits
Equal Resistance Method
Theory 15.3(A) Example 4

Total Resistance

6.70 OHMS

R₁ 20Ω   R₂ 20Ω   R₃ 20Ω

Copyright 2022, www.MikeHolt.com

Formula: R_T = $\dfrac{\text{Resistance of One Resistor}}{\text{Number of Resistors}}$

R_T =20Ω/3 resistors

R_T = 6.70Ω

▶Figure 15–11

Solution:

R_T = *Resistance of One Resistor/Number of Resistors*

R_T = *20Ω/3 resistors*

R_T = *6.70Ω*

Answer: *(d) 6.70Ω*

Note: *The total resistance is always smaller than the smallest resistor.*

(B) Product-Over-Sum Method. The Product-Over-Sum method is used to calculate the resistance of two parallel resistors of different values as determined by the formula: $R_T = (R_1 \times R_2)/(R_1 + R_2)$

▶ **Product-Over-Sum Method—
Two Resistors Example**

Question: *The resistance of a coffee pot is 16Ω (R_1), and the resistance of a skillet is approximately 13Ω (R_2). What is the total resistance of the two appliances if they are connected in parallel?* ▶**Figure 15–12**

(a) 7.20Ω   (b) 13Ω   (c) 16Ω   (d) 29Ω

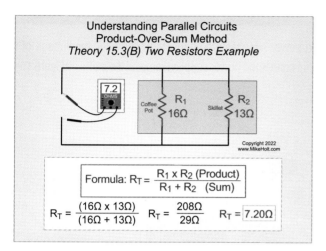

▶Figure 15–12

Solution:

$R_T = (R_1 \times R_2)/(R_1 + R_2)$

$R_T = (16\Omega \times 13\Omega)/(16\Omega + 13\Omega)$

$R_T = 208\Omega/29\Omega$

$R_T = 7.20\Omega$

Answer: (a) 7.20Ω

Note: The total resistance is always smaller than the smallest resistor.

(C) Reciprocal Method. The Reciprocal Method for determining the total resistance of a parallel circuit is used when there are more than two resistors of different values. Use the formula:
$R_T = 1/(1/R_1 + 1/R_2 + 1/R_3...$

▶ **Reciprocal Method Example 1**

Question: What is the resistance total of a 16Ω, 13Ω, and 36Ω resistor connected in parallel? ▶**Figure 15–13**

(a) 6Ω   (b) 13Ω   (c) 16Ω   (d) 36Ω

Solution:

$R_T = 1/(1/R_1 + 1/R_2 + 1/R_3)$

$R_T = 1/(1/16 + 1/13 + 1/36)$

$R_T = 1/(0.0625\Omega + 0.0769\Omega + 0.0278\Omega)$

$R_T = 1/0.1672\Omega$

$R_T = 6\Omega$

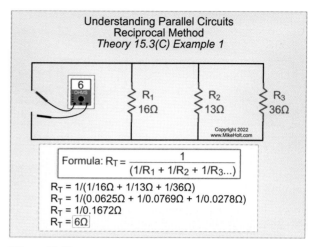

▶Figure 15–13

Note: If you use your calculator, add the reciprocals of all the resistors together.

$R_T = 1/(1/R_1 + 1/R_2 + 1/R_3)$

$R_T = 1/(1/16 + 1/13 + 1/36)$

$R_T = 1/(16 \ [press \ "1/\times"] + 13 \ [press \ "1/\times"] + 36 \ [press \ "1/\times"])$

$R_T = (0.1672\Omega) \ [press \ "1/\times"]$

$R_T = 5.98\Omega; \ round \ up \ to \ 6\Omega$

Answer: (a) 6Ω

Note: The total resistance is always smaller than the smallest resistor.

▶ **Reciprocal Method Example 2**

Question: A circuit has three resistors in parallel: 15Ω, 30Ω, and 45Ω. The circuit resistance is _____. ▶Figure 15–14

(a) 8.33Ω   (b) 9.10Ω   (c) 10.99Ω   (d) 12.22Ω

Solution:

$R_T = 1/(1/R_1 + 1/R_2 + 1/R_3)$

$R_T = 1/(1/15\Omega + 1/30\Omega + 1/45\Omega)$

$R_T = 1/(0.07\Omega + 0.03\Omega + 0.02\Omega)$

$R_T = 1/0.12\Omega$

$R_T = 8.33\Omega$

Answer: (a) 8.33Ω

Note: The answer will always be less than the smallest resistor.

• • •

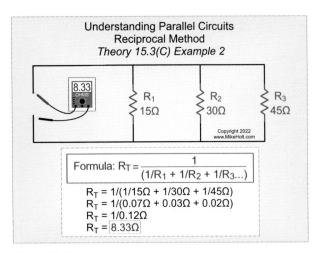

Understanding Parallel Circuits
Reciprocal Method
Theory 15.3(C) Example 2

Formula: $R_T = \dfrac{1}{(1/R_1 + 1/R_2 + 1/R_3...)}$

$R_T = 1/(1/15\Omega + 1/30\Omega + 1/45\Omega)$
$R_T = 1/(0.07\Omega + 0.03\Omega + 0.02\Omega)$
$R_T = 1/0.12\Omega$
$R_T = \boxed{8.33\Omega}$

▶Figure 15–14

15.4 Parallel Circuit Summary

A parallel circuit has the following characteristics: ▶Figure 15–15

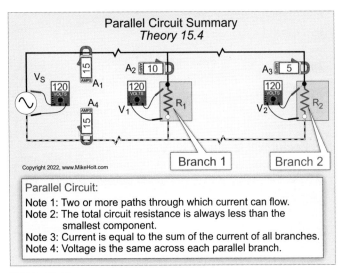

Parallel Circuit Summary
Theory 15.4

Branch 1   Branch 2

Parallel Circuit:
Note 1: Two or more paths through which current can flow.
Note 2: The total circuit resistance is always less than the
       smallest component.
Note 3: Current is equal to the sum of the current of all branches.
Note 4: Voltage is the same across each parallel branch.

▶Figure 15–15

Note 1:   Two or more paths through which current can flow.

Note 2:   The total circuit resistance is always less than the smallest
           component.

Note 3:   Current is equal to the sum of the current of all branches.

Note 4:   Voltage is the same across each parallel branch.

15.5 Parallel-Connected Power Supplies

When power supplies are connected in parallel, the voltage of the
parallel-connected power supplies remains the same. ▶Figure 15–16

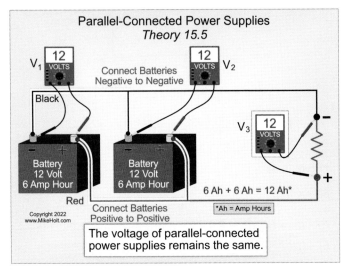

Parallel-Connected Power Supplies
Theory 15.5

Connect Batteries
Negative to Negative

Black

Battery
12 Volt
6 Amp Hour

Battery
12 Volt
6 Amp Hour

6 Ah + 6 Ah = 12 Ah*

Red   Connect Batteries   *Ah = Amp Hours
       Positive to Positive

The voltage of parallel-connected
power supplies remains the same.

▶Figure 15–16

Caution

CAUTION: When jumping a battery in parallel, place
the red cable clamps on the battery's positive (+) terminal
and the black cable clamps on its negative (–) terminal. Pay close
attention when terminating the cables on batteries to avoid causing
a short circuit (+) to (-) connection which could lead to an explosion.
▶Figure 15–17

Parallel-Connected Power Supplies
Theory 15.5 Caution

Vehicle 1   Vehicle 2

When jumping a battery in parallel, place the red
cable clamps on the battery's positive (+) terminal and
the black cable clamps on its negative (–) terminal.
Pay close attention to avoid causing a short circuit.

▶Figure 15–17

15.6 Practical Uses of Parallel Circuits

(A) General. Parallel circuits are commonly used for wiring receptacles, lighting, appliances, and equipment.

(1) Receptacles. Receptacles on a circuit are connected in parallel. This results in each receptacle having the same operating voltage. ▶Figure 15–18

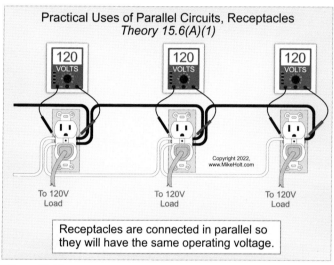

Practical Uses of Parallel Circuits, Receptacles
Theory 15.6(A)(1)

To 120V Load   To 120V Load   To 120V Load

Copyright 2022, www.MikeHolt.com

Receptacles are connected in parallel so they will have the same operating voltage.

▶Figure 15–18

▶ Receptacles Example

Question: Receptacles are connected in parallel so they will have the same operating _____.

(a) power   (b) power factor   (c) voltage   (d) current

Answer: *(c) voltage*

(2) Lighting. Lighting is connected in parallel, and each light will have the same operating voltage. ▶Figure 15–19

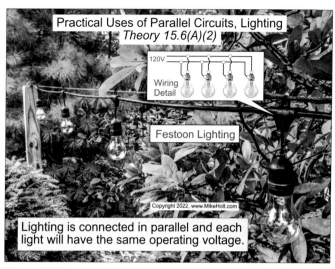

Practical Uses of Parallel Circuits, Lighting
Theory 15.6(A)(2)

120V

Wiring Detail

Festoon Lighting

Copyright 2022, www.MikeHolt.com

Lighting is connected in parallel and each light will have the same operating voltage.

▶Figure 15–19

(3) Appliances and Electrical Equipment. Appliances such as heat strips, water heaters, and some types of motors have their internal electrical components connected in parallel. ▶Figure 15–20

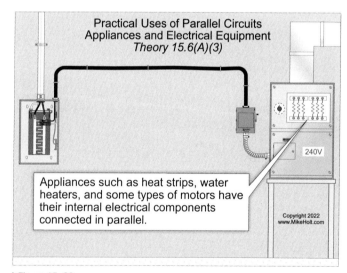

Practical Uses of Parallel Circuits
Appliances and Electrical Equipment
Theory 15.6(A)(3)

240V

Appliances such as heat strips, water heaters, and some types of motors have their internal electrical components connected in parallel.

Copyright 2022 www.MikeHolt.com

▶Figure 15–20

(B) Advantage of Parallel Circuits. One advantage of parallel circuits is that if one branch of a parallel circuit is opened, voltage is still provided to the other parallel branches. ▶Figure 15–21

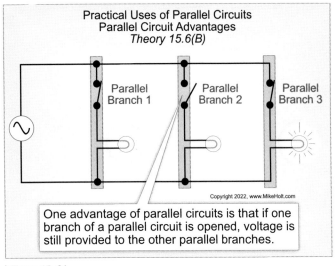

Practical Uses of Parallel Circuits
Parallel Circuit Advantages
Theory 15.6(B)

Parallel Branch 1

Parallel Branch 2

Parallel Branch 3

Copyright 2022, www.MikeHolt.com

One advantage of parallel circuits is that if one branch of a parallel circuit is opened, voltage is still provided to the other parallel branches.

▶Figure 15–21

UNIT 16

SERIES-PARALLEL CIRCUITS

16.1 Introduction

In this unit you will learn how to calculate total circuit resistance for series-parallel circuits.

16.2 Understanding Series-Parallel Circuits

A series-parallel circuit is one that contains some resistors in series and some in parallel. That portion of the circuit that includes resistors in series must comply with the rules for series circuits. That portion of the circuit that contains resistors in parallel must comply with the rules for parallel circuits. ▶Figure 16–1

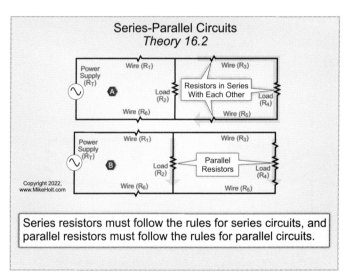

▶Figure 16–1

To understand series-parallel circuits, we must review the rules for determining resistance for series and parallel circuits.

(A) Series Circuit Resistance. The total resistance of a series circuit is equal to the sum of the resistances. ▶Figure 16–2

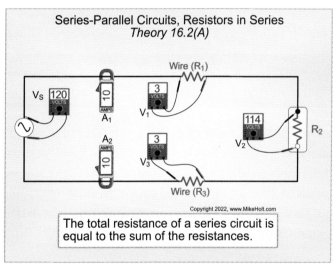

▶Figure 16–2

(B) Parallel Circuit Resistance. The total resistance of a parallel circuit must be calculated with one of the three methods covered in the previous unit. ▶Figure 16–3

▶ Method 1. Equal Resistance

▶ Method 2. Product-Over-Sum

▶ Method 3. Reciprocal

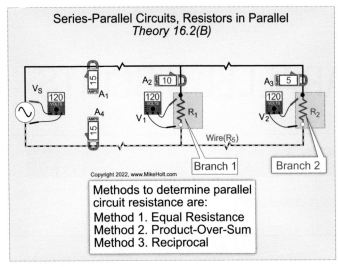

Series-Parallel Circuits, Resistors in Parallel
Theory 16.2(B)

Methods to determine parallel circuit resistance are:
Method 1. Equal Resistance
Method 2. Product-Over-Sum
Method 3. Reciprocal

▶Figure 16–3

16.3 Calculating Resistance in Series-Parallel Circuits

When determining the resistance for a series-parallel circuit, you need to keep breaking the circuit down to the part(s) of the circuit that is series and the part(s) that is parallel until you have only one resistance. Draw the circuit so you can see the series components and the parallel branches. Determine the series resistance and the parallel resistance, then redraw the circuit again.

▶ Resistance of Parallel Circuit Example

Question: What is the resistance of two 12Ω resistors connected in parallel?

(a) 2Ω   (b) 4Ω   (c) 6Ω   (d) 8Ω

Solution:

Use the Equal Resistance method to determine the resistance of the two 12Ω resistors connected in parallel.

R = Resistance of One Resistor/Number of Resistors

R = 12Ω/2 resistors

R = 6Ω

Answer: (c) 6Ω

▶ Resistance of Series Circuit Example

Question: What is the resistance of two 15Ω resistors connected in series?

(a) 24Ω   (b) 30Ω   (c) 36Ω   (d) 54Ω

Solution:

Determine the sum of the series-connected resistors:

$(R + R_1 + R_2)$
$R = 15Ω + 15Ω$
$R = 30Ω$

Answer: (b) 30Ω

▶ Resistance of Series-Parallel Circuits Example

Question: What is the total resistance of a series-parallel circuit: Resistors 1 and 4 are rated 15Ω each and resistors 2 and 3 are rated 12Ω each. Resistor 1 is in series with the parallel resistors 2 and 3, and resistor 4 is in series with parallel resistors 2 and 3.
▶Figure 16–4

(a) 24Ω   (b) 30Ω   (c) 36Ω   (d) 54Ω

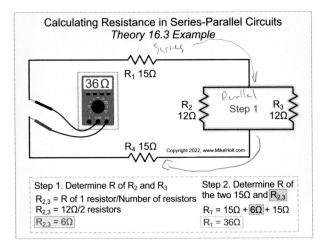

Calculating Resistance in Series-Parallel Circuits
Theory 16.3 Example

Step 1. Determine R of R_2 and R_3
$R_{2,3}$ = R of 1 resistor/Number of resistors
$R_{2,3}$ = 12Ω/2 resistors
$R_{2,3}$ = 6Ω

Step 2. Determine R of the two 15Ω and $R_{2,3}$
$R_T = 15Ω + 6Ω + 15Ω$
$R_T = 36Ω$

▶Figure 16–4

Solution:

Step 1: *Use the Equal Resistance method to determine the resistance of the two 12Ω resistors connected in parallel.*

**$R_{2,3}$ = Resistance of One Resistor/Number of
Resistors**

$R_{2,3}$ = 12Ω/2 resistors

$R_{2,3}$ = 6Ω

Step 2: *Determine the sum of the series-connected resistors:*

$(R_1 + R_{2,3} + R_4)$

$R = 15Ω + 6Ω + 15Ω$

Answer: (c) 36Ω

Understanding Electrical Theory | www.MikeHolt.com |

CHAPTER

6

PRACTICE QUESTIONS

CHAPTER 6—PRACTICE QUESTIONS

Unit 14—Series Circuits

14.2 Series Circuits

1. A series circuit can be envisioned as a circle where current leaves the power source and flows through every load in a _____ path before it returns to the power source.

   (a) single
   (b) parallel
   (c) multiple
   (d) various

2. If there is a break in a _____ circuit, the current in the circuit will stop flowing and none of the loads in the circuit will receive voltage.

   (a) series
   (b) parallel
   (c) multiwire
   (d) any of these

14.3 Understanding Series Circuits

3. In a series circuit, the total circuit resistance is equal to the _____ of all the resistances of all the resistors.

   (a) sum
   (b) product
   (c) square
   (d) square root

4. What is the total resistance of three resistors where R_1 is 15Ω, R_2 is 20Ω, and R_3 is 35Ω?

   (a) 50Ω
   (b) 70Ω
   (c) 100Ω
   (d) 150Ω

5. What is the total resistance of three resistors where R_1 is 35Ω, R_2 is 40Ω, and R_3 is 55Ω?

   (a) 50Ω
   (b) 70Ω
   (c) 130Ω
   (d) 150Ω

6. Kirchhoff's Current Law states that the current flowing through each resistor of a series circuit will be _____ the current leaving and returning to the power source.

   (a) directly proportional to
   (b) inversely proportional to
   (c) added to
   (d) the same value as

7. The current for a 240V circuit that has three resistors in series where R_1 is 15Ω, R_2 is 20Ω, and R_3 is 25Ω is _____.

   (a) 4A
   (b) 7A
   (c) 9A
   (d) 12A

8. The current for a 120V circuit that has three resistors in series where R_1 is 8Ω, R_2 is 12Ω, and R_3 is 30Ω is _____.

   (a) 2.40A
   (b) 3.70A
   (c) 4.90A
   (d) 5.20A

9. The current for a 208V circuit that has three resistors in series where R_1 is 1Ω, R_2 is 5Ω, and R_3 is 14Ω is _____.

   (a) 10.40A
   (b) 12.70A
   (c) 12.90A
   (d) 15.20A

10. The current for a 277V circuit that has three resistors in series where R_1 is 10Ω, R_2 is 10Ω, and R_3 is 10Ω is _____.

    (a) 4A
    (b) 7A
    (c) 9A
    (d) 12A

11. A 120V circuit has three resistors in series where R_1 is 10Ω, R_2 is 15Ω, and R_3 is 25Ω. The voltage across R_1 is _____.

    I = 2.4

    (a) 24V
    (b) 30V
    (c) 104V
    (d) 110V

12. A 120V circuit has three resistors in series where R_1 is 10Ω, R_2 is 15Ω, and R_3 is 15Ω. The voltage across R_2 or R_3 is _____.

    I = 3

    (a) 30V
    (b) 45V
    (c) 60V
    (d) 95V

13. A 240V circuit has three resistors in series where R_1 is 15Ω, R_2 is 15Ω, and R_3 is 15Ω. The voltage across R_2 or R_3 is _____.

    I = 5.3

    (a) 50V
    (b) 65V
    (c) 80V
    (d) 95V

14. A 240V circuit has three resistors in series where R_1 is 25Ω, R_2 is 25Ω, and R_3 is 30Ω. The voltage across R_1 is _____.

    I = 3

    (a) 45V
    (b) 55V
    (c) 65V
    (d) 75V

15. Kirchhoff's Voltage Law states that the source voltage of a series circuit is equal to the _____ of the voltages across all circuit resistors.

    (a) sum
    (b) product
    (c) square
    (d) square root

16. A 40Ω circuit has three resistors in series where R_1 is 60V, R_2 is 60V, and R_3 is 120V. The voltage source is equal to _____.

    (a) 60V
    (b) 90V
    (c) 120V
    (d) 240V

17. A 50Ω circuit has three resistors in series where R_1 is 60V, R_2 is 60V, and R_3 is 88V. The voltage source is equal to _____.

    (a) 60V
    (b) 90V
    (c) 120V
    (d) 208V

18. A 10A circuit has three resistors in series where R_1 is 4Ω, R_2 is 4Ω, and R_3 is 4Ω. The voltage source is equal to _____.

    (a) 120V
    (b) 130V
    (c) 140V
    (d) 200V

19. A 20A circuit has three resistors in series where R_1 is 4Ω, R_2 is 4Ω, and R_3 is 4Ω. The voltage source is equal to _____.

    (a) 230V
    (b) 240V
    (c) 277V
    (d) 480V

20. No matter how many resistances there are in a series circuit, the sum of the voltages across all of the resistances equals the voltage of the source according to the _____ Law of Proportion.

    (a) Voltage
    (b) Current
    (c) Resistance
    (d) Power

14.4 Series Circuit Summary

21. A series circuit has which of the following characteristics?

    (a) Circuit resistance is equal to the sum of the resistances.
    (b) Current is the same through all the resistors.
    (c) The total voltage across all resistors is equal to the voltage source.
    (d) all of these

14.5 Series-Connected Power Supplies

22. When power supplies are connected in series, the voltage of the _____ power supplies is equal to the sum of the power supply voltages.

    (a) series-connected
    (b) parallel-connected
    (c) multi-connected
    (d) none of these

23. If series-connected power supplies are not arranged positive (+) to negative (–), the circuit _____ will not equal the sum of the power supply voltages.

    (a) voltage
    (b) current
    (c) resistance
    (d) power

24. The voltage across two 24V batteries connected in series is _____.

    (a) 24V
    (b) 48V
    (c) 120V
    (d) 240V

25. The voltage of ten 52.70V solar panels connected in series is _____.

    (a) 277V
    (b) 480V
    (c) 527V
    (d) 600V

14.6 Applications of Series Circuits

26. _____ circuits are used for equipment control, signaling, and (at times) the internal wiring of equipment.

    (a) Series
    (b) Parallel
    (c) Multiwire
    (d) any of these

27. Series circuits are often used for _____ applications (starting and stopping) of electrical equipment.

    (a) special
    (b) control
    (c) special and control
    (d) none of these

28. Series circuits are often used to give a _____ something has occurred.

    (a) signal that
    (b) malfunction when
    (c) signal that or malfunction when
    (d) none of these

29. The internal wiring of many types of equipment, such as motor windings, can be connected in _____.

    (a) high-mode
    (b) low-mode
    (c) zig-zag
    (d) series

Unit 15—Parallel Circuits

15.2 Understanding Parallel Circuits

1. In a parallel circuit, the voltage across each resistance of the circuit is _____ the voltage source.

    (a) less than
    (b) equal to
    (c) greater than
    (d) less than or greater than

2. A 12V circuit has two 5Ω resistors connected in parallel. The voltage across any one of these resistors is _____.

   (a) 12V
   (b) 24V
   (c) 48V
   (d) 120V

3. A 120V circuit has two 20Ω resistors connected in parallel. The voltage across any one of these resistors is _____.

   (a) 12V
   (b) 24V
   (c) 48V
   (d) 120V

4. According to Kirchhoff's _____ Law, the total current of a parallel circuit equals the sum of the currents of all the branches.

   (a) Current
   (b) Voltage
   (c) Resistance
   (d) Power

5. A circuit has three 25A resistors connected in parallel. The current of this circuit is _____.

   (a) 35A
   (b) 45A
   (c) 65A
   (d) 75A

6. A circuit has three 15A resistors connected in parallel. The current of this circuit is _____.

   (a) 35A
   (b) 45A
   (c) 65A
   (d) 75A

7. A circuit has three 10A resistors connected in parallel. The current of this circuit is _____.

   (a) 30A
   (b) 40A
   (c) 60A
   (d) 70A

15.3 Parallel Circuit Resistance Calculations

8. The total resistance of a parallel circuit can be calculated by the _____ method.

   (a) Equal Resistance
   (b) Product-Over-Sum
   (c) Reciprocal
   (d) any of these

9. In a parallel circuit, the total circuit resistance is always _____ the smallest resistance.

   (a) greater than
   (b) less than
   (c) equal to
   (d) the square of

10. According to the _____ method, when all the resistances of the parallel circuit have the same resistance, divide the resistance of one resistance by the number of resistors in parallel.

    (a) Equal Resistance
    (b) Product-Over-Sum
    (c) Reciprocal
    (d) none of these

11. The total resistance of three 15Ω resistors connected in parallel is _____.

    (a) 5Ω
    (b) 10Ω
    (c) 20Ω
    (d) 30Ω

12. The total resistance of ten 50Ω resistors connected in parallel is _____.

    (a) 5Ω
    (b) 10Ω
    (c) 50Ω
    (d) 100Ω

13. A 240V circuit has three resistors in parallel where R_1 is 25Ω, R_2 is 25Ω, and R_3 is 25Ω. The resistance of this parallel circuit is _____.

    (a) 5.30Ω
    (b) 8.33Ω
    (c) 13.30Ω
    (d) 15.33Ω

14. A circuit has three 5Ω resistors connected in parallel. The resistance of this circuit is _____.

    (a) 1.66Ω
    (b) 2.26Ω
    (c) 4.76Ω
    (d) 5.66Ω

15. The Product-Over-Sum method is used to calculate the resistance of _____ parallel resistances of different values.

    (a) two
    (b) three
    (c) four
    (d) five

16. The resistance of a coffee pot is 16Ω (R_1), and the resistance of a skillet is approximately 13Ω (R_2). What is the total resistance of the two appliances if they are connected in parallel?

    (a) 7.20Ω
    (b) 13Ω
    (c) 16Ω
    (d) 29Ω

17. The resistance of a microwave is 15Ω (R_1), and the resistance of an oven is approximately 30Ω (R_2). What is the total resistance of the two appliances if they are connected in parallel?

    (a) 7.20Ω
    (b) 10Ω
    (c) 16Ω
    (d) 25Ω

18. The resistance of a toaster is 6Ω (R_1), and the resistance of a warming drawer is approximately 12Ω (R_2). What is the total resistance of the two appliances if they are connected in parallel?

    (a) 4Ω
    (b) 8Ω
    (c) 16Ω
    (d) 20Ω

19. The resistance of a rice cooker is 5Ω (R_1), and the resistance of an air fryer is approximately 10Ω (R_2). What is the total resistance of the two appliances if they are connected in parallel?

    (a) 3.33Ω
    (b) 5.20Ω
    (c) 7.16Ω
    (d) 8.29Ω

20. The _____ method for determining the total resistance of a parallel circuit is used when there are more than two resistors of different values.

    (a) Equal Resistance
    (b) Product-Over-Sum
    (c) Reciprocal
    (d) none of these

21. What is the resistance total of a 16Ω, a 13Ω, and a 36Ω resistor connected in parallel?

    (a) 6Ω
    (b) 13Ω
    (c) 16Ω
    (d) 36Ω

22. A circuit has three resistors in parallel: 15Ω, 30Ω, and 45Ω. The circuit resistance is _____.

    (a) 9Ω
    (b) 10Ω
    (c) 11Ω
    (d) 12Ω

15.4 Parallel Circuit Summary

23. A parallel circuit has which of the following characteristics?

    (a) The total circuit resistance is always less than the smallest component.
    (b) Current is equal to the sum of the current of all branches.
    (c) Voltage is the same across each parallel branch.
    (d) all of these

15.5 Parallel-Connected Power Supplies

24. When power supplies are connected in parallel, the voltage of the _____ power supplies remains the same.

    (a) series-connected
    (b) parallel-connected
    (c) multi-connected
    (d) none of these

15.6 Practical Uses of Parallel Circuits

25. _____ circuits are commonly used for wiring receptacles, lighting, appliances, and equipment.

    (a) Series
    (b) Parallel
    (c) Multiwire
    (d) any of these

26. Receptacles on a circuit are connected in parallel. This results in each receptacle having the same operating _____.

    (a) power
    (b) current
    (c) resistance
    (d) voltage

27. Lighting is connected in parallel, and each light will have the same operating _____.

    (a) power
    (b) current
    (c) resistance
    (d) voltage

28. Appliances such as heat strips, water heaters, and some types of motors have their internal electrical components connected in _____.

    (a) parallel
    (b) series
    (c) zig-zag
    (d) none of these

29. One advantage of parallel circuits is that if one branch of a parallel circuit is opened, _____ is still provided to the other parallel branches.

    (a) power
    (b) current
    (c) resistance
    (d) voltage

Unit—16 Series-Parallel Circuits

16.2 Understanding Series-Parallel Circuits

1. A _____ circuit is one that contains some resistances in series and some resistances in parallel with each other.

    (a) parallel
    (b) series
    (c) series-parallel
    (d) none of these

2. That portion of the series-parallel circuit that contains resistances in _____ must comply with the rules for series circuits.

    (a) series
    (b) parallel
    (c) series-parallel
    (d) parallel-series

3. That portion of the series-parallel circuit that contains resistances in _____ must comply with the rules for parallel circuits.

    (a) series
    (b) parallel
    (c) series-parallel
    (d) parallel-series

4. The total resistance of a _____ circuit is equal to the sum of the resistances.

    (a) series
    (b) parallel
    (c) series-parallel
    (d) parallel-series

5. The total resistance of a parallel circuit can be calculated by using the _____.

    (a) Equal Resistance method
    (b) Product-Over-Sum method
    (c) Reciprocal method
    (d) any of these

16.3 Calculating Resistance in Series-Parallel Circuits

6. When working with series-parallel circuits, it is best to _____ the circuit so you can see the series components and the parallel branches.

    (a) draw
    (b) photograph
    (c) configure
    (d) invert

CHAPTER 7

ALTERNATING CURRENT

Chapter 7—Alternating Current

Unit 17—Alternating Current Fundamentals

The major advantage of alternating current is that it can be transformed into different voltages to transmit power long distances. In this unit you will learn:

▸ how alternating current is produced

▸ the relationship of voltage and current waveforms

Unit 18—Inductance

When electrons move, the electromagnetic fields of the individual electrons combine to produce an overall electromagnetic field. The greater the current flow, the greater the overall electromagnetic field around the wire. The movement of electrons by an external electromagnetic field is called "induced current" and the associated potential that is established is called "induced voltage." In this unit you will learn:

▸ about self-inductance and mutual inductance

▸ the relationship between induced voltage and current

▸ how inductive reactance is calculated

Unit 19—Capacitance

Capacitors are electrical devices that store energy in an electrical field between closely spaced plates and can release that stored energy later. In this unit you will learn:

▸ what capacitance is

▸ how capacitive reactance is calculated

▸ common uses of capacitors

• • •

Unit 20—True Power, Power Factor, and Apparent Power

True power can only be produced when both the current and voltage are in-phase with each other. If the current and voltage are out-of-phase, the alternating-current circuit will have power factor. Apparent power is the power delivered to alternating-current circuits with power factor. In this unit you will learn:

▶ what true power and apparent power are

▶ the relationship between true power and apparent power

▶ the effects of power factor on alternating-current circuits

UNIT 17

ALTERNATING CURRENT FUNDAMENTALS

17.1 Introduction

The major advantage of alternating current is that it can be transformed into different voltages to transmit power long distances. In this unit you will learn:

▶ how alternating current is produced

▶ the relationship of voltage and current waveforms

17.2 How Alternating Current is Produced

(A) Magnetism. In 1831, Michael Faraday discovered that electricity could be produced from a source other than a battery. He knew that electricity could be used to produce an electromagnet and wondered if a magnet could be used to generate electricity. Faraday discovered that when he moved a magnet inside a coil of wire, he was able to measure a pulse of electric current with a measuring instrument called a "galvanometer." When he pulled the magnet out of the coil of wire, he measured another electrical pulse of current.

(B) Current Direction. Faraday discovered that a magnet that pushes into or pulls out of a coil of wire causes the current in the wire to move in a specific direction relative to the movement of the magnetic field of the magnet. When a magnetic field moves through a coil of wire, the lines of force of the magnetic field cause the electrons in the wire to flow in a specific direction and when the magnetic field moves in the opposite direction, electrons in the wire flow in the opposite direction. ▶Figure 17–1

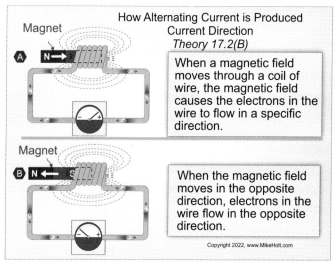

How Alternating Current is Produced
Current Direction
Theory 17.2(B)

When a magnetic field moves through a coil of wire, the magnetic field causes the electrons in the wire to flow in a specific direction.

When the magnetic field moves in the opposite direction, electrons in the wire flow in the opposite direction.

Copyright 2022, www.MikeHolt.com

▶Figure 17–1

(C) Alternating-Current Generator. Generators can be used to produce alternating-current flow. To do so, a magnetic field must have motion relative to a coil of wire. A simple ac generator can be constructed with loops of wire rotating within the magnetic field between opposite poles of a stationary magnet. ▶Figure 17–2

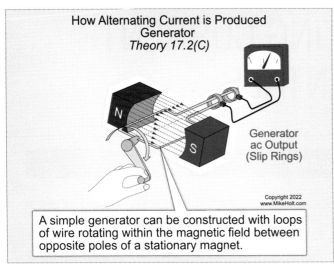

How Alternating Current is Produced
Generator
Theory 17.2(C)

Generator ac Output (Slip Rings)

A simple generator can be constructed with loops of wire rotating within the magnetic field between opposite poles of a stationary magnet.

▶Figure 17–2

Author's Comment:

▶ According to the Drift Theory, electrons wiggle back and forth no more than one inch per ½ cycle in 60 Hz alternating-current circuits.

17.3 Waveforms

A waveform is a mathematical representation (a graph) used to visualize the level and direction of current and voltage in a circuit. One way to see the different characteristics of waveforms is by using an oscilloscope. ▶Figure 17–3

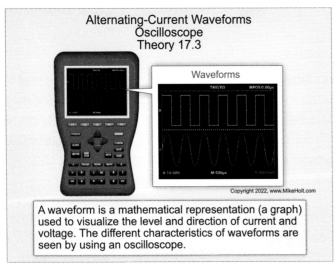

Alternating-Current Waveforms
Oscilloscope
Theory 17.3

Waveforms

A waveform is a mathematical representation (a graph) used to visualize the level and direction of current and voltage. The different characteristics of waveforms are seen by using an oscilloscope.

▶Figure 17–3

(A) Direct-Current Waveforms. Direct-current (dc) power sources push and pull electrons in the circuit in one direction and the polarity of the voltage waveform is positive because the electrons flow from the negative to positive terminals of the power source.

(1) Battery. Direct-current voltage produced by a battery has a constant magnitude and the polarity is always the same. When dc voltage from a battery is plotted on a graph, it looks like a flat line. ▶Figure 17–4

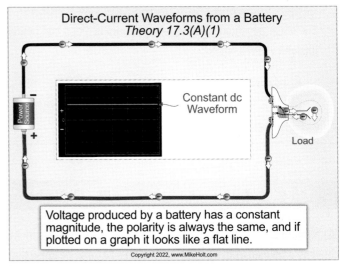

Direct-Current Waveforms from a Battery
Theory 17.3(A)(1)

Constant dc Waveform

Load

Voltage produced by a battery has a constant magnitude, the polarity is always the same, and if plotted on a graph it looks like a flat line.

▶Figure 17–4

(2) Solar PV. Direct-current voltage produced by a solar cell is a function of the irradiation of the sun's rays. At night the voltage will be almost zero, and as the sun rises, the voltage will increase to peak voltage. As the sun sets, the voltage decreases again to nearly zero. When dc voltage from a solar cell for a 24-hour period is plotted on a graph, it looks like an arc. ▶Figure 17–5

(3) Full-Wave Rectifier Diode. A rectifier is a device that converts alternating current to direct current. Direct current from a full-wave rectifier supplied by ac power has a varying magnitude because the polarity is always the same, so the waveform appears as a ripple with positive polarity. The combination of alternating-current and direct-current waveforms result in a pulsating waveform. ▶Figure 17–6

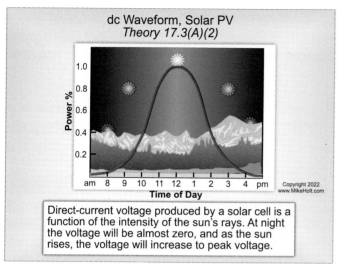

dc Waveform, Solar PV
Theory 17.3(A)(2)

Direct-current voltage produced by a solar cell is a function of the intensity of the sun's rays. At night the voltage will be almost zero, and as the sun rises, the voltage will increase to peak voltage.

▶Figure 17–5

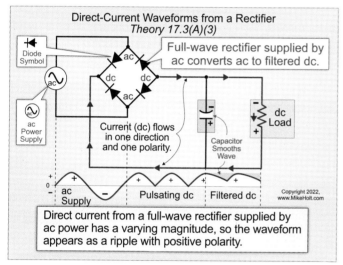

Direct-Current Waveforms from a Rectifier
Theory 17.3(A)(3)

Full-wave rectifier supplied by ac converts ac to filtered dc.

Current (dc) flows in one direction and one polarity.

Capacitor Smooths Wave

Direct current from a full-wave rectifier supplied by ac power has a varying magnitude, so the waveform appears as a ripple with positive polarity.

▶Figure 17–6

(B) Alternating-Current Waveforms. Most commercial alternating-current power is produced by some type of generator using wind, steam, or water. An alternating-current waveform represents the level and direction of the voltage for every instant of time during one full revolution of the generator's rotor.

(1) Polarity. The voltage and current waveforms for alternating-current generators begin with a positive polarity for the first 180° and then change to a negative polarity.

(2) Sinusoidal Waveform. The waveform for an alternating-current generator is symmetrical, with positive values above and negative values below the zero-reference line on the graph. This waveform is called a "sine wave" or a "sinusoidal waveform." ▶Figure 17–7

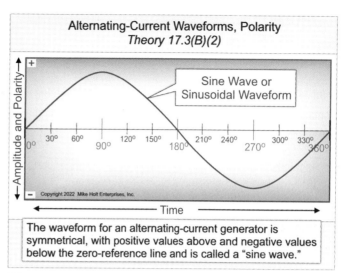

Alternating-Current Waveforms, Polarity
Theory 17.3(B)(2)

Sine Wave or Sinusoidal Waveform

The waveform for an alternating-current generator is symmetrical, with positive values above and negative values below the zero-reference line and is called a "sine wave."

▶Figure 17–7

(a) Degrees. The relationship of the voltage and current waveforms to the generator's rotor position is from 0° to 360° as follows: ▶Figure 17–8

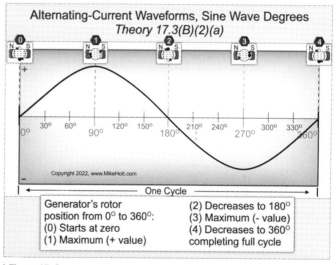

Alternating-Current Waveforms, Sine Wave Degrees
Theory 17.3(B)(2)(a)

One Cycle

Generator's rotor position from 0° to 360°:	(2) Decreases to 180°
(0) Starts at zero	(3) Maximum (- value)
(1) Maximum (+ value)	(4) Decreases to 360° completing full cycle

▶Figure 17–8

Point (0). The voltage/current waveform starts at the zero value when the generator's rotor is not turning.

Point (1). As the generator rotor turns through the electromagnetic field, the voltage/current increases from zero to a maximum value at 90° of the 360° in a positive polarity.

Point (2). As the generator rotor continues to turn through the electromagnetic field, the positive polarity voltage/current decreases from the maximum value at 90° to 180°.

Point (3). As the generator rotor continues to turn through the electromagnetic field, the voltage/current increases from zero to a maximum value at 270° of the 360° in the negative polarity.

Point (4). As the generator rotor continues to turn through the electromagnetic field, the negative polarity voltage/current decreases from the maximum value at 270° to 360°.

(3) Nonsinusoidal Waveform. A nonsinusoidal waveform is produced when nonlinear loads distort the voltage and current sine waves.
▶Figure 17–9

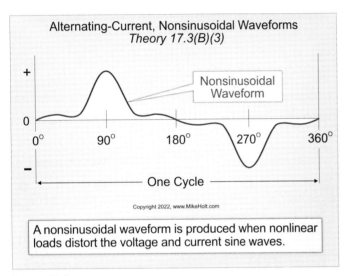

▶Figure 17–9

(a) Nonlinear Load. A nonlinear load is a load where the shape of the current waveform does not follow the shape of the applied sinusoidal voltage waveform. Examples of nonlinear loads that contribute to nonsinusoidal waveforms include computer power supplies, electronic ballasts for fluorescent lighting fixtures, LED drivers, and adjustable-speed drives for motors. A nonsymmetrical waveform is more common than a symmetrical sine wave in today's world of electronics.
▶Figure 17–10

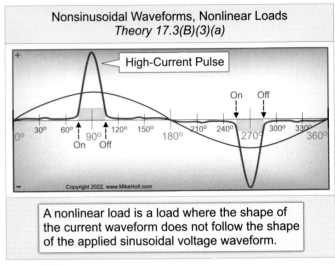

▶Figure 17–10

(b) Harmonics. Nonlinear loads produce "harmonics" which are waveforms that cycle at a frequency that is a multiple of the fundamental frequency. If an electronic load has an abrupt change in impedance (such as a sudden change from high to low), it causes current pulses that reflect back into the power distribution system. ▶Figure 17–11

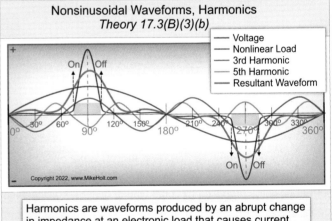

▶Figure 17–11

17.4 Frequency

The full rotation of an alternating-current generator is equal to 360° and its frequency output is expressed as "cycles per second" measured in "Hertz" (Hz) in honor of Heinrich Hertz. Electrical power generated in the United States and Canada have their generators rotate at speeds that are a multiple of 60 rotations per second; therefore, the frequency is 60 Hz. Some other parts of the world have their generators rotate at multiples of 50 rotations per second, or 50 Hz. ▶**Figure 17–12**

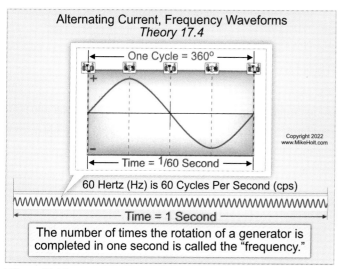

Alternating Current, Frequency Waveforms
Theory 17.4

One Cycle = 360°

Copyright 2022 www.MikeHolt.com

Time = ¹/60 Second

60 Hertz (Hz) is 60 Cycles Per Second (cps)

Time = 1 Second

The number of times the rotation of a generator is completed in one second is called the "frequency."

▶Figure 17–12

17.5 In-Phase Waveforms

If the voltage and current waveforms begin and end simultaneously, then the two waveforms are "in-phase" with each other. This means that, at every instant, the current is exactly in step with the voltage, so the current and voltage waveforms will reach their zero and peak values at the same time. ▶**Figure 17–13**

17.6 Out-of-Phase Waveforms

When the voltage and current waveforms reach their zero and peak values at different times, the waveforms are said to be "out-of-phase" with each other. When describing the relationship between voltage and current, the reference waveform is always voltage. ▶**Figure 17–14**

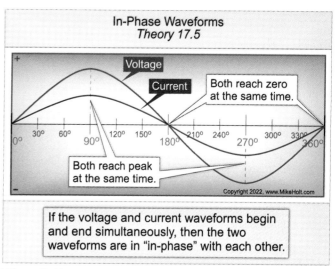

In-Phase Waveforms
Theory 17.5

Voltage
Current
Both reach zero at the same time.
Both reach peak at the same time.

Copyright 2022, www.MikeHolt.com

If the voltage and current waveforms begin and end simultaneously, then the two waveforms are in "in-phase" with each other.

▶Figure 17–13

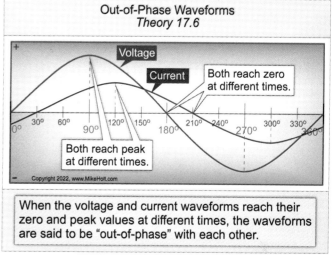

Out-of-Phase Waveforms
Theory 17.6

Voltage
Current
Both reach zero at different times.
Both reach peak at different times.

Copyright 2022, www.MikeHolt.com

When the voltage and current waveforms reach their zero and peak values at different times, the waveforms are said to be "out-of-phase" with each other.

▶Figure 17–14

(A) Current Waveform Leads Voltage Waveform. In a purely capacitive circuit, the current waveform leads the voltage waveform by as much as 90°. When shown as a waveform, the current waveform begins and finishes its cycle before the voltage waveform. ▶**Figure 17–15**

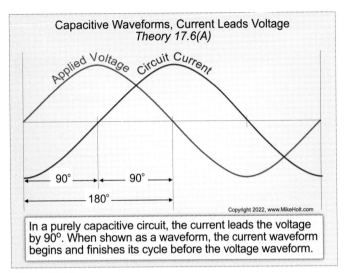

▶Figure 17-15

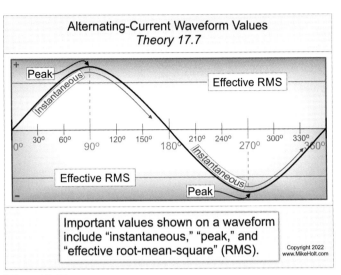

▶Figure 17-17

(B) Current Waveform Lags Voltage Waveform. In a purely inductive circuit, the current waveform lags the voltage waveform by as much as 90°. When shown as a waveform, the current waveform begins and finishes its cycle after the voltage waveform. ▶Figure 17-16

(A) Instantaneous Waveform Value. The instantaneous value of a waveform is the value at a specific moment in time starting at zero, having a peak value, and ending at zero. ▶Figure 17-18

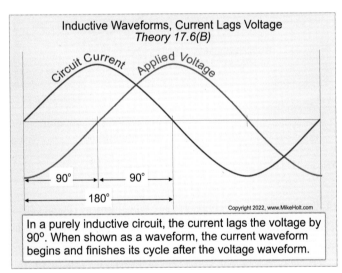

▶Figure 17-16

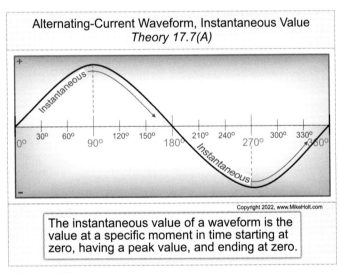

▶Figure 17-18

17.7 Alternating-Current Waveform Values

Important ac waveform values include "instantaneous," "peak," and "effective root-mean-square" (RMS). ▶Figure 17-17

(B) Peak Waveform Value. The peak value of a waveform is the maximum value the waveform reaches, for both positive and negative polarities. The peak value is determined by the following formula: ▶Figure 17-19

Peak = Effective (RMS) × 1.414

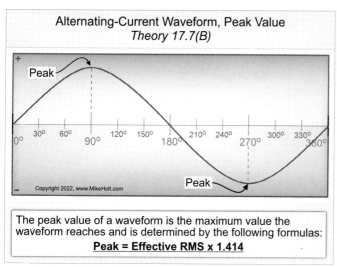

Alternating-Current Waveform, Peak Value
Theory 17.7(B)

The peak value of a waveform is the maximum value the waveform reaches and is determined by the following formulas:
Peak = Effective RMS x 1.414

▶Figure 17–19

▶ Peak Value Example 1

Question: The peak current, in amperes, of a circuit with a load having an effective (RMS) current of 10A is _____. ▶Figure 17–20

(a) 14A   (b) 15A   (c) 16A   (d) 17A

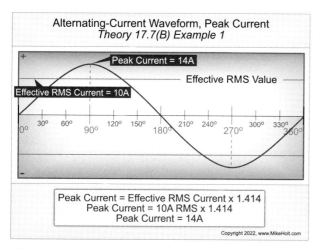

Alternating-Current Waveform, Peak Current
Theory 17.7(B) Example 1

Peak Current = Effective RMS Current x 1.414
Peak Current = 10A RMS x 1.414
Peak Current = 14A

▶Figure 17–20

Solution:

Peak Current = Effective (RMS) Current × 1.414
Peak Current = 10A RMS × 1.414

Answer: (a) 14A

▶ Peak Value Example 2

Question: The peak voltage of a circuit having an effective (RMS) voltage of 277V is _____. ▶Figure 17–21

(a) 170V   (b) 277V   (c) 300V   (d) 392V

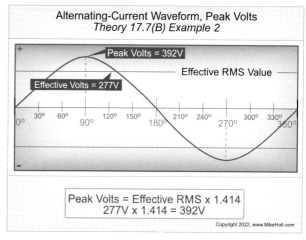

Alternating-Current Waveform, Peak Volts
Theory 17.7(B) Example 2

Peak Volts = Effective RMS x 1.414
277V x 1.414 = 392V

▶Figure 17–21

Solution:

Peak Voltage = Effective Voltage × 1.414
Peak Voltage = 277V RMS × 1.414

Answer: (d) 392V

(C) Effective (RMS) Waveform Value. The effective ac voltage is equal to the dc voltage that would provide the same heat generation if applied to a resistor. The effective RMS value of a waveform is determined by the following formula: ▶Figure 17–22

Effective (RMS) = Peak × 0.707

Author's Comment:

▶ Root-Mean-Square (RMS) voltage describes the calculation steps (in reverse) necessary to determine the effective ac voltage. ▶Figure 17–23

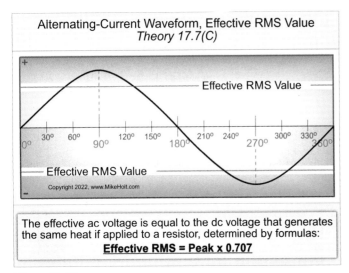

Alternating-Current Waveform, Effective RMS Value
Theory 17.7(C)

The effective ac voltage is equal to the dc voltage that generates the same heat if applied to a resistor, determined by formulas:
Effective RMS = Peak x 0.707

▶Figure 17–22

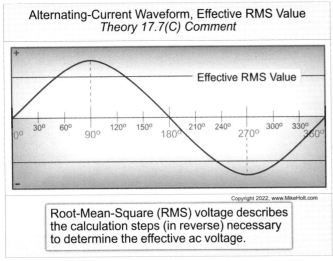

Alternating-Current Waveform, Effective RMS Value
Theory 17.7(C) Comment

Root-Mean-Square (RMS) voltage describes the calculation steps (in reverse) necessary to determine the effective ac voltage.

▶Figure 17–23

▶ **Effective (RMS) Value Example**

Question: What is the effective (RMS) voltage of a circuit with a peak value of 170V? ▶**Figure 17–24**

(a) 100V   (b) 110V   (c) 115V   (d) 120V

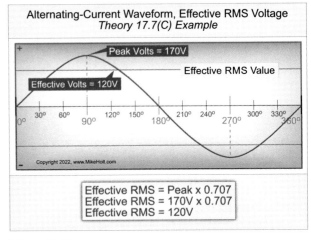

Alternating-Current Waveform, Effective RMS Voltage
Theory 17.7(C) Example

Effective RMS = Peak x 0.707
Effective RMS = 170V x 0.707
Effective RMS = 120V

▶Figure 17–24

Solution:

Effective (RMS) = Peak × 0.707
Effective (RMS) = 170V × 0.707

Answer: (d) 120V

Step 1:   *Square.* Square the instantaneous ac voltage values.

Step 2:   *Mean.* Determine the mean (average) of the instantaneous ac voltages from Step 1.

Step 3:   *Root.* Calculate the square root value of the mean (average) from Step 2.

INDUCTANCE

18.1 Introduction

When electrons move, the electromagnetic fields of the individual electrons combine to produce an overall electromagnetic field. The greater the current flow, the greater the overall electromagnetic field around the wire. The movement of electrons by an external electromagnetic field is called "induced current" and the associated potential that is established is called "induced voltage." In this unit you will learn:

▸ about self-inductance and mutual inductance

▸ the relationship between induced voltage and current

▸ how inductive reactance is calculated

18.2 How Inductance Works

As alternating current flows through a wire, an expanding and collapsing electromagnetic field expands from the center of the wire to its outside and then collapses back to the center of the wire. The effect of relative motion between an alternating electromagnetic field and a wire is known as "inductance."

There are two models of inductance, self- and mutual induction.

18.3 Self-Inductance

(A) Self-Induced Voltage. When alternating current flows in a wire, the expanding and collapsing electromagnetic field from the center to the outside of the wire self-induces an opposing voltage in the wire. This self-induced opposing voltage is known as "counter-electromotive force" (CEMF). ▸Figure 18–1

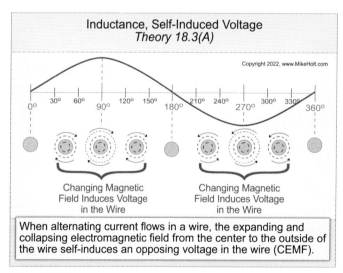

When alternating current flows in a wire, the expanding and collapsing electromagnetic field from the center to the outside of the wire self-induces an opposing voltage in the wire (CEMF).

▸Figure 18–1

(1) Self-Induced Voltage and Applied Current. Self-induced voltage is 90° out-of-phase with the applied current. When alternating current increases, the polarity of the counter-electromotive force within the wire from self-induction opposes the increase in current. When alternating current decreases, the polarity of the counter-electromotive force from self-induction attempts to prevent the current from decreasing. ▸Figure 18–2

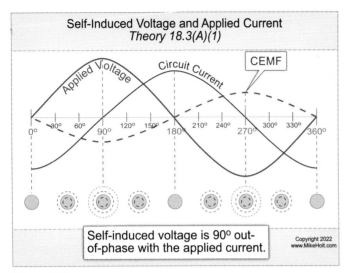

▶Figure 18–2

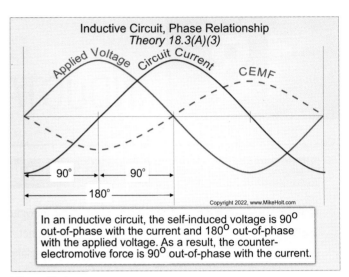

▶Figure 18–4

(2) Self-Induced Voltage and Applied Voltage. Self-induced voltage is 180° out-of-phase with the applied voltage. When the applied voltage increases or decreases, the polarity of the counter-electromotive force opposes the change in applied voltage. When the applied voltage is at its maximum in one direction, the counter-electromotive force is at its maximum in the opposite direction. ▶Figure 18–3

(B) Wire Shape. The amount of self-induced voltage within a wire is determined by its physical shape and the magnitude of the current. A straight wire will have less self-induced voltage than a wire formed into a coil. ▶Figure 18–5

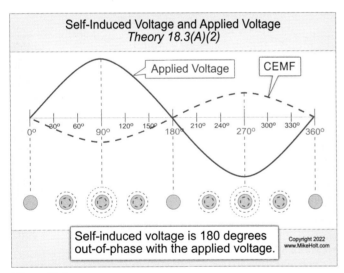

▶Figure 18–3

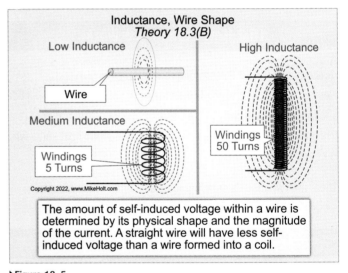

▶Figure 18–5

18.4 Mutual Inductance

(3) Phase Relationship. In an inductive circuit, the self-induced voltage is 90° out-of-phase with the current and 180° out-of-phase with the applied voltage. As a result, the counter-electromotive force is 90° out-of-phase with the applied current. ▶Figure 18–4

(A) Induced Voltage. Mutual induction occurs when one coil of wire (winding) induces a voltage onto another coil of wire (winding) because of the expanding and collapsing electromagnetic fields of adjacent windings. ▶Figure 18–6

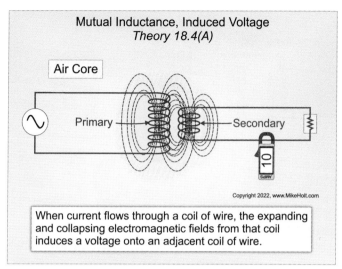

Mutual Inductance, Induced Voltage
Theory 18.4(A)

Air Core

Primary — Secondary

When current flows through a coil of wire, the expanding and collapsing electromagnetic fields from that coil induces a voltage onto an adjacent coil of wire.

▶Figure 18–6

(B) Field Intensity. The electromagnetic field intensity of windings can be increased by inserting a soft iron core into the middle of the windings, which results in greater mutual inductance between the windings. ▶Figure 18–7

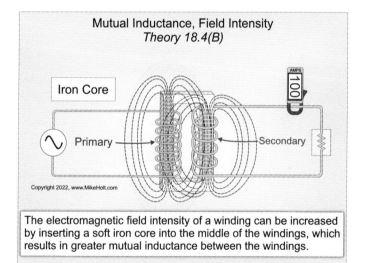

Mutual Inductance, Field Intensity
Theory 18.4(B)

Iron Core

Primary — Secondary

The electromagnetic field intensity of a winding can be increased by inserting a soft iron core into the middle of the windings, which results in greater mutual inductance between the windings.

▶Figure 18–7

18.5 Inductive Reactance

An inductor opposes any change in alternating current. When the current increases, the inductor opposes the increase and when the current decreases, the inductor will try to keep the current the same. The counter-electromotive force resulting from a purely inductive circuit is 90° out-of-phase with the current. ▶Figure 18–8

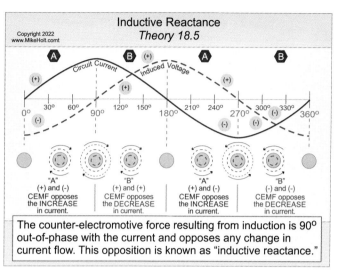

Inductive Reactance
Theory 18.5

Copyright 2022
www.MikeHolt.comt

The counter-electromotive force resulting from induction is 90° out-of-phase with the current and opposes any change in current flow. This opposition is known as "inductive reactance."

▶Figure 18–8

This opposition to current flow is known as "inductive reactance," is abbreviated as "X_L," is measured ohms, and expressed by the formula:
$$X_L = 2 \times \pi \times f \times L$$

"π" is 3.14

"f" is the frequency measured in hertz

"L" is inductance measured in Henrys

▶ Inductive Reactance Example

Question: What is the inductive reactance for the windings of a 5 hp motor operating at 60 Hz with an inductance of 0.10 Henrys?

(a) 17Ω   (b) 38Ω   (c) 42Ω   (d) 48Ω

Solution:

$X_L = 2 \times \pi \times f \times L$

$\pi = 3.14$
$f = 60 \text{ Hz}$
$L = 0.10H$

$X_L = 2 \times 3.14 \times 60 \text{ Hz} \times 0.10H$
$X_L = 38Ω$

Answer: (b) 38Ω

18.6 Uses of Induction

Figuring out how to harness the power of induction was Nikola Tesla's life's work. His discoveries and advances in alternating current changed the industrial landscape of the world by making the use of alternating-current electricity practical. The most significant uses of induction for the electrical industry include equipment such as motors, generators, relays, and transformers. ▶Figure 18–9

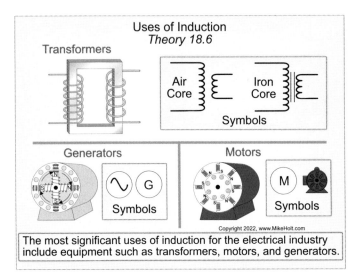

▶Figure 18–9

UNIT
19

CAPACITANCE

19.1 Introduction

Capacitors are electrical devices that store energy in an electrical field between closely spaced plates and can release that stored energy later. In this unit you will learn:

▸ what capacitance is

▸ how capacitive reactance is calculated

▸ common uses of capacitors

19.2 Capacitance in Capacitors

(A) General. Capacitance is the property of an electrical circuit that enables it to store electrical energy and release that energy later. In a capacitive circuit, the current waveform leads the voltage waveform by 90°. Devices that intentionally introduce capacitance into circuits are called "capacitors." ▸**Figure 19-1**

(B) Determining Capacitance. Capacitance exists whenever an insulating material (dielectric) separates two conductive materials that have a voltage between them. Factors that determine capacitance are the surface area of the conductive materials, the distance between the conductive materials, and the insulating material or "dielectric" between the conductive materials. ▸**Figure 19-2**

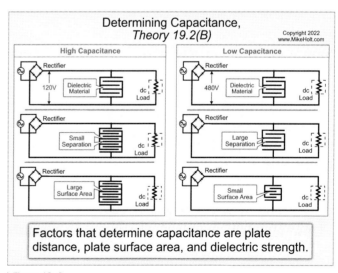

Factors that determine capacitance are plate distance, plate surface area, and dielectric strength.

▸Figure 19-2

Capacitance in Capacitors Theory 19.2(A)

Capacitance is the property of an electrical circuit that enables it to store electrical energy and release it later. Devices that intentionally introduce capacitance into circuits are called "capacitors."

▸Figure 19-1

19.3 Capacitor Charge and Discharge

(A) Charging. When a capacitor has a voltage between the conductive materials (plates), the capacitor is said to have a charge. One plate has an excess of electrons, and the other plate has a lack of electrons. The plate with the excess electrons has a negative charge (–), while the plate that lacks electrons has a positive charge (+). ▶Figure 19–3

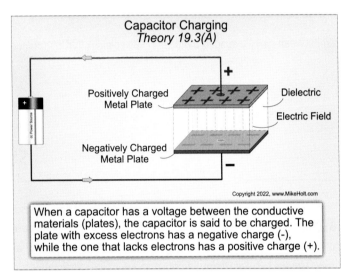

Capacitor Charging
Theory 19.3(A)

Positively Charged Metal Plate
Dielectric
Electric Field
Negatively Charged Metal Plate

When a capacitor has a voltage between the conductive materials (plates), the capacitor is said to be charged. The plate with excess electrons has a negative charge (-), while the one that lacks electrons has a positive charge (+).

Copyright 2022, www.MikeHolt.com

▶Figure 19–3

(B) Discharging. To discharge a capacitor, a conductive path is required between its positive (+) and negative (–) terminals. The charged electrons on the negative plate will move to the positive plate until the electric charge of the two plates is balanced. Even after the power has been removed, capacitors can present a shock hazard and must be discharged. ▶Figure 19–4

(C) Shorting. If the capacitor is overcharged, the electrons from the negative plate can be pulled through the capacitor's dielectric insulation to the positive plate. If this happens, the capacitor is said to have shorted. ▶Figure 19–5

19.4 Capacitive Reactance

A capacitor opposes any change in voltage. In a purely capacitive circuit, the current waveform leads the voltage waveform by as much as 90°. ▶Figure 19–6

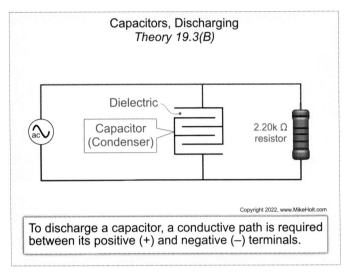

Capacitors, Discharging
Theory 19.3(B)

Dielectric
Capacitor (Condenser)
2.20k Ω resistor

To discharge a capacitor, a conductive path is required between its positive (+) and negative (–) terminals.

Copyright 2022, www.MikeHolt.com

▶Figure 19–4

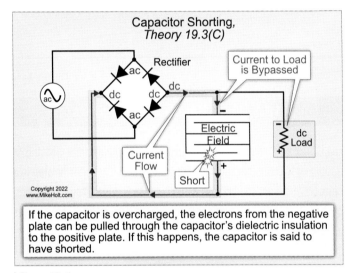

Capacitor Shorting,
Theory 19.3(C)

Rectifier
Current to Load is Bypassed
Current Flow
Electric Field
Short
dc Load

If the capacitor is overcharged, the electrons from the negative plate can be pulled through the capacitor's dielectric insulation to the positive plate. If this happens, the capacitor is said to have shorted.

Copyright 2022 www.MikeHolt.com

▶Figure 19–5

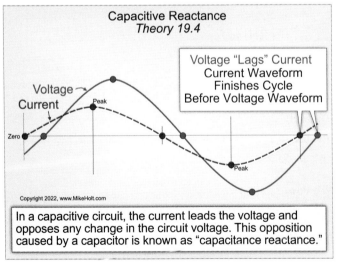

Capacitive Reactance
Theory 19.4

Voltage "Lags" Current
Current Waveform Finishes Cycle Before Voltage Waveform

Voltage
Current
Zero
Peak
Peak

In a capacitive circuit, the current leads the voltage and opposes any change in the circuit voltage. This opposition caused by a capacitor is known as "capacitance reactance."

Copyright 2022, www.MikeHolt.com

▶Figure 19–6

This opposition to the change in voltage caused by a capacitor is known as "capacitive reactance," is abbreviated as "X_C," and is measured in ohms as expressed by the formula:

$$X_C = 1/(2 \pi \times f \times C)$$

"π" is 3.14

"f" is the frequency in hertz

"C" is the capacitance in microfarads (µf), one millionth (10^{-6}) of a farad

▶ **Capacitive Reactance Example**

Question: The capacitive reactance in ohms for a 45 µf (0.000045f) capacitor connected to a 60 Hz, air-conditioning unit is _____.

(a) 17Ω   (b) 32Ω   (c) 59Ω   (d) 62Ω

Solution:

$$X_C = 1/(2 \pi \times f \times C)$$

$\pi = 3.14$

$f = 60$ Hz

$C = 45$ µf, or 45/1,000,000 or 0.000045f

$X_C = 1/(2 \times 3.14 \times 60Hz \times 0.000045f)$

$X_C = 5.90Ω$

Answer: (c) 59Ω

19.5 Uses of Capacitors

Capacitors are used to start single-phase motors, reduce utility bills, improve power quality, and act as filters in electronic power supplies.

(A) Starting Single-Phase Motors. Single-phase ac motors require the use of a "start" capacitor to initiate the rotation of the motor. ▶Figure 19–7

(B) Power Factor Correction.

(1) Service Equipment or Panels. Capacitors located at service equipment or electrical panels are primarily intended to reduce power factor penalties imposed by the electric utility.

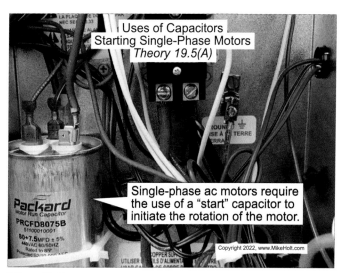

Uses of Capacitors
Starting Single-Phase Motors
Theory 19.5(A)

Single-phase ac motors require the use of a "start" capacitor to initiate the rotation of the motor.

Copyright 2022, www.MikeHolt.com

▶Figure 19–7

(2) Individual Loads. Capacitors located at the load will result in a reduction of circuit current that reduces circuit voltage drop and wire power losses.

(C) Capacitors in Electronic Power Supplies.

(1) Electronic Power Supplies. A full-wave rectifier can be used when ac voltage needs to be converted to dc voltage for use by electronic equipment. A rectifier diode converts alternating current to direct current by allowing the alternating current to flow only in one direction. A capacitor can be added to the electronic circuit to help smooth out the voltage waveform. ▶Figure 19–8

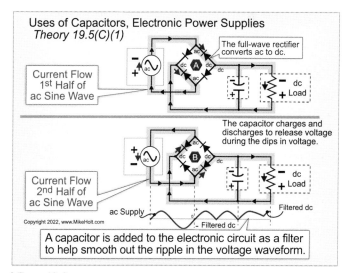

Uses of Capacitors, Electronic Power Supplies
Theory 19.5(C)(1)

The full-wave rectifier converts ac to dc.

Current Flow
1st Half of
ac Sine Wave

dc
Load

The capacitor charges and discharges to release voltage during the dips in voltage.

Current Flow
2nd Half of
ac Sine Wave

dc
Load

ac Supply

Filtered dc

Filtered dc

Copyright 2022, www.MikeHolt.com

A capacitor is added to the electronic circuit as a filter to help smooth out the ripple in the voltage waveform.

▶Figure 19–8

(2) Rectifier Diodes.

(a) Single Rectifier Diode. A single rectifier diode can only provide current flow for one-half of the ac sine wave, which is not very practical for devices needing constant current to operate properly.

(b) Full-Wave Bridge Rectifier Diode. Connecting four rectifiers into a "full-wave bridge rectifier" circuit provides a "bridge" circuit that allows different rectifiers to alternately provide direct current to the load during each half of the sine wave alternation. A full-wave rectifier keeps the voltage polarity constant with a pulsating dc current.
▶Figure 19–9

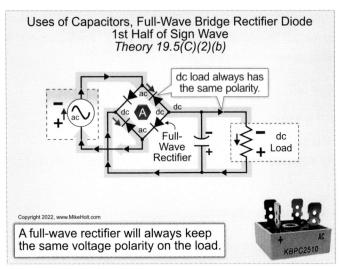

Uses of Capacitors, Full-Wave Bridge Rectifier Diode
1st Half of Sign Wave
Theory 19.5(C)(2)(b)

dc load always has the same polarity.

Full-Wave Rectifier

dc Load

Copyright 2022, www.MikeHolt.com

A full-wave rectifier will always keep the same voltage polarity on the load.

KBPC2510

▶Figure 19–9

UNIT 20

TRUE POWER, POWER FACTOR, AND APPARENT POWER

20.1 Introduction

True power can only be produced when both the current and voltage are in-phase with each other. If the current and voltage are out-of-phase, the alternating-current circuit will have power factor. Apparent power is the power delivered to alternating-current circuits with power factor. In this unit you will learn:

▸ what true power and apparent power are

▸ the relationship between true power and apparent power

▸ the effects of power factor on alternating-current circuits

---

20.2 True Power

True power is the electrical energy consumed in a circuit supplying resistive loads such as incandescent lighting and resistive heating. True power, for resistive loads, is measured in watts as expressed by the formula: **P = E × I**.

▸ True Power Example

Question: What is the approximate power consumed for a 32.60A resistive heater rated 230V? ▸**Figure 20–1**

(a) 2,353W   (b) 3,541W   (c) 5,136W   (d) 7,498W

Solution:

P = E × I

E = 230V, voltage given

I = 32.60A, amperes given

P = 230V × 32.60A

P = 7,498W

Answer: *(d) 7,498W*

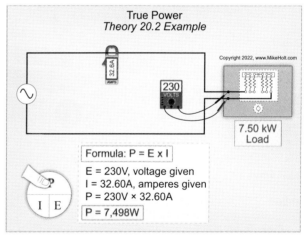

▸Figure 20–1

20.3 Power Losses of Wires

Power in a circuit can be either useful or wasted; the wasted work is still energy used and is called "power loss." The heating of wires, transformer windings, motor windings, and many other loads result in power loss of the wires. Power loss in a wire is directly proportional to the length of the wire and the square of the current. If the current is doubled, the power loss will be increased by 400 percent. Wire power loss in watts is determined by the formula: $P = I^2 \times R$.

▶ Power Losses of Wires Example

Question: What is the approximate power loss of a circuit carrying 16A having a total wire resistance of 0.30Ω? ▶Figure 20–2

(a) 22.40W   (b) 76.80W   (c) 154.20W   (d) 310.20W

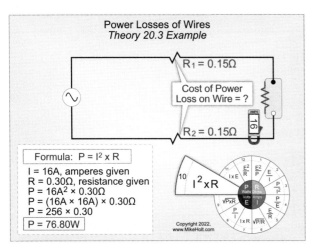

▶Figure 20–2

Solution:

$P = I^2 \times R$

I = 16A, amperes given

R = 0.30Ω, resistance given

P = 16A² × 0.30Ω

P = (16A × 16A) × 0.30Ω

P = 256A × 0.30Ω

P = 76.80W

Answer: (b) 76.80W

20.4 Power Losses at Terminals

Loose wire connections at terminals result in a high resistive contact point which can cause the terminals to overheat. Terminals for wires must be tightened to manufacturer's torque specifications to prevent fires caused by excessive heating at the terminals. The power loss in watts at a terminal can be determined by the formula: $P = I^2 \times R$.

▶ Power Losses at Terminal Example 1

Question: The power loss of a terminal carrying 50A with a contact resistance of 0.40Ω is _____. ▶Figure 20–3

(a) 1,000W   (b) 1,200W   (c) 1,400W   (d) 1,500W

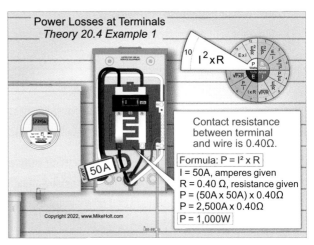

▶Figure 20–3

Solution:

$P = I^2 \times R$

I = 50A, amperes given

R = 0.40 Ω, resistance given

P = (50A × 50A) × 0.40Ω

P = 2,500A × 0.40Ω

P = 1,000W

Answer: (a) 1,000W

▶ Power Losses at Terminal Example 2

Question: *The power loss of a terminal carrying 25A with a contact resistance of 0.20Ω is _____.* ▶Figure 20–4

(a) 125W   (b) 131W   (c) 141W   (d) 151W

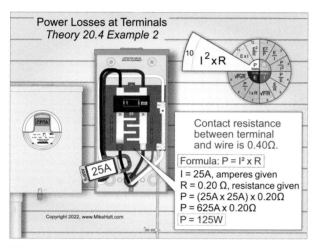

Power Losses at Terminals
Theory 20.4 Example 2

$I^2 \times R$

Contact resistance between terminal and wire is 0.40Ω.

Formula: P = I² x R
I = 25A, amperes given
R = 0.20 Ω, resistance given
P = (25A x 25A) x 0.20Ω
P = 625A x 0.20Ω
P = 125W

Copyright 2022, www.MikeHolt.com

▶Figure 20–4

Solution:

$P = I^2 \times R$

I = 25A, amperes given

R = 0.20Ω, resistance given

$P = (25A \times 25A) \times 0.20\Omega$

$P = 625A \times 0.20\Omega$

$P = 125W$

Answer: *(a) 125W*

20.5 Equipment Efficiency

Efficiency describes how much input energy is used for the intended purpose. Efficiency is expressed as a ratio of output watts to input watts using the formula: **Efficiency = Output Watts/Input Watts**. ▶Figure 20–5

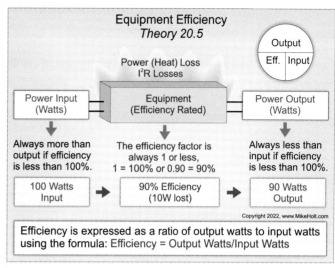

Equipment Efficiency
Theory 20.5

Output
Eff. Input

Power (Heat) Loss
I²R Losses

Power Input (Watts)	Equipment (Efficiency Rated)	Power Output (Watts)

Always more than output if efficiency is less than 100%.

The efficiency factor is always 1 or less, 1 = 100% or 0.90 = 90%

Always less than input if efficiency is less than 100%.

100 Watts Input → 90% Efficiency (10W lost) → 90 Watts Output

Copyright 2022, www.MikeHolt.com

Efficiency is expressed as a ratio of output watts to input watts using the formula: Efficiency = Output Watts/Input Watts

▶Figure 20–5

▶ Calculating Efficiency Example

Question: *The power supply output is rated 6.20A at 17.50V, and the input is rated 1.40A at 100V. What is the approximate efficiency of the power supply?*

(a) 75 percent   (b) 86 percent   (c) 90 percent   (d) 95 percent

Solution:

Efficiency = Output Watts/Input Watts

Output Watts = E × I
Output Watts = 19.50V × 6.20A
Output Watts = 121W

Input Watts = E × I
Input Watts = 100V × 1.40A
Input Watts = 140W

Efficiency = Output Watts/Input Watts
Efficiency = 121W/140A
Efficiency = 0.86 or 86 percent

Answer: *(b) 86 percent*

20.6 Cost of Power

Your electric bill is based on the energy consumed during a month, multiplied by the cost of the energy in "kilowatt hours" (kWh). ▶Figure 20–6

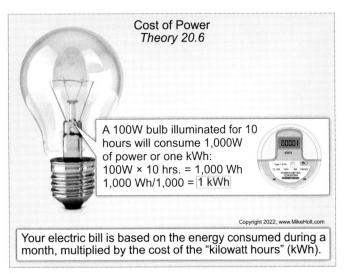

Cost of Power Theory 20.6

A 100W bulb illuminated for 10 hours will consume 1,000W of power or one kWh:
100W × 10 hrs. = 1,000 Wh
1,000 Wh/1,000 = 1 kWh

Copyright 2022, www.MikeHolt.com

Your electric bill is based on the energy consumed during a month, multiplied by the cost of the "kilowatt hours" (kWh).

▶Figure 20–6

▶ Cost of Power, Loss for Light Bulbs Example

Question: The cost of electricity is 13 cents per kWh. What does it cost to supply ten 100W loads ten hours a day for 30 days?

(a) $2.30   *(b) $3.60*   *(c) $4.10*   *(d) $5.60*

Solution:

Step 1: Determine the power consumed for the month:

Power for the Month = 100W × 10 Hours a Day × 30 days

Power for the Month = 30,000 Wh

Step 2: Convert the answer in Step 1 to kWh:

P = 30,000 Wh/1,000

P = 30 kWh

Step 3: Determine the cost for the month:

Cost for the Month = 13 cents per kWh × 30 kWh

Cost for the Month = $3.60

Answer: (b) $3.60

▶ Cost of Power, Loss for Wire Example

Question: The cost of electricity is 13 cents per kWh. What does it cost for the year to heat up two 10 AWG wires having a total resistance of 0.24Ω supplying a 24A load that operates for 20 hours each day? ▶Figure 20–7

(a) $131   *(b) $141*   *(c) $151*   *(d) $161*

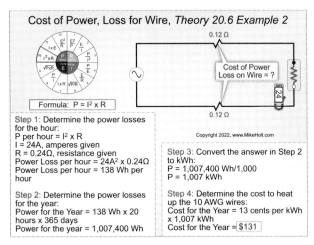

Cost of Power, Loss for Wire, *Theory 20.6 Example 2*

Formula: P = I² x R

Step 1: Determine the power losses for the hour:
P per hour = I² x R
I = 24A, amperes given
R = 0.24Ω, resistance given
Power Loss per hour = 24A² x 0.24Ω
Power Loss per hour = 138 Wh per hour

Step 2: Determine the power losses for the year:
Power for the Year = 138 Wh x 20 hours x 365 days
Power for the year = 1,007,400 Wh

Step 3: Convert the answer in Step 2 to kWh:
P = 1,007,400 Wh/1,000
P = 1,007 kWh

Step 4: Determine the cost to heat up the 10 AWG wires:
Cost for the Year = 13 cents per kWh x 1,007 kWh
Cost for the Year = $131

Copyright 2022, www.MikeHolt.com

▶Figure 20–7

Solution:

Step 1: Determine the power losses for the hour:

P per Hour = I² × R

I = 24A, amperes given

R = 0.24Ω, resistance given

Power Loss Per Hour = 24A² × 0.24Ω

Power Loss Per Hour = 138 Wh per hour

Step 2: Determine the power losses for the year:

Power for the Year = 138 Wh × 20 hours × 365 days

Power for the year = 1,007,400 Wh

Step 3: Convert the answer in Step 2 to kWh:

P = 1,007,400 Wh/1,000

P = 1,007 kWh

Step 4: Determine the cost to heat up the 10 AWG wires:

Cost for the Year = 13 cents per kWh × 1,007 kWh

Cost for the Year = $131

Answer: (a) $131

20.7 Power Factor

Power factor occurs when the voltage waveform is out-of-phase with the current waveform due to inductance or capacitance. ▶Figure 20–8

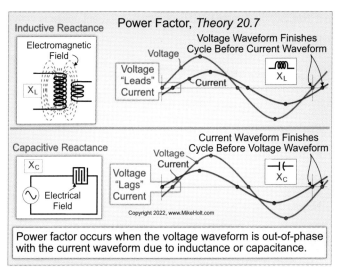

▶Figure 20–8

"Power factor percentage" is the relationship between true power and apparent power as determined by the formula:

Power Factor % = True Power (Watts)/Apparent Power (VA)

▶ Power Factor (PF) Example 1

Question: What is the power factor percentage for a 120V ballast rated 0.75A supplying two lamps, each rated 42W? ▶Figure 20–9

(a) 75 percent   (b) 89 percent   (c) 93 percent   (d) 95 percent

Solution:

Step 1: *Determine the formula and knowns:*

PF = Watts/VA

Watts = 42W × 2 bulbs, watts given

Watts = 84W

VA = Ballast Volts × Amperes (VA)

Volts = 120V, volts given

Amperes = 0.75A, amperes given

VA = 120V × 0.75A

VA = 90 VA

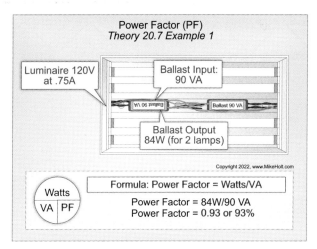

▶Figure 20–9

Step 2: *Determine the power factor percentage:*

PF = Watts/VA

Watts = 84W

VA = 90 VA

PF = 84W/90 VA

PF = 0.93 or 93 percent

Answer: (c) 93 percent

▶ Power Factor (PF) Example 2

Question: The power factor rating for a 250W high-bay light at 277V rated 1.20A is _____. ▶Figure 20–10

(a) 75 percent   (b) 80 percent   (c) 90 percent   (d) 100 percent

Solution:

Step 1: *Determine the formula and knowns:*

PF = W/VA

Watts = 250W, watts given

VA = V × A

V = 277V, volts given

A = 1.20A, amperes given

VA = 277V × 1.20A

VA = 332 VA

• • •

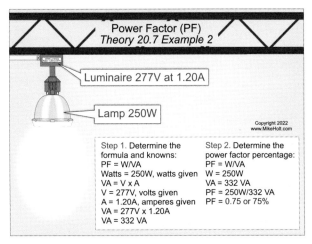

▶Figure 20–10

Step 2: *Determine the power factor percentage:*

$$PF = W/VA$$

$$W = 250W$$

$$VA = 332\ VA$$

$$PF = 250W/332\ VA$$

$$PF = 0.75\ or\ 75\ percent$$

Answer: (a) 75 percent

(A) Unity Power Factor. When an ac circuit supplies power to a purely resistive load, such as incandescent lighting or resistive heating elements, the voltage and current waveforms will be in-phase with each other. This condition is called "unity power factor." ▶**Figure 20–11**

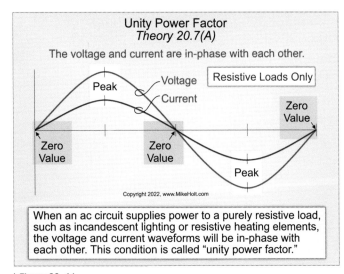

▶Figure 20–11

20.8 Apparent Power

In an inductive load such as a motor, the voltage and current waveforms do not reach their zero and peak values at the same time. Apparent power is a measurement of the amount of electrical energy supplied to a load, *not* the energy used by the load. Apparent power is determined by the formulas:

Apparent Power = Volts × Amperes

Apparent Power = True Power/Power Factor Percentage

▶ **Apparent Power—Volts × Amperes Example**

Question: *What is the apparent power of a 120V motor rated 16A?*
▶Figure 20–12

(a) 1,632 VA   (b) 1,800 VA   (c) 1,920 VA   (d) 2,400 VA

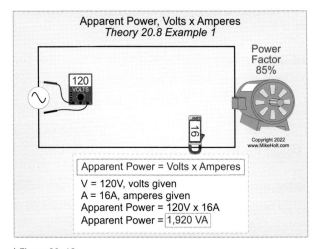

▶Figure 20–12

Solution:

Apparent Power = Volts × Amperes

V = 120V, volts given

A = 16A, amperes given

Apparent Power = 120V × 16A

Apparent Power = 1,920 VA

Answer: (c) 1,920 VA

▶ Apparent Power—True Power/Power Factor Percentage Example

Question: *What is the apparent power of an 80W load having a power factor of 90 percent?* ▶Figure 20-13

(a) 80.89 VA   (b) 80.98 VA   (c) 88.90 VA   (d) 89.98 VA

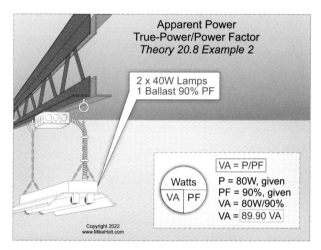

▶Figure 20-13

Solution:

Apparent Power = True Power/Power Factor Percentage

True Power = 80W, given

Power Factor Percentage = 90 percent, given

Apparent Power = 80W/90 percent
Apparent Power = 88.90 VA

Answer: (c) 88.90 VA

20.9 Apparent Power versus True Power

True power is expressed in watts and apparent power is expressed in VA. True power is equal to or less than apparent power, and apparent power is equal to or greater than true power. The formula for true power, when power factor applies, is:

True Power = Apparent Power × Power Factor Percentage

▶ Apparent Power versus True Power Example

Question: *What is the true power of a 16A load rated 120V with a power factor of 85 percent?* ▶Figure 20-14

(a) 1,632W   (b) 1,800W   (c) 1,920W   (d) 2,400W

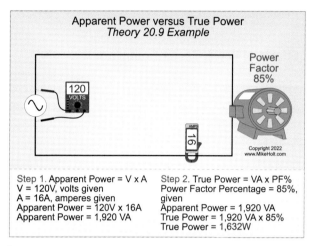

▶Figure 20-14

Solution:

Step 1: *Determine the apparent power:*

Apparent Power = V × A

V = 120V, volts given

A = 16A, amperes given

Apparent Power = 120V × 16A
Apparent Power = 1,920 VA

Step 2: *Determine the true power:*

True Power = Apparent Power × Power Factor Percentage

Power Factor Percentage = 85 percent, given

Apparent Power = 1,920 VA

True Power = 1,920 VA × 85 percent
True Power = 1,632W

Answer: (a) 1,632W

20.10 Effects of Power Factor on Circuits

Alternating-current circuits are sized based on volt-amperes. Since apparent power (VA) is greater than true power (W) because of power factor, fewer loads can be placed on a circuit, resulting in more circuits on panels, and the possibility of larger transformers being required.

▶ Effects of Power Factor Example 1

Question: What is the minimum number of 120V, 20A circuits required to supply one hundred 150W incandescent luminaires? ▶Figure 20–15

(a) 4 circuits   (b) 5 circuits   (c) 6 circuits   (d) 7 circuits

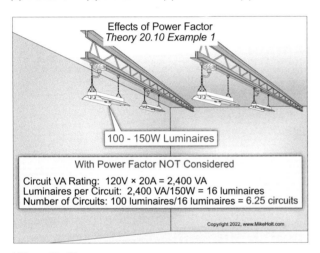

▶Figure 20–15

Solution:

Step 1: *Determine the Circuit VA Rating:*

Circuit VA Rating = Volts × Amperes

Circuit VA Rating = 120V × 20A

Circuit VA Rating = 2,400 VA

Step 2: *Determine the Luminaires per Circuit:*

Luminaires per Circuit = Circuit VA Rating/Load

Luminaires per Circuit = 2,400 VA/150W

Luminaires per Circuit = 16 luminaires

Step 3: *Determine the Minimum Number of Circuits:*

Minimum Number of Circuits = Total luminaires/16 luminaires per circuit

Minimum. Number of Circuits = 100 luminaires/16 luminaires per circuit

Minimum. Number of Circuits = 6.25 circuits

Answer: (d) 7 circuits

▶ Effects of Power Factor Example 2

Question: How many 120V, 20A circuits are required for one hundred 150W LED luminaires with a power factor of 85 percent? ▶Figure 20–16

(a) 4 circuits   (b) 5 circuits   (c) 6 circuits   (d) 8 circuits

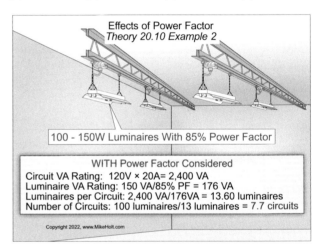

▶Figure 20–16

Solution:

Step 1: *Determine the Circuit VA Rating:*

Circuit VA Rating = Volts × Amperes

Circuit VA Rating = 120V × 20A

Circuit VA Rating = 2,400 VA

Step 2: *Determine the Luminaires VA:*

Luminaire VA = Watts/Power Factor Percent

Luminaire VA = 150W/85 percent

Luminaire VA = 176 VA

Step 3: *Determine the Luminaires VA:*

Luminaires per Circuit = Circuit VA Rating/Load VA

Luminaires per Circuit = 2,400 VA/176 VA

Luminaires per Circuit = 13.60 luminaires

Step 4: *Determine the Minimum Number of Circuits for One Hundred 150W LED Luminaires:*

*Minimum Number of Circuits = Total luminaires/
13 luminaires per circuit*

*Minimum Number of Circuits = 100 luminaires/
13 luminaires*

Minimum Number of Circuits = 7.70 circuits

Answer: *(d) 8 circuits*

CHAPTER 7—PRACTICE QUESTIONS

Unit 17—Alternating Current Fundamentals

17.2 How Alternating Current is Produced

1. Michael Faraday discovered that when he moved a(an) _____ inside a coil of wire, he was able to measure a pulse of electric current with a measuring instrument called a "galvanometer."

   (a) iron rod
   (b) piece of metal
   (c) magnet
   (d) all of these

2. When a magnetic field moves through a coil of wire, the lines of force of the magnetic field cause the electrons in the wire to flow in a(an) _____ direction and when the magnetic field moves in the opposite direction, electrons in the wire flow in the _____ direction.

   (a) specific, opposite
   (b) opposite, specific
   (c) southerly, northerly
   (d) none of these

3. _____ can be used to produce alternating-current flow and to do so a magnetic field must have motion relative to a coil of wire.

   (a) Generators
   (b) PV systems
   (c) Batteries
   (d) all of these

4. A simple ac generator consists of a loop of wire rotating between the _____ fields between the opposite poles of a magnet.

   (a) magnetic
   (b) static
   (c) gravity
   (d) all of these

17.3 Waveforms

5. A waveform is a mathematical representation (a graph) used to visualize the level and direction of _____ and _____ in a circuit.

   (a) power, resistance
   (b) current, voltage
   (c) watts, impedance
   (d) any of these

6. Direct-current (dc) power sources push and pull electrons in the circuit in _____ direction(s) from the negative to positive terminals of the power source.

   (a) reverse
   (b) opposing
   (c) one
   (d) none of these

7. Direct-current voltage produced by a battery has a constant magnitude and the _____ is always the same.

   (a) intensity
   (b) latitude
   (c) polarity
   (d) none of these

8. When dc voltage from a solar cell for a 24-hour period is plotted on a graph, it looks like a(an) _____.

    (a) arc
    (b) flat line
    (c) circle
    (d) square

9. In circuits with a full-wave rectifier diode, the combination of alternating-current and direct-current waveforms results in a _____ waveform.

    (a) sinusoidal
    (b) symmetrical
    (c) sine
    (d) pulsating

10. An alternating-current _____ represents the level and direction of the voltage for every instant of time during one full revolution of the generator's rotor.

    (a) waveform
    (b) graph
    (c) curve
    (d) circuit

11. The voltage and current waveform for alternating-current generators begins with a _____ polarity for the first 180° and then changes to a _____ polarity.

    (a) negative, positive
    (b) positive, negative
    (c) positive, positive
    (d) negative, negative

12. A _____ waveform is symmetrical with positive values above and negative values below the zero-reference level.

    (a) nonsinusoidal
    (b) nonsymmetrical
    (c) sinusoidal
    (d) any of these

13. The relationship of the voltage and current waveforms to the generator's rotor position is from 0° to _____.

    (a) 90°
    (b) 120°
    (c) 180°
    (d) 360°

14. A nonsinusoidal waveform is produced when _____ loads distort the voltage and current sinusoidal waveform.

    (a) linear
    (b) resistive
    (c) inductive
    (d) nonlinear

15. A nonlinear load is a load where the shape of the current waveform does not follow the _____ of the applied sinusoidal voltage waveform.

    (a) shape
    (b) color
    (c) direction
    (d) orientation

16. Nonlinear loads produce "_____" which are waveforms that cycle at a frequency that is a multiple of the fundamental frequency.

    (a) capacitors
    (b) resistors
    (c) inductors
    (d) harmonics

17.4 Frequency

17. The full rotation of an alternating-current generator is equal to 360° and its frequency output is expressed as "cycles per second" measured in "_____."

    (a) degrees
    (b) sine waves
    (c) phases
    (d) Hertz

17.5 In-Phase Waveforms

18. If the voltage and current waveforms begin and end simultaneously, then the two waveforms are "_____" with each other.

    (a) in-phase
    (b) out-of-phase
    (c) coupled
    (d) any of these

17.6 Out-of-Phase Waveforms

19. When the voltage and current waveforms reach their zero and peak values at different times, the waveforms are said to be "_____" with each other.

    (a) in-phase
    (b) out-of-phase
    (c) in-phase or out-of-phase
    (d) none of these

20. When describing the relationship between voltage and current, the reference waveform is always _____.

    (a) current
    (b) resistance
    (c) voltage
    (d) none of these

21. In a purely capacitive circuit, the current waveform _____ the voltage waveform by as much as 90°.

    (a) leads
    (b) lags
    (c) is in-phase with
    (d) none of these

22. In a purely inductive circuit, the current waveform _____ the voltage waveform by as much as 90°.

    (a) leads
    (b) lags
    (c) is in-phase with
    (d) none of these

17.7 Alternating-Current Waveform Values

23. The important value(s) shown on an ac waveform is(are) "_____."

    (a) instantaneous
    (b) peak
    (c) effective RMS
    (d) all of these

24. "_____" is the value of the voltage or current waveform at a specific moment in time.

    (a) Peak
    (b) Root-mean-square
    (c) Effective
    (d) Instantaneous

25. "_____" is the maximum value that ac current or voltage reaches, for both positive and negative polarities.

    (a) Peak
    (b) Root-mean-square
    (c) Instantaneous
    (d) none of these

26. The peak value is equal to the effective value _____.

    (a) times 0.707
    (b) times 1.414
    (c) divided by 2
    (d) times 0.58

27. What is the peak current of a circuit with a 12A effective RMS load?

    (a) 15A
    (b) 17A
    (c) 19A
    (d) 20A

28. What is the peak current of a circuit with a 20A effective RMS load?

    (a) 25.70A
    (b) 28.28A
    (c) 29.10A
    (d) 30.80A

29. The peak voltage of an alternating-current circuit having an effective RMS voltage of 240V is _____.

    (a) 170V
    (b) 339V
    (c) 392V
    (d) 480V

30. The peak voltage of an alternating-current circuit having an effective RMS voltage of 480V is _____.

    (a) 570.18V
    (b) 639.85V
    (c) 678.72V
    (d) 780.92V

31. _____ ac voltage or ac current is the equivalent value of dc voltage or dc current that would produce the same amount of heat in a resistor.

    (a) Peak
    (b) Effective
    (c) Instantaneous
    (d) none of these

32. The effective value of 120V is equal to the peak value of 170V _____.

    (a) times 0.314
    (b) times 0.707
    (c) divided by 0.707
    (d) divided by 0.314

33. What is the effective RMS voltage of a circuit with a peak value of 392V?

    (a) 120V
    (b) 208V
    (c) 277V
    (d) 300V

34. What is the effective RMS voltage of a circuit with a peak value of 340V?

    (a) 120V
    (b) 208V
    (c) 240V
    (d) 300V

35. What is the effective RMS voltage of a circuit with a peak value of 295V?

    (a) 120V
    (b) 208V
    (c) 277V
    (d) 300V

36. What is the effective RMS current of a circuit with a peak value of 15A?

    (a) 10.60A
    (b) 20.80A
    (c) 27.70A
    (d) 30.20A

37. "_____" describes the steps necessary to determine the effective voltage or current value.

    (a) Peak
    (b) Root-Mean-Square
    (c) Instantaneous
    (d) none of these

Unit 18—Inductance

18.2 How Inductance Works

1. The effect of relative motion between an alternating electro-magnetic field and a wire is known as "_____."

    (a) voltage
    (b) current
    (c) magnetism
    (d) inductance

18.3 Self-Inductance

2. When alternating current flows in wire, the expanding and collapsing electromagnetic field from the center to the outside of the wire self-_____ an opposing voltage in the wire.

    (a) applies
    (b) induces
    (c) distorts
    (d) any of these

3. Self-induced voltage is also known as "_____."

    (a) reactance
    (b) counter-electromotive force
    (c) capacitance
    (d) none of these

4. Self-induced voltage is _____ out-of-phase with the applied current.

    (a) 90°
    (b) 120°
    (c) 180°
    (d) 360°

5. When alternating current increases, the polarity of the counter-electromotive force within the wire from self-induction _____ the increase in current.

    (a) aids
    (b) attracts
    (c) opposes
    (d) repels

6. When alternating current decreases, the polarity of the counter-electromotive force from _____ attempts to prevent the current from decreasing.

    (a) capacitance
    (b) self-induction
    (c) magnetism
    (d) none of these

7. Self-induced voltage is _____ out-of-phase with the applied voltage.

    (a) 90°
    (b) 120°
    (c) 180°
    (d) 360°

8. When the applied voltage increases or decreases, the polarity of the counter-electromotive force _____ the change in applied voltage.

    (a) aids
    (b) attracts
    (c) opposes
    (d) repels

9. When the _____ is at its maximum in one direction, the CEMF is at its maximum in the opposite direction.

    (a) applied current
    (b) applied voltage
    (c) induced voltage
    (d) induced current

10. In an inductive circuit, the self-induced voltage is 90° out-of-phase with the current waveform and _____ out-of-phase with the applied voltage.

    (a) 90°
    (b) 120°
    (c) 180°
    (d) 360°

11. In a purely inductive circuit, the CEMF is _____ out-of-phase with the applied current.

    (a) 90°
    (b) 120°
    (c) 180°
    (d) 360°

12. The amount of self-induced voltage within a wire is determined by its physical _____ and the magnitude of the current.

    (a) shape
    (b) nature
    (c) order
    (d) none of these

13. A straight wire will have _____ self-induced voltage than a wire formed into a coil.

    (a) higher
    (b) less
    (c) more
    (d) any of these

18.4 Mutual Inductance

14. _____ induction occurs when one coil of wire induces a voltage onto another coil of wire because of the expanding and collapsing electromagnetic fields of adjacent windings.

    (a) Mutual
    (b) Self
    (c) Voltage
    (d) Current

15. The electromagnetic field intensity of a winding can be increased by inserting a(an) _____ core into the middle of the windings, which results in greater mutual inductance between the windings.

    (a) air
    (b) soft iron
    (c) plastic
    (d) none of these

18.5 Inductive Reactance

16. The counter-electromotive force opposes the change in current flowing in the wire. This is called "inductive reactance" and is abbreviated _____.

    (a) X_L
    (b) X_C
    (c) Z
    (d) none of these

18.6 Uses of Induction

17. The most significant use(s) of induction for the electrical industry include equipment such as _____.

    (a) motors
    (b) transformers
    (c) generators
    (d) all of these

Unit 19—Capacitance

19.2 Capacitance in Capacitors

1. "_____" is a property of an electrical circuit that enables it to store electrical energy and release that energy later.

    (a) Capacitance
    (b) Induction
    (c) Self-induction
    (d) none of these

2. The factor(s) that determine the capacitance of a capacitor are the _____ the plates.

    (a) surface area of
    (b) distance between
    (c) dielectric between
    (d) all of these

19.3 Capacitor Charge and Discharge

3. When a capacitor has a voltage between the plates, it is said to have a "_____."

    (a) inductor
    (b) charge
    (c) discharge
    (d) short

4. To discharge a capacitor, all that is required is a(an) _____ path between the positive and negative terminals of the capacitor.

    (a) conductive
    (b) insulating
    (c) open
    (d) all of these

5. Even after the power has been removed, capacitors can present a shock hazard and must be _____.

    (a) induced
    (b) charged
    (c) discharged
    (d) shorted

6. If a capacitor is overcharged, the electrons from the negative plate can be pulled through the insulation to the positive plate. The capacitor is then said to have "_____."

    (a) charged
    (b) discharged
    (c) induced
    (d) shorted

19.4 Capacitive Reactance

7. A capacitor opposes any change in voltage. In a purely capacitive circuit, the current waveform _____.

    (a) leads the voltage waveform by as much as 90°
    (b) lags the voltage waveform by as much as 90°
    (c) leads the voltage waveform by as much as 180°
    (d) lags the voltage waveform by as much as 180°

8. The opposition offered to the flow of alternating current by a capacitor is called "capacitive reactance," is expressed in ohms (Ω), and abbreviated _____.

    (a) X_C
    (b) X_L
    (c) Z
    (d) none of these

19.5 Uses of Capacitors

9. _____ are used to start single-phase motors, reduce utility bills, improve power quality, and as filters in electronic power supplies.

    (a) Capacitors
    (b) Inductors
    (c) Capacitors or Inductors
    (d) none of these

10. Single-phase motors use a "_____" capacitor to initiate the rotation of the motor.

    (a) start
    (b) end
    (c) special
    (d) none of these

11. Capacitors located at service equipment or electrical panels are primarily intended to reduce _____ penalties imposed by the electric utility.

    (a) energy
    (b) efficiency
    (c) power factor
    (d) all of these

12. Capacitors located at the load will result in a(an) _____ of circuit current that reduces circuit voltage drop and wire power losses.

    (a) increase
    (b) reduction
    (c) shorting out
    (d) none of these

Unit 20—True Power, Power Factor, and Apparent Power

20.2 True Power

1. To determine the true power for _____ loads, use the formula P = E × I.

   (a) resistive
   (b) inductive
   (c) capacitive
   (d) all of these

2. What is the approximate power consumed by a 30A resistive heater rated 240V?

   (a) 2,350W
   (b) 3,500W
   (c) 5,000W
   (d) 7,200W

3. What is the approximate power consumed by a 15A incandescent light bulb rated 115V?

   (a) 1,725W
   (b) 2,570W
   (c) 3,505W
   (d) 5,200W

4. What is the approximate power consumed by a 20A water heater rated 208V?

   (a) 2,350W
   (b) 3,500W
   (c) 4,160W
   (d) 4,200W

20.3 Power Losses of Wires

5. Power in a circuit can be either useful or wasted, the wasted work is still energy used and is called "_____."

   (a) resistance
   (b) inductive reactance
   (c) capacitive reactance
   (d) power losses

6. Power losses in a wire are directly proportional to the length of the wire and the square of the current. If the current is doubled, the power loss will be increased by _____ percent.

   (a) 100
   (b) 200
   (c) 300
   (d) 400

7. What is the approximate power loss of a circuit carrying 6A having a total wire resistance of 0.60Ω?

   (a) 22W
   (b) 75W
   (c) 150W
   (d) 320W

20.4 Power Losses at Terminals

8. The power loss in watts at a terminal can be determined by the formula _____.

   (a) $P = I^2 \times R$
   (b) $R = E^2/P$
   (c) $E = I \times R$
   (d) $I = E/R$

9. The power loss of a terminal carrying 25A with a contact resistance of 0.20Ω is _____.

   (a) 100W
   (b) 125W
   (c) 140W
   (d) 150W

10. The power loss of a terminal carrying 50A with a contact resistance of 0.40Ω is _____.

    (a) 200W
    (b) 300W
    (c) 400W
    (d) 500W

20.5 Equipment Efficiency

11. Efficiency is expressed as a ratio of _____ watts to input watts.

    (a) output
    (b) input
    (c) kilo
    (d) none of these

12. Efficiency describes how much _____ energy is used for its intended purpose.

    (a) output
    (b) input
    (c) kilo
    (d) none of these

13. If the output power is 1,320W and the input power is 1,800W, what is the efficiency of the equipment?

    (a) 62 percent
    (b) 73 percent
    (c) 80 percent
    (d) 100 percent

14. If the input power of a 1 hp dc motor is 1,128W and the output power is 746W, what is the efficiency of the motor?

    (a) 66 percent
    (b) 74 percent
    (c) 87 percent
    (d) 100 percent

15. If the output power is 1,600W and the equipment is 88 percent efficient, what are the input amperes at 120V?

    (a) 10A
    (b) 15A
    (c) 20A
    (d) 25A

16. If a transformer is 97 percent efficient, for every 1 kW input, there will be _____ output.

    (a) 970W
    (b) 1,000W
    (c) 1,030W
    (d) 1,200W

20.6 Cost of Power

17. Electric bills are based on the energy consumed during a month, multiplied by the cost of the energy in _____ hours.

    (a) kilowatt
    (b) voltage
    (c) ohm
    (d) amp

18. The cost of electricity is 13 cents per kWh. What does it cost to supply ten 100W loads ten hours a day for thirty days?

    (a) $2.30
    (b) $3.60
    (c) $4.10
    (d) $5.60

19. The cost of electricity is 13 cents per kWh. What does it cost for the year to heat up two 10 AWG wires having a total resistance of 0.24Ω supplying a 24A load that operates for 20 hours each day?

    (a) $131
    (b) $141
    (c) $151
    (d) $161

20. What does it cost per year (at 9 cents per kWh) for ten 150W recessed luminaires to operate if they are turned on for six hours a day?

    (a) $150
    (b) $300
    (c) $500
    (d) $800

21. What does it cost per year (at 8 cents per kWh) for the power loss of a 12 AWG wire (100 ft long) that has a total resistance of 0.40Ω and a current flow of 16A that operates 10 hours each day?

    (a) $30
    (b) $50
    (c) $70
    (d) $80

20.7 Power Factor

22. Alternating-current inductive or capacitive reactive loads cause the voltage and current waveforms to be _____ with each other.

    (a) in-phase
    (b) out-of-phase
    (c) in sync
    (d) none of these

23. _____ is the relationship between true power and apparent power.

    (a) Alternating-current power
    (b) Power factor percentage
    (c) Direct-current power
    (d) Reactive power

24. The formula for determining power factor percentage is **Power Factor % = _____.**

    (a) True Power/Apparent Power
    (b) Apparent Power/True Power
    (c) Watts/Impedance
    (d) Capacitance/Inductance

25. What is the power factor for a ballast at 120V rated 0.85A supplying two bulbs, each rated 40W?

    (a) 78 percent
    (b) 89 percent
    (c) 93 percent
    (d) 95 percent

26. The power factor rating for a 300W high-bay light at 277V rated 1.20A is _____.

    (a) 75 percent
    (b) 80 percent
    (c) 90 percent
    (d) 100 percent

27. When an ac circuit supplies power to a purely resistive load, the circuit voltage and current are in-phase with each other. This condition is called "_____ power factor."

    (a) capacitive
    (b) inductive
    (c) unity
    (d) any of these

20.8 Apparent Power

28. The _____ power of an ac circuit equals volts times amperes.

    (a) apparent
    (b) true
    (c) real
    (d) reactive

29. What is the apparent power of a 120V load rated 18A?

    (a) 1,632 VA
    (b) 1,800 VA
    (c) 1,920 VA
    (d) 2,160 VA

30. What is the apparent power of an 84W load having a power factor of 90 percent?

    (a) 80.33 VA
    (b) 80.98 VA
    (c) 89.90 VA
    (d) 93.33 VA

20.9 Apparent Power versus True Power

31. True power is equal to or _____ than apparent power, and apparent power is equal to or _____ than true power.

    (a) greater, less
    (b) less, greater
    (c) equal, equal
    (d) none of these

32. What is the true power of a 120V load rated 18A with a power factor of 95 percent?

    (a) 1,632W
    (b) 1,800W
    (c) 2,052W
    (d) 2,400W

33. What is the true power of a 240V load rated 28A with a power factor of 90 percent?

    (a) 4,632W
    (b) 5,880W
    (c) 6,048W
    (d) 7,405W

20.10 Effects of Power Factor on Circuits

34. Since apparent power (VA) is greater than true power (W) because of power factor, _____ loads can be placed on a circuit, so more circuits on panels, and larger transformers might be required.

    (a) fewer
    (b) more
    (c) larger
    (d) any of these

35. What is the true power of a 120V circuit operating at 10A with unity power factor?

    (a) 1,200 VA
    (b) 2,400 VA
    (c) 1,200W
    (d) 2,400W

36. What size transformer is required for a 240V, 100A, single-phase noncontinuous load (unity power factor)?

    (a) 15 kVA
    (b) 25 kVA
    (c) 37.50 kVA
    (d) 50 kVA

37. What size transformer is required for a 240V, 100A, single-phase noncontinuous load with a power factor of 85 percent?

    (a) 15 kVA
    (b) 25 kVA
    (c) 37.50 kVA
    (d) 50 kVA

38. How many 120V, 20A circuits are required for forty-two, 300W incandescent luminaires (noncontinuous load)?

    (a) 3 circuits
    (b) 4 circuits
    (c) 5 circuits
    (d) 6 circuits

39. How many 120V, 20A circuits are required for forty-two, 300W luminaires (assume this is a noncontinuous inductive load) that have a power factor of 85 percent?

    (a) 5 circuits
    (b) 6 circuits
    (c) 7 circuits
    (d) 8 circuits

CHAPTER 8

MOTORS, GENERATORS, RELAYS, AND TRANSFORMERS

Chapter 8—Motors, Generators, Relays, and Transformers

Unit 21—Motors

Electric motors are among the most common loads connected to an electrical system. A motor is a rotating machine that converts electrical energy into mechanical energy. In this unit you will learn:

- motor basics
- motor starting, running, and locked-rotor amperes
- motor calculations involving horsepower and nameplate ratings
- about dual-voltage motors and reversing the rotation of alternating-current motors

Unit 22—Generators

A generator is a device that converts mechanical energy into electrical energy. Generators produce most of the electric power in the world and are used in residential, commercial, and industrial facilities for primary, backup, and temporary power. In this unit you will learn:

- generator basics
- the differences between single- and three-phase generators
- how to calculate generator output volt-amperes and amperes

Unit 23—Relays

A relay is a switch that uses a coil to operate one or more sets of contacts. In this unit you will learn:

- how relays operate
- about normally open and normally closed relay contacts

• • •

Unit 24—Transformers

A transformer uses electromagnetism to convert input voltage into a different output voltage. In this unit you will learn:

▸ the uses of transformers

▸ about different types of transformers

▸ how to calculate primary and secondary current

▸ the differences between delta/wye- and delta/delta-connected transformers

UNIT 21

MOTORS

21.1 Introduction

Electric motors are among the most common loads connected to an electrical system. A motor is a rotating machine that converts electrical energy into mechanical energy. In this unit you will learn:

▸ motor basics

▸ motor starting, running, and locked-rotor amperes

▸ motor calculations involving horsepower and nameplate ratings

▸ about dual-voltage motors and reversing the rotation of alternating-current motors

---

21.2 Alternating-Current Motor Principles

(A) Motor Components. A motor uses opposing electromagnetic fields to turn the motor shaft. The stationary electromagnetic field is created by a stator and a rotating electromagnetic field is created by a rotor. ▸Figure 21–1

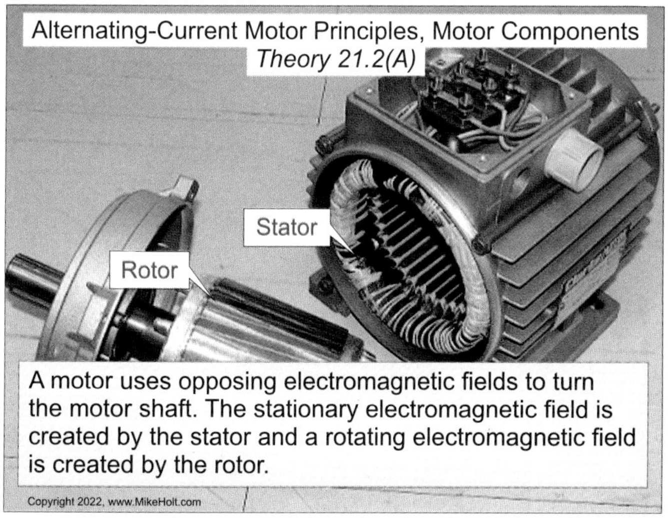

![Alternating-Current Motor Principles, Motor Components Theory 21.2(A). Stator, Rotor labeled. A motor uses opposing electromagnetic fields to turn the motor shaft. The stationary electromagnetic field is created by the stator and a rotating electromagnetic field is created by the rotor. Copyright 2022, www.MikeHolt.com]

▸Figure 21–1

(B) Motor Motion. The law of attraction and repulsion states that electromagnetic fields of the same polarity repel each other and those of opposite polarity attract each other. In an ac induction motor, the stator produces a rotating magnetic field that induces current in the rotor windings. The rotor current generates a magnetic field in opposition to the magnetic field of the stator, thereby causing the motor to turn. ▸Figure 21–2

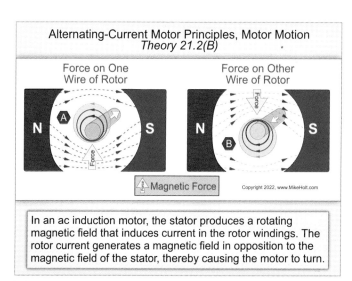

Alternating-Current Motor Principles, Motor Motion
Theory 21.2(B)

Force on One Wire of Rotor — Force on Other Wire of Rotor — N, S, A, B, Force, Magnetic Force. Copyright 2022, www.MikeHolt.com

In an ac induction motor, the stator produces a rotating magnetic field that induces current in the rotor windings. The rotor current generates a magnetic field in opposition to the magnetic field of the stator, thereby causing the motor to turn.

▸Figure 21–2

(C) Rotor and Stator Field Interaction. The electromagnetic field from the rotor causes a downward and upward force against the stator's electromagnetic field. This electromagnetic field interaction creates the momentum for the motor to rotate. ▶Figure 21–3

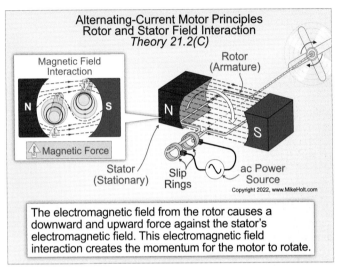

Figure 21-3 — Alternating-Current Motor Principles — Rotor and Stator Field Interaction — Theory 21.2(C)

The electromagnetic field from the rotor causes a downward and upward force against the stator's electromagnetic field. This electromagnetic field interaction creates the momentum for the motor to rotate.

▶Figure 21–3

21.3 Motor Horsepower Rating

The mechanical output of a motor is rated in horsepower (hp), and one horsepower of mechanical work is equal to 746 watts. The formulas to determine the horsepower size or output watts of a motor are: ▶Figure 21–4

Output Watts = Horsepower × 746W

Horsepower = Output Watts/746W

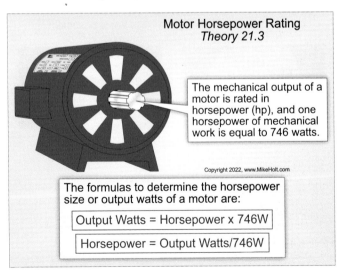

Figure 21-4 — Motor Horsepower Rating — Theory 21.3

The mechanical output of a motor is rated in horsepower (hp), and one horsepower of mechanical work is equal to 746 watts.

The formulas to determine the horsepower size or output watts of a motor are:

Output Watts = Horsepower x 746W

Horsepower = Output Watts/746W

▶Figure 21–4

▶ Output Watts Example

Question: *What are the output watts of a 10 hp single-phase motor?* ▶Figure 21–5

(a) 5.46 kW   *(b) 6.64 kW*   *(c) 7.46 kW*   *(d) 8.64 kW*

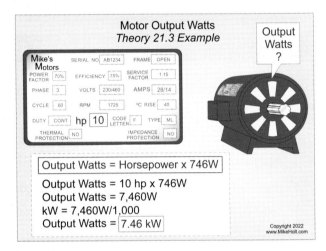

Figure 21-5 — Motor Output Watts — Theory 21.3 Example

Output Watts = Horsepower x 746W
Output Watts = 10 hp x 746W
Output Watts = 7,460W
kW = 7,460W/1,000
Output Watts = 7.46 kW

▶Figure 21–5

Solution:

Output Watts = Horsepower × 746W

Output Watts = 10 hp × 746W

Output Watts = 7,460W

Output Watts = 7,460W/1,000

Output Watts = 7.46 kW

Answer: *(c) 7.46kW*

▶ **Horsepower Size Example**

Question: *What size motor will produce 15 kW of output mechanical work?* ▶Figure 21–6

(a) 5 hp   (b) 10 hp   (c) 20 hp   (d) 30 hp

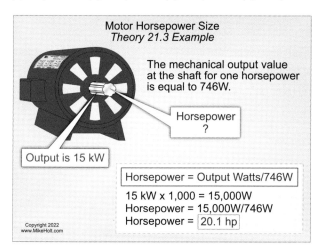

Motor Horsepower Size
Theory 21.3 Example

The mechanical output value at the shaft for one horsepower is equal to 746W.

Horsepower ?

Output is 15 kW

Horsepower = Output Watts/746W

15 kW x 1,000 = 15,000W
Horsepower = 15,000W/746W
Horsepower = 20.1 hp

Copyright 2022 www.MikeHolt.com

▶Figure 21–6

Solution:

Horsepower = Output Watts/746W

Output Watts = 15 kW × 1,000
Output Watts = 15,000W

Horsepower = 15,000W/746W
Horsepower = 20 hp

Answer: *(c) 20 hp*

21.4 Motor Amperes

(A) Motor Starting Amperes. When voltage is applied to a motor, only the motor's wire resistance opposes current flow. Because its wire resistance is so low, the motor has initial starting amperes between six and ten times the motor's nameplate running amperes. ▶Figure 21–7 and ▶Figure 21–8

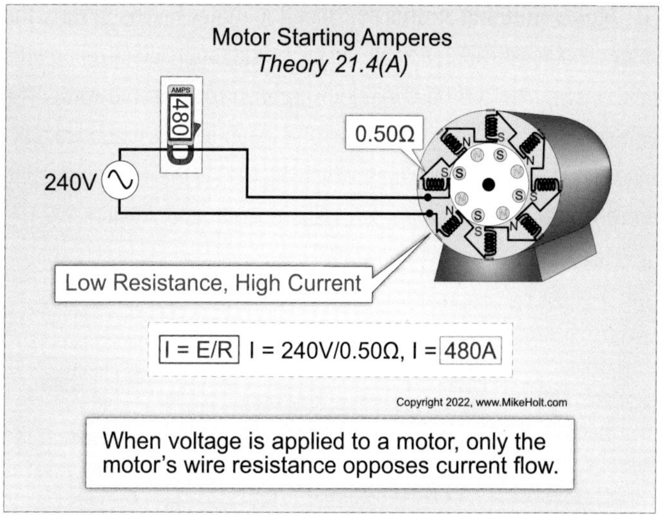

Motor Starting Amperes
Theory 21.4(A)

AMPS 480

240V ~

0.50Ω

Low Resistance, High Current

I = E/R I = 240V/0.50Ω, I = 480A

Copyright 2022, www.MikeHolt.com

When voltage is applied to a motor, only the motor's wire resistance opposes current flow.

▶Figure 21–7

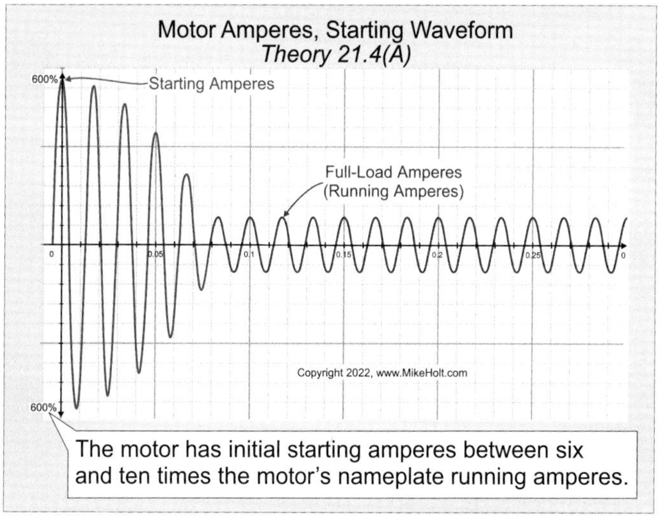

Motor Amperes, Starting Waveform
Theory 21.4(A)

600%
Starting Amperes

Full-Load Amperes
(Running Amperes)

Copyright 2022, www.MikeHolt.com

600%

The motor has initial starting amperes between six and ten times the motor's nameplate running amperes.

▶Figure 21–8

▶ **Motor Starting Amperes Example**

Question: *The starting current for a motor will be about _____ times the motor's nameplate full-load amperes.*

(a) three   (b) four   (c) five   (d) six

Answer: *(d) six*

(B) Motor Running Amperes. Once the motor begins to turn, the rotor windings are increasingly cut by the stationary electromagnetic field, increasing the counter-electromotive force in the rotor. The counter-electromotive force in the rotor increases the inductive reactance (X_L) in the rotor windings, which decreases the motor's starting current to its running amperes. ▶Figure 21–9 and ▶Figure 21–10

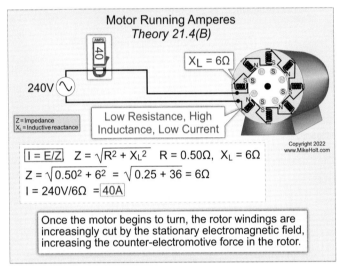

Motor Running Amperes
Theory 21.4(B)

240V

$X_L = 6\Omega$

Low Resistance, High Inductance, Low Current

Z = Impedance
X_L = Inductive reactance

Copyright 2022
www.MikeHolt.com

$\boxed{I = E/Z}$ $Z = \sqrt{R^2 + X_L^2}$ R = 0.50Ω, $X_L = 6\Omega$

$Z = \sqrt{0.50^2 + 6^2} = \sqrt{0.25 + 36} = 6\Omega$

I = 240V/6Ω = $\boxed{40A}$

Once the motor begins to turn, the rotor windings are increasingly cut by the stationary electromagnetic field, increasing the counter-electromotive force in the rotor.

▶Figure 21–9

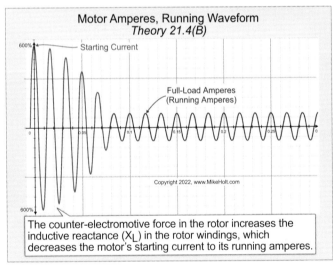

Motor Amperes, Running Waveform
Theory 21.4(B)

Starting Current

Full-Load Amperes
(Running Amperes)

Copyright 2022, www.MikeHolt.com

The counter-electromotive force in the rotor increases the inductive reactance (X_L) in the rotor windings, which decreases the motor's starting current to its running amperes.

▶Figure 21–10

(C) Locked-Rotor Amperes (LRA).

(1) General. Locked-rotor current (LRC), which is also called "locked-rotor amperes" (LRA), is the current drawn by the motor when voltage is applied to the motor and its shaft (rotor) is prevented from turning. Locked-rotor current, or locked-rotor amperes, occurs when the rotating part of the motor winding becomes jammed and counter-electromotive force (self-inductance/CEMF) is no longer present. This condition decreases wire impedance (ac resistance plus reactance) to the point that the winding wire effectively becomes a resistor. The locked-rotor current is typically between six to ten times the motor nameplate full-load amperes. ▶Figure 21–11

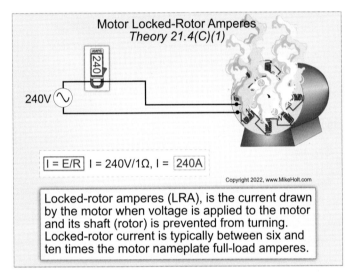

Motor Locked-Rotor Amperes
Theory 21.4(C)(1)

240V

$\boxed{I = E/R}$ I = 240V/1Ω, I = $\boxed{240A}$

Copyright 2022, www.MikeHolt.com

Locked-rotor amperes (LRA), is the current drawn by the motor when voltage is applied to the motor and its shaft (rotor) is prevented from turning. Locked-rotor current is typically between six and ten times the motor nameplate full-load amperes.

▶Figure 21–11

(2) Locked Rotor Hazard. A motor that operates at locked-rotor current (LRC) will cause its winding to overheat to the point where the wire winding's insulation and lubrication will be damaged. Most motors can sustain locked-rotor current for less than one minute.

21.5 Motor Nameplate Amperes

(A) Nameplate Amperes. The motor nameplate amperes indicate the current the motor is expected to draw at its rated horsepower, rated voltage, efficiency, and power factor. The motor nameplate amperes rating is commonly referred to as the motor "full-load amperes" (FLA). ▶Figure 21–12

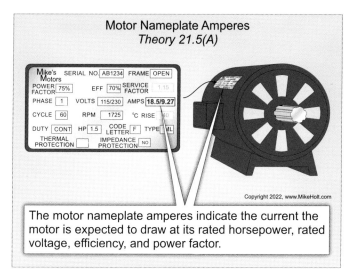

Figure 21–12

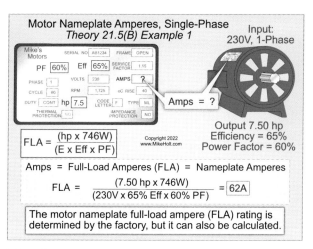

Figure 21–13

(B) Calculating Motor Nameplate Amperes. The motor nameplate amperes (FLA) can be determined using the following formulas:

Single-Phase FLA = (hp × 746W)/(E × Eff × PF)

Three-Phase FLA = (hp × 746W)/(E × 1.732 × Eff × PF)

▶ Single-Phase Motor FLA Example 1

Question: The motor nameplate amperes for a 7.50 hp, 230V, single-phase motor with an efficiency rating of 65 percent and a power factor of 60 percent is _____. ▶Figure 21–13

(a) 32A   (b) 42A   (c) 52A   (d) 62A

Solution:

Motor FLA, Single-Phase = (hp × 746W)/(E × Eff × PF)

FLA = (7.50 hp × 746W)/(230V × 65% Eff × 60% PF)
FLA = 5,595W/89.7
FLA = 62A

Answer: (d) 62A

▶ Single-Phase Motor FLA Example 2

Question: The nameplate full-load ampere rating for a 1 hp, 115V single-phase motor will be _____ if the motor operates at an efficiency rating of 70 percent with a power factor of 70 percent. ▶Figure 21–14

(a) 13.20A   (b) 14.20A   (c) 15.20A   (d) 16.20A

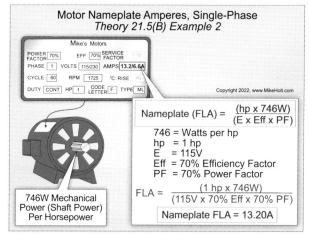

Figure 21–14

Solution:

Motor FLA, Single-Phase = (hp × 746W)/(E × Eff × PF)

Motor FLA = (1 hp × 746W)/(115V × 70% Eff × 70% PF)
Motor FLA = 746W/56.35
Motor FLA = 13.20A

Answer: (a) 13.20A

▶ **Three-Phase Motor FLA Example**

Question: The motor nameplate amperes for a 10 hp, 208V, three-phase motor with an efficiency rating of 95 percent and a power factor of 90 percent is _____. ▶Figure 21–15

(a) 13A   (b) 19A   (c) 24A   (d) 33A

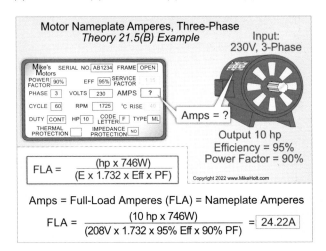

▶Figure 21–15

Solution:

Motor FLA, Three-Phase = (hp × 746W)/(E × 1.732 × Eff × PF)

Motor FLA = (10 hp × 746W)/(208V ×1.732 × 95% Eff × 90% PF)

Motor FLA = 7,460W/308

Motor FLA = 24.22A

Answer: (c) 24A

21.6 Dual-Voltage Motors

(A) High and Low Voltage. Dual-voltage motors are made with two sets of windings. The windings are connected in parallel for operation at the lower motor nameplate voltage rating and in series for operation at the higher voltage rating. ▶Figure 21–16

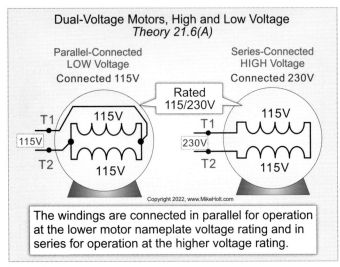

The windings are connected in parallel for operation at the lower motor nameplate voltage rating and in series for operation at the higher voltage rating.

▶Figure 21–16

(1) High and Low Voltage Connections.

(a) Higher Voltage Connection. When a motor is connected to the higher voltage rating for a 115/230V or 230/460V motor, the current rating will be half the current rating than if it is connected to the lower voltage rating. ▶Figure 21–17

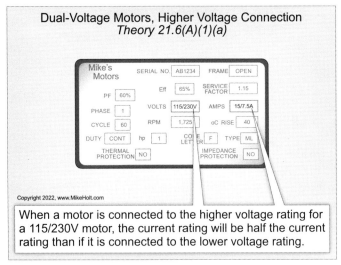

When a motor is connected to the higher voltage rating for a 115/230V motor, the current rating will be half the current rating than if it is connected to the lower voltage rating.

▶Figure 21–17

(b) Lower Voltage Connection. When a motor is connected to the lower voltage rating for a 115/230V or 230/460V motor, the current rating will be twice the current rating than if it is connected to the higher voltage rating. ▶Figure 21–18

Dual-Voltage Motors, Lower Voltage Connection
Theory 21.6(A)(1)(b)

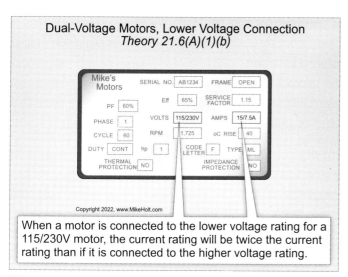

Mike's Motors

	SERIAL NO. AB1234	FRAME	OPEN
PF 60%	Eff 65%	SERVICE FACTOR	1.15
PHASE 1	VOLTS 115/230V	AMPS	15/7.5A
CYCLE 60	RPM 1,725	oC RISE	40
DUTY CONT	hp 1	CODE LETTER F	TYPE ML
THERMAL PROTECTION NO		IMPEDANCE PROTECTION	NO

Copyright 2022, www.MikeHolt.com

When a motor is connected to the lower voltage rating for a 115/230V motor, the current rating will be twice the current rating than if it is connected to the higher voltage rating.

▶Figure 21–18

(2) Motor Volt-Amperes. Whether a dual-voltage motor is connected to the higher or lower voltage, the motor VA will remain the same. The motor volt-amperes are determined by the formula:

Single-Phase VA = Volts × Amperes

▶ **Motor Volt-Amperes Example**

Question: The volt-amperes for a 5 hp, 230V single-phase motor with a nameplate rating of 29A is _____.

(a) 6,670 VA   (b) 7,805 VA   (c) 8,990 VA   (d) 9,000 VA

Solution:

VA = V × A
VA = 230V × 29A
VA = 6,670 VA

Answer: (a) 6,670 VA

21.7 Reversing the Rotation of Alternating-Current Motors

(A) Single-Phase. Some ac single-phase motors are constructed so their direction of rotation can be reversed. To reverse a single-phase ac induction motor, it is necessary to change the relative polarity of the start winding in relation to the run winding. The motor nameplate will contain the information for forward and reverse operation.

(B) Three-Phase. A three-phase motor can be reversed by swapping any two of the three-phase wires at any point in the circuit to the motor. The industry practice is to reverse the Phase A and Phase C wires. ▶Figure 21–19

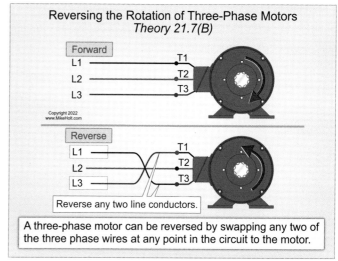

Reversing the Rotation of Three-Phase Motors
Theory 21.7(B)

Forward
L1 ——— T1
L2 ——— T2
L3 ——— T3

Copyright 2022 www.MikeHolt.com

Reverse
L1 ——— T1
L2 ——— T2
L3 ——— T3

Reverse any two line conductors.

A three-phase motor can be reversed by swapping any two of the three phase wires at any point in the circuit to the motor.

▶Figure 21–19

Caution

⚡ **CAUTION:** If a three-phase motor loses a phase while it is operating, the rotor will continue to turn but at a reduced speed and torque. Eventually, the reduced torque will cause the current flow on the other two phases to increase and will most likely damage the stator winding if the motor does not have overload protection.

21.8 Alternating-Current Motor Types

(A) Alternating-Current Squirrel-Cage Induction Motor. Three-phase ac squirrel-cage induction motors are used in almost all major industrial applications. They are called squirrel-cage motors because the rotor consists of bars that are either parallel to the shaft or at a slight angle and are connected at the ends by shorting rings. These bars resemble a hamster or squirrel cage if you remove the core material around them.

(B) Synchronous Motor. In a synchronous motor, the rotor is locked in step with the rotating stator field and is dragged along at the synchronous speed of the rotating electromagnetic field. Synchronous motors maintain their speed with a high degree of accuracy. Small synchronous motors are used for clock motors. Large synchronous motors are often found in large industrial facilities driving loads such as compressors, crushers, and large pumps.

(C) Wound-Rotor Induction Motor. Wound-rotor induction motors are used only in special applications because of their complexity. Wound-rotor induction motors only operate on three-phase ac power. They are like induction motors; however, the rotor windings are connected in a wye configuration and the points of the wye are brought out through slip rings to an external controller.

(D) Universal Motor. Universal motors are fractional horsepower motors that operate equally well on ac and dc. They are used for vacuum cleaners, electric drills, mixers, and light household appliances. These motors have the inherent disadvantage associated with dc motors, which is the need for commutation. The problem with commutators is that as the motor operates, parts rub against each other and wear out.

UNIT
22

GENERATORS

22.1 Introduction

A generator is a device that converts mechanical energy into electrical energy. Generators produce most of the electric power in the world and are used in residential, commercial, and industrial facilities for primary, backup, and temporary power. In this unit you will learn:

▸ generator basics

▸ the differences between single- and three-phase generators

▸ how to calculate generator output volt-amperes and amperes

22.2 Generator Prime Mover

A generator produces electrical energy by converting mechanical energy from a "prime mover" into electricity. A prime mover can be a combustion engine, steam turbine, water movement from a dam, or air movement from wind turbines. ▸Figure 22–1

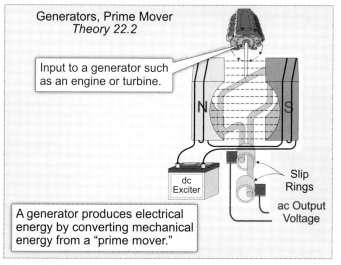

Generators, Prime Mover
Theory 22.2

Input to a generator such as an engine or turbine.

N   S

dc Exciter

Slip Rings

ac Output Voltage

A generator produces electrical energy by converting mechanical energy from a "prime mover."

▸Figure 22–1

22.3 Alternating-Current Generators

(A) Single-Phase.

(1) Generator Output Voltage. In generators that produce large quantities of electricity, the wire coils are stationary, and an electromagnetic field revolves within them. Voltage is created by a generator when the electromagnetic field of the rotor cuts through the stator winding. The voltage produced in the wire loop is dependent on the number of turns of wire, the strength of the electromagnetic field, and the speed at which the rotor rotates. ▸Figure 22–2

A magnetic field is produced by electromagnetism thereby allowing the intensity of the magnetic field (lines of force) to be modified to control the generator's output voltage.

(2) Generator Voltage Frequency. The frequency of a generator depends on the number of stator poles and the speed of the rotor. The most common configurations of stators that provide an output frequency of 60 hertz are 2-pole (3,600 RPM), 4-pole (1,800 RPM), and 6-pole (1,200 RPM).

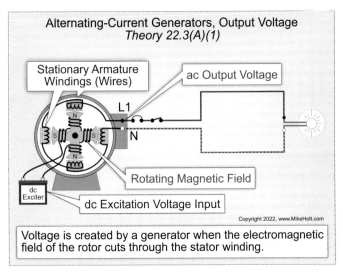

Alternating-Current Generators, Output Voltage
Theory 22.3(A)(1)

Voltage is created by a generator when the electromagnetic field of the rotor cuts through the stator winding.

▶Figure 22–2

(B) Three-Phase Generators. Three-phase alternating-current generators work on the same basic principle as single-phase ac generators. The primary difference between single- and three-phase generators is the layout of the windings. Three-phase ac generators have three sets of equally spaced windings, each of which are physically 120° out-of-phase with each other creating three voltage outputs that are 120° out-of-phase with each other. ▶Figure 22–3

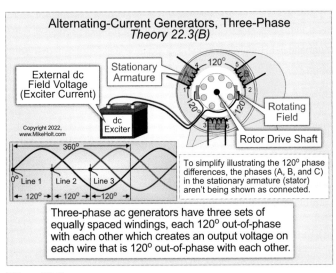

Alternating-Current Generators, Three-Phase
Theory 22.3(B)

To simplify illustrating the 120° phase differences, the phases (A, B, and C) in the stationary armature (stator) aren't being shown as connected.

Three-phase ac generators have three sets of equally spaced windings, each 120° out-of-phase with each other which creates an output voltage on each wire that is 120° out-of-phase with each other.

▶Figure 22–3

22.4 Generator Output Current

The output current of a generator is determined by the following formulas:

Single-Phase: $I = VA/E$

Three-Phase: $I = VA/(E \times 1.732)$

▶ **Generator Output Current—Single-Phase Example**

Question: The output current for a single-phase, 24 kVA, 240V generator is _____. ▶Figure 22–4

(a) 50A   (b) 70A   (c) 90A   (d) 100A

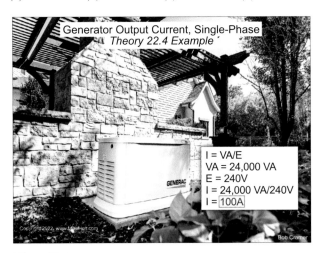

Generator Output Current, Single-Phase
Theory 22.4 Example

$I = VA/E$
$VA = 24,000 VA$
$E = 240V$
$I = 24,000 VA/240V$
$I = \boxed{100A}$

▶Figure 22–4

Solution:

$I = VA/E$
$VA = 24,000 VA$
$E = 240V$

$I = 24,000 VA/240V$
$I = 100A$

Answer: (d) 100A

▶ **Generator Output Current—Three-Phase Example**

Question: The current for a three-phase, 36 kVA, 120/208V generator is _____. ▶Figure 22–5

(a) 100A   *(b) 110A*   *(c) 125A*   *(d) 150A*

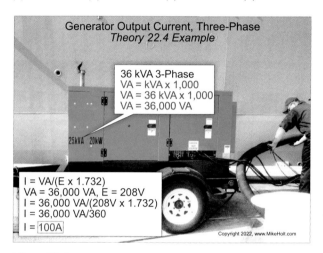

▶Figure 22–5

Solution:

I = VA/(E × 1.732)

VA = 36,000 VA

E = 208V

I = 36,000 VA/(208V × 1.732)

I = 36,000 VA/360

I = 100A

Answer: (a) 100A

22.5 Single-Phase and Three-Phase Generator Voltages

(A) Single-Phase Generator Voltages. Single-phase voltage can originate from a single-phase generator. ▶Figure 22–6

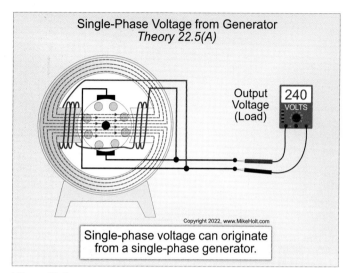

▶Figure 22–6

(B) Three-Phase Generator Voltages. Voltages in a three-phase circuit originate from a generator where the voltage of each phase wire is out-of-phase with each other by 120°. ▶Figure 22–7

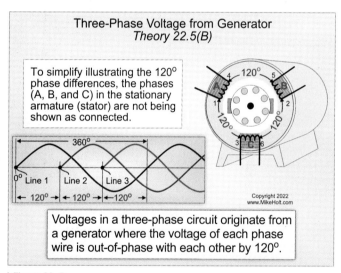

▶Figure 22–7

22.6 Electrical Industry Voltages

(A) Nominal System Voltage. The nominal system voltage is a voltage used for circuit calculations. For example, 120/240V, 120/208V, or 277/480V are nominal system voltages. ▶Figure 22–8

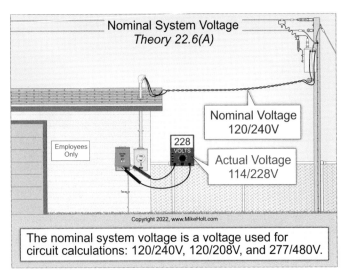

Nominal System Voltage
Theory 22.6(A)

Nominal Voltage
120/240V

Actual Voltage
114/228V

The nominal system voltage is a voltage used for circuit calculations: 120/240V, 120/208V, and 277/480V.

▶Figure 22–8

(B) Utility Voltage Range. In accordance with ANSI C84.1, the utility voltage must be no more than 105 percent and not less than 90 percent of the nominal system voltage. This means that for a 120/240V nominal voltage system, the utility must provide a voltage of not less than 108/216V (90 percent) or not more than 126/252V (105 percent). ▶Figure 22–9

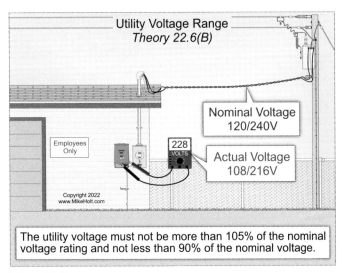

Utility Voltage Range
Theory 22.6(B)

Nominal Voltage
120/240V

Actual Voltage
108/216V

The utility voltage must not be more than 105% of the nominal voltage rating and not less than 90% of the nominal voltage.

▶Figure 22–9

(C) Actual Voltage. The actual voltage at any point in the electrical system is the voltage that is measured by a voltmeter. ▶Figure 22–10

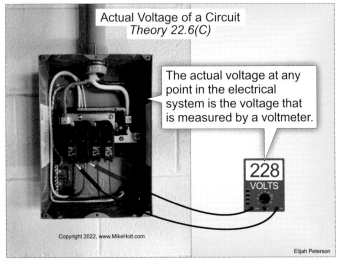

Actual Voltage of a Circuit
Theory 22.6(C)

The actual voltage at any point in the electrical system is the voltage that is measured by a voltmeter.

228 VOLTS

Elijah Peterson

▶Figure 22–10

(D) Equipment Voltage Rating.

(1) Minimum Electrical Equipment Voltage. Equipment must be connected to a nominal system voltage per their specifications. In accordance with ANSI C84.1, the minimum voltage at the equipment cannot be less than 90 percent of the nominal system voltage.

(2) Minimum Motor Voltage. Motors must be connected to a nominal voltage in accordance with their specifications. In accordance with the NEMA MG1-standard, the minimum voltage at the motor cannot be less than 90 percent of the motor's nameplate voltage rating.

UNIT

23

RELAYS

23.1 Introduction

A relay is a switch that uses an electromagnetic coil to operate one or more sets of contacts. In this unit you will learn: ▶Figure 23–1

▸ how relays operate

▸ about normally open and normally closed relay contacts

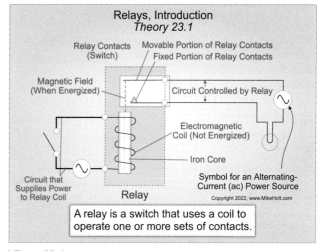

▶Figure 23–1

23.2 How Relays Operate

(A) Electromagnetic Relay. An electromagnetic relay uses an electromagnetic field to open or close a contact. One part of the relay contact is fixed, and the other part of the relay contact moves to open or close the relay contact by an electromagnetic field. ▶Figure 23–2

(B) Relay Sequence of Operation. The sequence of operation for a relay, where the contact(s) is open and when the relay is not energized is as follows: ▶Figure 23–3

Step 1: Closing the switch provides electrical energy to energize the relay.

Step 2: The coil of the relay becomes energized once the switch is closed.

Step 3: The coil creates an electromagnetic field once it is energized.

Step 4: The electromagnetic field attracts the armature (to close the contact).

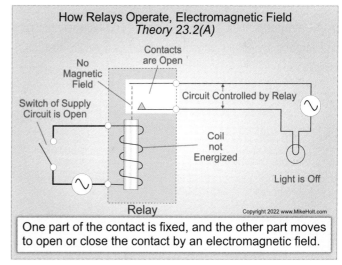

▶Figure 23–2

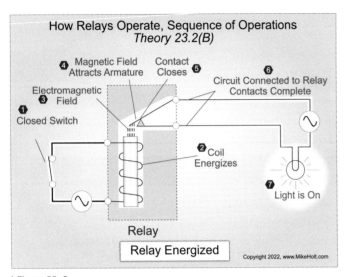

▶Figure 23–3

Step 5: The electromagnetic field from the coil closes the normally open (NO) contact.

Step 6: The circuit connected to the relay contacts is completed.

Step 7: The light is on.

23.3 Relay Contacts

Relays can contain contacts that are normally open, normally closed, or both normally open and normally closed.

(A) NO Contacts. If the contact of the relay is open when the coil is de-energized, then the contact is identified as normally open (NO). ▶Figure 23–4

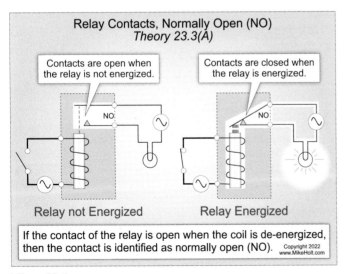

▶Figure 23–4

(B) NC Contacts. If the contact of the relay is closed when the coil is de-energized, then the contact is identified as normally closed (NC). ▶Figure 23–5

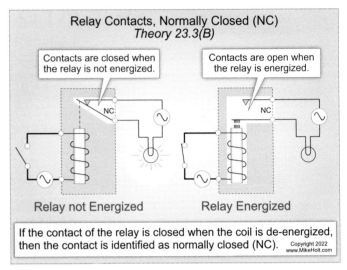

▶Figure 23–5

(C) NO and NC Contacts. Some relays have both NO and NC contacts. When the relay coil is not energized, the NC contacts are closed, and the NO contacts are open. When the relay coil is energized, the NC contacts open and the NO contacts close. ▶Figure 23–6

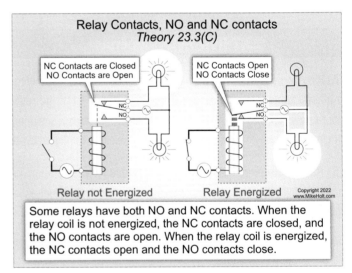

▶Figure 23–6

UNIT

24

TRANSFORMERS

24.1 Introduction

A transformer uses electromagnetism to convert input voltage into a different output voltage. In this unit you will learn:

▶ the uses of transformers

▶ about different types of transformers

▶ how to calculate primary and secondary current

▶ the differences between delta/wye- and delta/delta-connected transformers

24.2 Types of Transformers

There are many types of transformers ranging from high-voltage utility transmission and distribution transformers to simple low-voltage power supplies for doorbells and lighting. ▶Figure 24–1

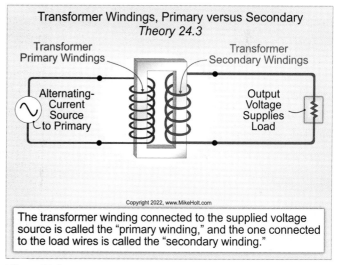

Types of Transformers
Theory 24.2

Copyright 2022
www.MikeHolt.com

There are many types of transformers ranging from high-voltage utility transmission and distribution transformers to simple low-voltage transformers for doorbells and lighting.

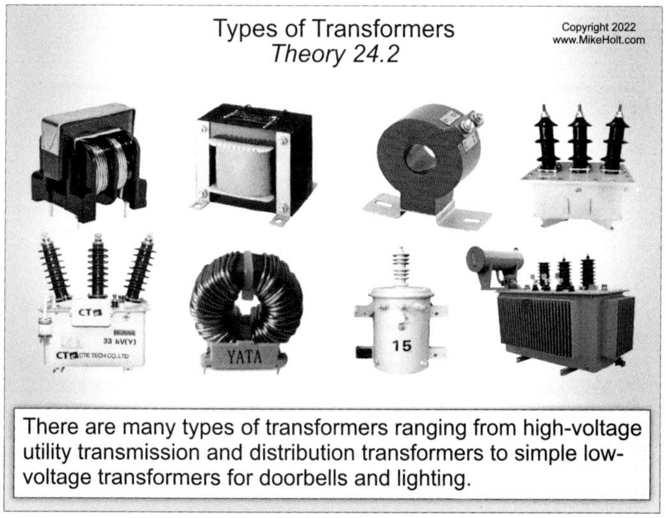

▶Figure 24–1

24.3 Primary versus Secondary

The transformer winding connected to the supplied voltage source is called the "primary winding," and the winding connected to the load wires is called the "secondary winding." ▶Figure 24–2

Transformer Windings, Primary versus Secondary
Theory 24.3

Transformer
Primary Windings

Transformer
Secondary Windings

Alternating-
Current
Source
to Primary

Output
Voltage
Supplies
Load

Copyright 2022, www.MikeHolt.com

The transformer winding connected to the supplied voltage source is called the "primary winding," and the one connected to the load wires is called the "secondary winding."

▶Figure 24–2

24.4 Transformer Mutual Induction

Transformers can be used to either increase, decrease, or maintain the same output voltage as the input voltage. A transformer consists of a primary winding and a secondary winding, which are electrically insulated from each other. Both the primary and secondary windings are wound on the same iron core, so the electromagnetic field from the primary winding cuts the secondary winding, which induces a voltage on the secondary. ▶Figure 24–3

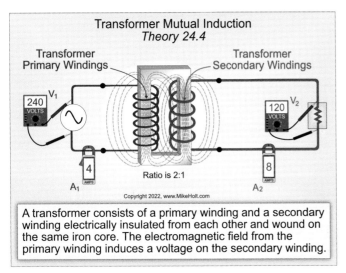

Transformer Mutual Induction
Theory 24.4

A transformer consists of a primary winding and a secondary winding electrically insulated from each other and wound on the same iron core. The electromagnetic field from the primary winding induces a voltage on the secondary winding.

▶Figure 24–3

24.5 Secondary Induced Voltage

The voltage on the secondary winding is a function of the number of secondary wire loops cut by the primary electromagnetic field. The voltage induced on the secondary winding equals the sum of the voltages induced in each secondary wire loop. ▶Figure 24–4

24.6 Transformer Turns Ratios

(A) Winding Turns Ratio. The relationship between the number of primary winding turns compared to the number of secondary winding turns is called the transformer "winding turns ratio" and the formula for calculations is: ▶Figure 24–5

Winding Turns Ratio = Primary Turns:Secondary Turns

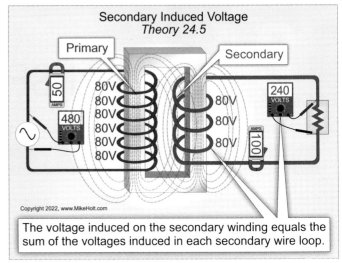

Secondary Induced Voltage
Theory 24.5

The voltage induced on the secondary winding equals the sum of the voltages induced in each secondary wire loop.

▶Figure 24–4

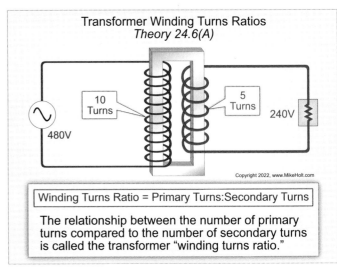

Transformer Winding Turns Ratios
Theory 24.6(A)

Winding Turns Ratio = Primary Turns:Secondary Turns

The relationship between the number of primary turns compared to the number of secondary turns is called the transformer "winding turns ratio."

▶Figure 24–5

▶ **Winding Turns Ratio Example**

Question: A transformer has a primary winding of ten turns and a secondary winding of two turns. The winding turns ratio of this transformer is _____. ▶Figure 24–6

(a) 3:1   (b) 4:1   (c) 5:1   (d) 10:1

Solution:

Winding Turns Ratio = Primary Turns:Secondary Turns
Winding Turns Ratio = 10/2
Winding Turns Ratio = 5:1

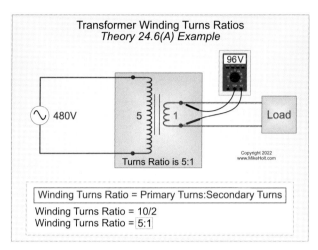

▶Figure 24–6

Answer: (c) 5:1

(B) Voltage Turns Ratio. The relationship between the primary voltage and secondary voltage is called the transformer "voltage turns ratio" and the formula for calculations is: ▶Figure 24–7

Voltage Turns Ratio = Primary Volts:Secondary Volts

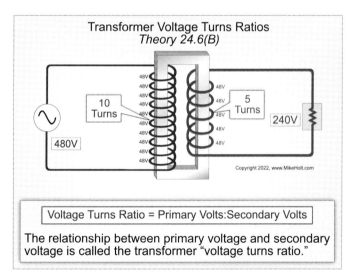

▶Figure 24–7

▶ **Voltage Turns Ratio Example**

Question: If the primary voltage of a transformer is 480V and the secondary is 120V, the voltage turns ratio will be _____.
▶Figure 24–8

(a) 1:4   (b) 2:4   (c) 4:1   (d) 4:20

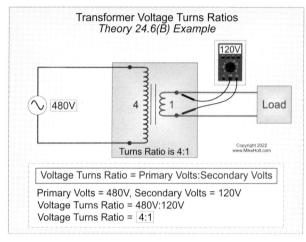

▶Figure 24–8

Solution:

Voltage Turns Ratio = Primary Volts:Secondary Volts

Primary Volts = 480V
Secondary Volts = 120V

Voltage Turns Ratio = 480V:120V
Voltage Turns Ratio = 4:1

Answer: (c) 4:1

(C) Secondary Voltage. The secondary voltage of a transformer is determined by the following formula:

Secondary Voltage = Primary Volts/Voltage Turns Ratio

▶ **Secondary Volts Example 1**

Question: *The secondary voltage of a 5:1 transformer is _____ if the primary is 120V.* ▶Figure 24–9

(a) 3V   (b) 6V   (c) 12V   (d) 24V

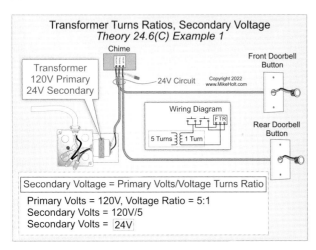

▶Figure 24–9

Solution:

Secondary Voltage = Primary Volts/Turns Ratio

Primary Volts = 120V

Voltage Turns Ratio = 5:1

Secondary Volts = 120V/5

Secondary Volts = 24V

Answer: (d) 24V

▶ **Secondary Volts Example 2**

Question: *The secondary voltage of a 4:1 turns ratio transformer is _____ if the primary is 480V.* ▶Figure 24–10

(a) 120V   (b) 208V   (c) 277V   (d) 480V

Solution:

Secondary Voltage = Primary Volts/Turn Ratio

Primary Volts = 480V

Voltage Turns Ratio = 4:1

Secondary Volts = 480V/4

Secondary Volts = 120V

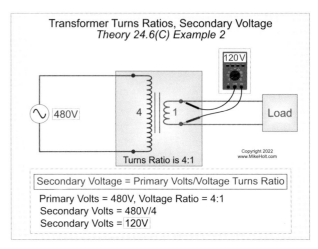

▶Figure 24–10

Answer: (a) 120V

24.7 Isolation Transformers (1:1)

If the primary and secondary windings of a transformer have the same number of wire loops (turns), the secondary output voltage will be the same as the primary input voltage. This type of transformer is called an "isolation transformer" which is a special purpose transformer primarily used for large computers, medical devices, and laboratory instruments. ▶Figure 24–11

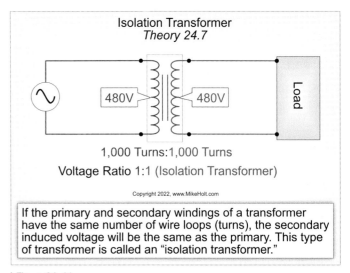

▶Figure 24–11

24.8 Autotransformers

Autotransformers use a single winding for both the primary and secondary and are often referred to as "buck-boost transformers."
▶Figure 24–12

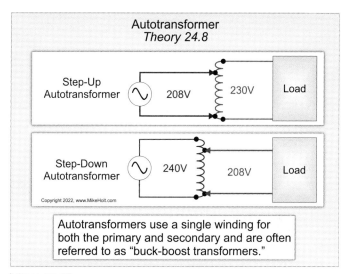

Autotransformer
Theory 24.8

Step-Up Autotransformer — 208V — 230V — Load

Step-Down Autotransformer — 240V — 208V — Load

Copyright 2022, www.MikeHolt.com

Autotransformers use a single winding for both the primary and secondary and are often referred to as "buck-boost transformers."

▶Figure 24–12

The disadvantage of an autotransformer is the lack of electrical isolation between the primary and secondary windings. A short circuit between the primary and secondary wires can lead to the primary voltage being directly applied to the connected equipment.

24.9 Transformer kVA Rating

Transformers are commonly sized between 3 kVA and 2,500 kVA.
▶Figure 24–13

24.10 Transformer Current Flow

When a load is connected to the secondary of a transformer, the primary winding electromagnetic field induces voltage in the secondary winding resulting in a secondary current. The secondary current flow creates an electromagnetic field in the secondary winding that induces a counter-electromotive force in the primary winding. As a result, less primary counter-electromotive force is generated, and the primary current will increase in proportion to the increase in the secondary current.
▶Figure 24–14

Transformer kVA Rating*, *Theory 24.9*	
Single-Phase	Three-Phase
3	15
5	30
10	45
15	75
25	112.50
37.50	150
50	225
75	300
100	500
167	750
250	1,000
333	1,500
500	2,000
833	2,500

Copyright 2022 www.MikeHolt.com

*Not a complete list of standard sizes.

▶Figure 24–13

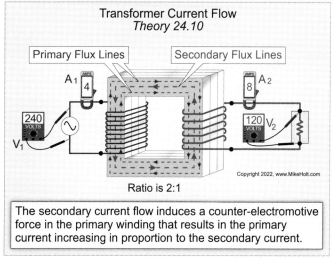

Transformer Current Flow
Theory 24.10

Primary Flux Lines   Secondary Flux Lines

A_1 4   8 A_2

240 VOLTS V_1 120 VOLTS V_2

Copyright 2022, www.MikeHolt.com

Ratio is 2:1

The secondary current flow induces a counter-electromotive force in the primary winding that results in the primary current increasing in proportion to the secondary current.

▶Figure 24–14

24.11 Transformer Current Rating

(A) Secondary Current. The secondary current of a transformer is determined by one of the following formulas:

Single-Phase Secondary Current = Transformer VA/Volts

Three-Phase Secondary Current = Transformer VA/ (Volts × 1.732)

▶ **Single-Phase Secondary Line Current Example 1**

Question: *What is the secondary current for a fully loaded single-phase, 25 kVA, 480V to 240V transformer?* ▶Figure 24–15

(a) 52A   *(b) 104A*   *(c) 208A*   *(d) 250A*

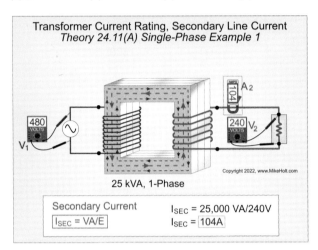

▶Figure 24–15

Solution:

$I_{SEC} = VA/E$

VA = 25,000

E = 240V

$I_{SEC} = 25,000\ VA/240V$

$I_{SEC} = 104A$

Answer: *(b) 104A*

▶ **Single-Phase Secondary Line Current Example 2**

Question: *The secondary current for a fully loaded single-phase, 37.50 kVA, 480V to 240V transformer is _____.* ▶Figure 24–16

(a) 108A   *(b) 130A*   *(c) 140A*   *(d) 156A*

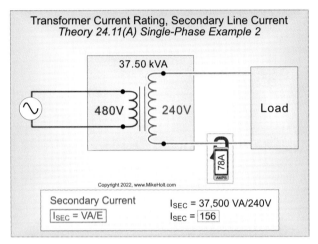

▶Figure 24–16

Solution:

$I_{SEC} = VA/E$

VA = 37,500

E = 240V

$I_{SEC} = 37,500\ VA/240V$

$I_{SEC} = 156.25A$

Answer: *(d) 156A*

▶ Three-Phase Secondary Line Current Example 1

Question: *What is the secondary current for a fully loaded three-phase, 75 kVA, 480V to 208Y/120V transformer?* ▶Figure 24–17

(a) 104A   (b) 140A   (c) 208A   (d) 500A

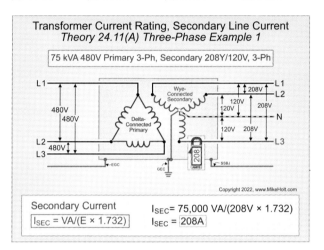

▶Figure 24–17

Solution:

$I_{SEC} = VA/(E \times 1.732)$

VA = 75,000

E = 208V

$I_{SEC} = 75,000 \ VA/(208V \times 1.732)$

$I_{SEC} = 75,000 \ VA/360.26V$

$I_{SEC} = 208A$

Answer: (c) 208A

▶ Single-Phase Primary Line Current Example

Question: *What is the primary current for a fully loaded single-phase, 25 kVA, 480V to240V transformer?* ▶Figure 24–18

(a) 52A   (b) 72A   (c) 82A   (d) 614A

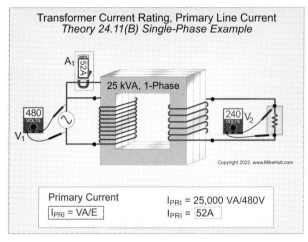

▶Figure 24–18

Solution:

$I_{PRI} = VA/E$

VA = 25,000

E = 480V

$I_{PRI} = 25,000 \ VA/480V$

$I_{PRI} = 52A$

Answer: (a) 52A

(B) Primary Current. The primary current of a transformer is determined by one of the following formulas:

Single-Phase Primary Current = Transformer VA/Volts

Three-Phase Primary Current = Transformer VA/(Volts × 1.732)

▶ **Three-Phase Primary Line Current Example 1**

Question: *What is the primary current for a fully loaded three-phase, 75 kVA, 480 to 208Y/120V transformer?* ▶Figure 24–19

(a) 10A   *(b) 70A*   *(c) 80A*   *(d) 90A*

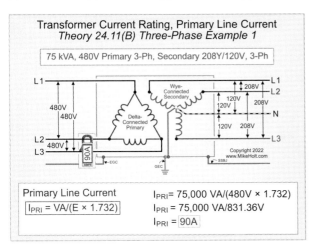

▶Figure 24–19

Solution:

$I_{PRI} = VA/(E \times 1.732)$

VA = 75,000

E = 480V

$I_{PRI} = 75,000\ VA/(480V \times 1.732)$

$I_{PRI} = 75,000\ VA/831.36V$

$I_{PRI} = 90A$

Answer: (d) 90A

▶ **Three-Phase Primary Line Current Example 2**

Question: *The primary current for a fully loaded three-phase, 37.50 kVA, 480V to 208Y/120V transformer is _____.* ▶Figure 24–20

(a) 45A   *(b) 55A*   *(c) 65A*   *(d) 75A*

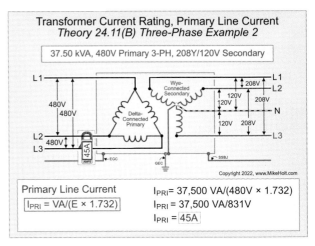

▶Figure 24–20

Solution:

$I_{PRI} = VA/(E \times 1.732)$

VA = 37,500

E = 480V

$I_{PRI} = 37,500\ VA/(480V \times 1.732)$

$I_{PRI} = 37,500\ VA/831V$

$I_{PRI} = 45A$

Answer: (a) 45A

24.12 Transformer Configurations

(A) Single-Phase Transformer Windings. Single-phase transformers contain a primary and a secondary winding mounted on a single laminated iron core. ▶Figure 24–21

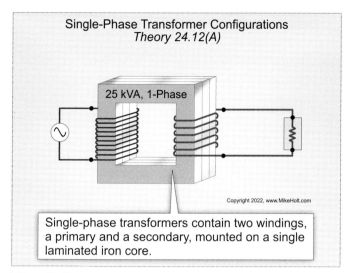

Single-Phase Transformer Configurations
Theory 24.12(A)

25 kVA, 1-Phase

Single-phase transformers contain two windings, a primary and a secondary, mounted on a single laminated iron core.

▶Figure 24–21

(B) Three-Phase Transformer Windings. Three-phase transformers are constructed with three sets of single-phase windings that are connected together to create a three-phase system. The two most common three-phase transformer configurations are Delta and Wye. ▶Figure 24–22 and ▶Figure 24–23

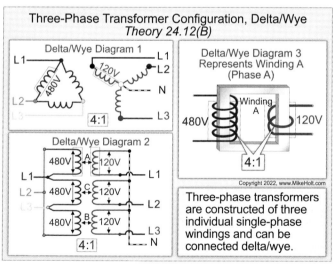

Three-Phase Transformer Configuration, Delta/Wye
Theory 24.12(B)

Delta/Wye Diagram 1

Delta/Wye Diagram 3
Represents Winding A
(Phase A)

4:1

480V   120V

Delta/Wye Diagram 2

4:1

Three-phase transformers are constructed of three individual single-phase windings and can be connected delta/wye.

▶Figure 24–22

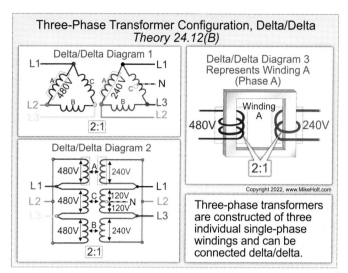

Three-Phase Transformer Configuration, Delta/Delta
Theory 24.12(B)

Delta/Delta Diagram 1

2:1

Delta/Delta Diagram 3
Represents Winding A
(Phase A)

480V   240V

2:1

Delta/Delta Diagram 2

2:1

Three-phase transformers are constructed of three individual single-phase windings and can be connected delta/delta.

▶Figure 24–23

24.13 Delta/Wye Transformers

(A) Primary Winding Configuration. The primary windings of a three-phase delta/wye transformer are connected end-to-end with each other. The primary circuit wires are connected to each point where the winding leads meet. ▶Figure 24–24

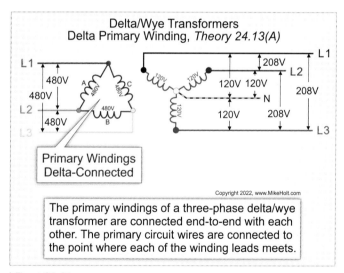

Delta/Wye Transformers
Delta Primary Winding, *Theory 24.13(A)*

480V   208V
480V   120V 120V
480V   120V   208V
120V   208V

Primary Windings
Delta-Connected

The primary windings of a three-phase delta/wye transformer are connected end-to-end with each other. The primary circuit wires are connected to the point where each of the winding leads meets.

▶Figure 24–24

(B) Secondary Winding Configuration. The secondary windings of a three-phase delta/wye transformer have one end of each secondary winding connected to a common point. The secondary wires are connected to the secondary winding leads that are not connected to the common point. The wye-connected secondary windings have four wires which can supply line-to-line loads and line-to-neutral loads. ▶Figure 24–25

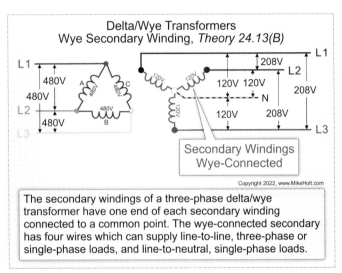

Delta/Wye Transformers
Wye Secondary Winding, *Theory 24.13(B)*

The secondary windings of a three-phase delta/wye transformer have one end of each secondary winding connected to a common point. The wye-connected secondary has four wires which can supply line-to-line, three-phase or single-phase loads, and line-to-neutral, single-phase loads.

▶Figure 24–25

(C) System Voltages.

(1) Line-to-Line Voltage. The voltage between any two primary wires is the "primary line-to-line voltage," while the voltage between any two secondary wires is the "secondary line-to-line voltage." ▶Figure 24–26

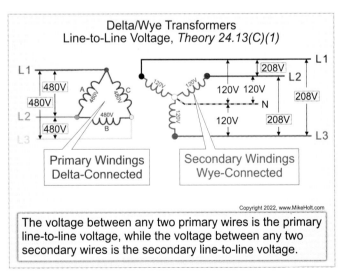

Delta/Wye Transformers
Line-to-Line Voltage, *Theory 24.13(C)(1)*

Primary Windings
Delta-Connected

Secondary Windings
Wye-Connected

The voltage between any two primary wires is the primary line-to-line voltage, while the voltage between any two secondary wires is the secondary line-to-line voltage.

▶Figure 24–26

Author's Comment:

▶ The line-to-line voltage for a three-phase, 4-wire, secondary wye-connected transformer is equal to the line-to-neutral voltage times 1.732. ▶Figure 24–27

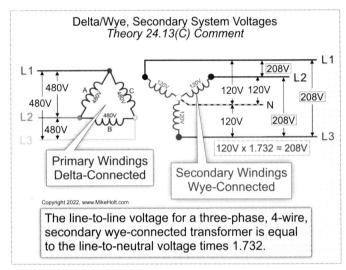

Delta/Wye, Secondary System Voltages
Theory 24.13(C) Comment

Primary Windings
Delta-Connected

Secondary Windings
Wye-Connected

120V x 1.732 = 208V

The line-to-line voltage for a three-phase, 4-wire, secondary wye-connected transformer is equal to the line-to-neutral voltage times 1.732.

▶Figure 24–27

(2) Line-to-Neutral Voltage. Line-to-neutral voltage is the voltage between a phase wire and a neutral wire. ▶Figure 24–28

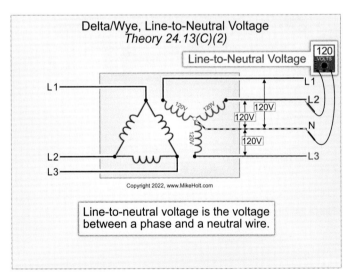

Delta/Wye, Line-to-Neutral Voltage
Theory 24.13(C)(2)

Line-to-Neutral Voltage

Line-to-neutral voltage is the voltage between a phase and a neutral wire.

▶Figure 24–28

24.14 Delta/Delta (High-Leg) Transformers

(A) Primary Winding Configuration. The primary windings of a three-phase delta/delta (high-leg) transformer are connected end-to-end with each other. The primary circuit wires are connected to each point where the winding leads meet. ▶Figure 24–29

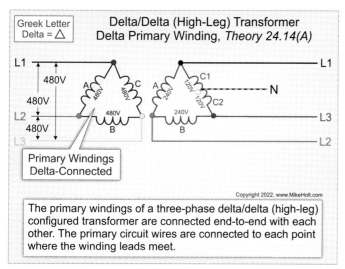

Delta/Delta (High-Leg) Transformer
Delta Primary Winding, *Theory 24.14(A)*

Primary Windings
Delta-Connected

The primary windings of a three-phase delta/delta (high-leg) configured transformer are connected end-to-end with each other. The primary circuit wires are connected to each point where the winding leads meet.

▶Figure 24–29

(B) Secondary Winding Configuration. The secondary windings of a three-phase delta/delta (high-leg) transformer have the secondary windings connected end-to-end with each other. The load wires are connected to each point where the secondary winding leads meet. A delta-connected high-leg transformer can supply line-to-line loads and line-to-neutral loads. ▶Figure 24–30

(C) System Voltages.

(1) Line-to-Line Voltage. The voltage between any two primary wires is known as the "primary line-to-line voltage," while the voltage between any two secondary wires is referred to as the "secondary line-to-line voltage." ▶Figure 24–31

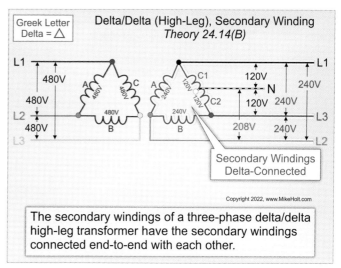

Delta/Delta (High-Leg), Secondary Winding
Theory 24.14(B)

Secondary Windings
Delta-Connected

The secondary windings of a three-phase delta/delta high-leg transformer have the secondary windings connected end-to-end with each other.

▶Figure 24–30

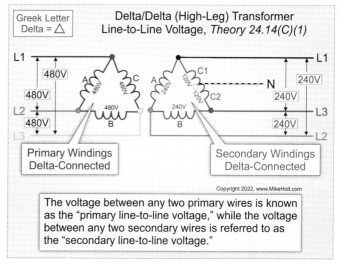

Delta/Delta (High-Leg) Transformer
Line-to-Line Voltage, *Theory 24.14(C)(1)*

Primary Windings
Delta-Connected

Secondary Windings
Delta-Connected

The voltage between any two primary wires is known as the "primary line-to-line voltage," while the voltage between any two secondary wires is referred to as the "secondary line-to-line voltage."

▶Figure 24–31

(2) Line-to-Neutral Voltage. The line-to-neutral voltage is the voltage between a phase wire and the neutral wire. In a delta/delta high-leg 4-wire system, the Line 1- and Line 3-to-neutral voltage is 120V, and the Line 2-to-neutral voltage will be 208V.

Author's Comment:

▶ The Line 2 wire is often called the "high-leg," "wild-leg," or "stinger-leg." The high-leg line-to-neutral voltage is equal to 120V × 1.732 = 208V. ▶Figure 24–32

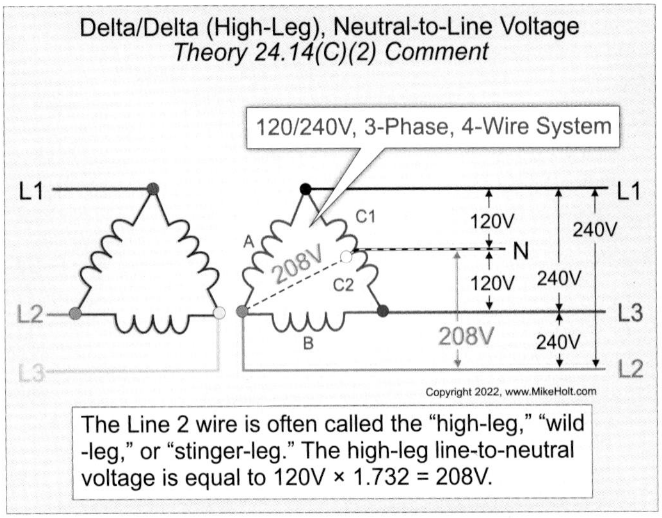

Delta/Delta (High-Leg), Neutral-to-Line Voltage
Theory 24.14(C)(2) Comment

120/240V, 3-Phase, 4-Wire System

L1 — L1
C1
A
208V
C2
N
120V 240V
120V 240V
L2 — L3
B
208V 240V
L3 — L2

Copyright 2022, www.MikeHolt.com

The Line 2 wire is often called the "high-leg," "wild-leg," or "stinger-leg." The high-leg line-to-neutral voltage is equal to 120V × 1.732 = 208V.

▶Figure 24–32

CHAPTER 8

PRACTICE QUESTIONS

CHAPTER 8—PRACTICE QUESTIONS

Unit 21—Motors

21.2 Alternating-Current Motor Principles

1. A motor uses opposing electromagnetic fields in order to rotate the motor shaft. The stationary electromagnetic field is created by the _____, and the rotating electromagnetic field is created by the _____.

   (a) stator, rotor
   (b) rotor, stator
   (c) winding A, winding B
   (d) none of these

2. In an ac induction motor, the stator produces a rotating magnetic field that induces current in the rotor windings. The rotor current generates a magnetic field in opposition to the magnetic field of the stator, thereby causing the motor to _____.

   (a) explode
   (b) turn
   (c) jam
   (d) lock up

3. The electromagnetic field on one side of the rotor causes a(an) _____ force and on the other side a(an) _____ force against the stator's magnetic field.

   (a) downward, upward
   (b) upward, downward
   (c) spinning, static
   (d) none of these

21.3 Motor Horsepower Rating

4. Motors are used to convert electrical energy into mechanical work and the output mechanical work of a motor is rated in horsepower, were 1 hp = _____.

   (a) 476W
   (b) 674W
   (c) 746W
   (d) 840W

5. What size motor in horsepower is required to produce approximately 30 kW of output watts?

   (a) 20 hp
   (b) 30 hp
   (c) 40 hp
   (d) 50 hp

6. What size motor in horsepower is required to produce approximately 60 kW of output watts?

   (a) 50 hp
   (b) 60 hp
   (c) 70 hp
   (d) 80 hp

7. What size motor in horsepower is required to produce approximately 110 kW of output watts?

   (a) 75 hp
   (b) 100 hp
   (c) 125 hp
   (d) 150 hp

8.   What are the approximate output in watts of a 15 hp motor?

(a) 11 kW
(b) 15 kW
(c) 22 kW
(d) 31 kW

9.   What are the approximate output watts of a 5 hp motor?

(a) 3.75 kW
(b) 4.75 kW
(c) 6.75 kW
(d) 7.75 kW

10. What are the approximate output in watts of a 25 hp?

(a) 18.65 kW
(b) 19.50 kW
(c) 22.75 kW
(d) 31.45 kW

21.4 Motor Amperes

11. When a motor starts, the current drawn is between six and ten times the motor's nameplate _____.

(a) lock-rotor amperes
(b) running amperes
(c) voltage
(d) none of these

12. Once a motor begins turning, the rotor windings are increasingly cut by the stationary magnetic field, resulting in an increasing counter-electromotive force in the _____.

(a) stator
(b) rotor
(c) shaft
(d) any of these

13. A motor that operates at _____ will cause its windings to overheat to the point where the wire windings' insulation and lubrication will be damaged.

(a) FLA
(b) FLC
(c) LRC
(d) any of these

21.5 Motor Nameplate Amperes

14. The nameplate motor FLA rating describes the motor current rating when it carries its rated horsepower, rated _____, efficiency, and power factor.

(a) power
(b) resistance
(c) CEMF
(d) voltage

15. The motor nameplate amperes rating is commonly referred to as the motor "_____."

(a) FLA
(b) FLC
(c) LRA
(d) any of these

16. What is the nameplate FLA for a 5 hp, 230V, single-phase motor with 93 percent power factor and 87 percent efficiency?

(a) 10A
(b) 20A
(c) 28A
(d) 35A

17. What is the nameplate FLA for a 20 hp, 208V, three-phase motor with 90 percent power factor and 80 percent efficiency?

(a) 51A
(b) 58A
(c) 65A
(d) 80A

21.6 Dual-Voltage Motors

18. Dual-voltage ac motors are made with two field windings. The field windings are connected in _____ for low-voltage operation and in _____ for high-voltage operation.

    (a) series, parallel
    (b) parallel, series
    (c) series, series
    (d) parallel, parallel

19. For a dual-voltage 230/460V motor, the field windings are connected in parallel for _____ operation and in series for _____ operation.

    (a) 230V, 460V
    (b) 460V, 230V
    (c) 230V, 230V
    (d) 460V, 460V

20. When a motor is connected to the higher voltage rating for a 115/230V or 230/460V motor, the current rating will be _____ the current rating than if it is connected to the lower voltage rating.

    (a) half
    (b) twice
    (c) triple
    (d) none of these

21. When a motor is connected to the lower voltage rating for a 115/230V or 230/460V motor, the current rating will be _____ the current rating than if it is connected to the higher voltage rating.

    (a) half
    (b) twice
    (c) triple
    (d) none of these

22. Whether a dual-voltage motor is connected to the high or low voltage, the _____ of the motor will remain the same.

    (a) voltage
    (b) current
    (c) resistance
    (d) volt-amperes

23. The volt-amperes for a 3 hp, 230V, single-phase motor with a nameplate rating of 15A is _____.

    (a) 3,450 VA
    (b) 6,670 VA
    (c) 8,990 VA
    (d) 9,000 VA

24. The volt-amperes for a 5 hp, 208V, single-phase motor with a nameplate rating of 28.50A is _____.

    (a) 4,350 VA
    (b) 5,928 VA
    (c) 8,991 VA
    (d) 9,289 VA

25. The volt-amperes for a 7.50 hp, 115V, single-phase motor with a nameplate rating of 75A is _____.

    (a) 5,450 VA
    (b) 6,675 VA
    (c) 8,625 VA
    (d) 9,090 VA

21.7 Reversing the Rotation of Alternating-Current Motors

26. Swapping _____ of the line wires can reverse a three-phase ac motor's rotation.

    (a) one
    (b) two
    (c) three
    (d) four

21.8 Alternating-Current Motor Types

27. Three-phase ac _____ motors are used in almost all major industrial applications.

    (a) wound-rotor
    (b) induction
    (c) synchronous
    (d) squirrel-cage

28. In a(an) _____ motor, the rotor is locked in step with the rotating stator field and is dragged along at the speed of the rotating magnetic field.

    (a) wound-rotor
    (b) induction
    (c) synchronous
    (d) squirrel-cage

29. _____ induction motors are used only in special applications because of their complexity.

    (a) Wound-rotor
    (b) Universal
    (c) Synchronous
    (d) Squirrel-cage

30. _____ motors are fractional horsepower motors that operate equally well on ac and dc and are used for vacuum cleaners, electric drills, mixers, and light household appliances.

    (a) Alternating-current
    (b) Universal
    (c) Wound-rotor
    (d) Synchronous

Unit 22—Generators

22.2 Generator Prime Mover

1. A generator produces electrical energy by converting mechanical energy from a "_____."

    (a) heat source
    (b) prime mover
    (c) solar PV system
    (d) chemical activity

22.3 Alternating-Current Generators

2. _____ is created by a generator when the electromagnetic field of the rotor cuts through the stator winding.

    (a) Voltage
    (b) Current
    (c) Resistance
    (d) Power

3. The _____ of a generator depends on the number of stator poles and the speed of the rotor.

    (a) voltage
    (b) current
    (c) resistance
    (d) frequency

4. Three-phase alternating-current generators have three sets of equally spaced windings, each winding is _____ out-of-phase with each other.

    (a) 90°
    (b) 120°
    (c) 180°
    (d) 240°

22.4 Generator Output Current

5. The approximate output current for a single-phase, 22 kVA, 240V generator is _____.

    (a) 50A
    (b) 70A
    (c) 90A
    (d) 100A

6. The approximate output current for a three-phase, 48 kVA, 120/208V generator is _____.

    (a) 100A
    (b) 110A
    (c) 125A
    (d) 130A

22.5 Single-Phase and Three-Phase Generator Voltages

7. _____ voltage can originate from a single-phase generator.

    (a) Single-phase
    (b) Three-phase
    (c) Single-phase or Three-phase
    (d) none of these

8. Voltages in a three-phase circuit originate from a _____ where the voltage of each phase wire is out-of-phase with each other by 120°.

    (a) generator
    (b) transformer
    (c) motor
    (d) all of these

22.6 Electrical Industry Voltages

9. The _____ system voltage is a voltage used for circuit calculations.

    (a) actual
    (b) nominal
    (c) equipment
    (d) utility

10. In accordance with ANSI C84.1, the _____ voltage must be no more than 105 percent and not less than 90 percent of the nominal system voltage.

    (a) transformer
    (b) generator
    (c) equipment
    (d) utility

11. The _____ voltage at any point in the electrical system is the voltage that is measured by a voltmeter.

    (a) actual
    (b) nominal
    (c) equipment
    (d) utility

12. In accordance with ANSI C84.1, the minimum voltage at the _____ cannot be less than 90 percent of the nominal system voltage.

    (a) service
    (b) utility
    (c) equipment
    (d) none of these

13. In accordance with the NEMA MG1-standard, the minimum voltage at a motor cannot be less than 90 percent of the motor's nameplate _____ rating.

    (a) voltage
    (b) starting current
    (c) locked-rotor
    (d) none of these

Unit 23—Relays

23.2 How Relays Operate

1. An electromagnetic _____ uses electromagnetism to open or close a contact.

   (a) motor
   (b) generator
   (c) transformer
   (d) relay

23.3 Relay Contacts

2. "Normally _____" means that the contacts are open when the coil is de-energized.

   (a) open
   (b) closed
   (c) powered
   (d) none of these

3. "Normally _____" means the contacts are closed when the coil is energized.

   (a) open
   (b) closed
   (c) powered
   (d) none of these

4. When the relay coil is energized, the NC contacts _____ and the NO contacts _____.

   (a) open, close
   (b) close, open
   (c) open, open
   (d) close, close

Unit 24—Transformers

24.3 Primary versus Secondary

1. The transformer winding that is connected to the source is called the "_____" winding and the transformer winding that is connected to the load is called the "_____" winding.

   (a) secondary, primary
   (b) primary, secondary
   (c) high-leg, low-leg
   (d) none of these

24.4 Transformer Mutual Induction

2. Both the primary and secondary windings are wound on the same iron core, so the electromagnetic field from the primary winding cuts the secondary winding, which induces a voltage on the _____.

   (a) primary
   (b) secondary
   (c) motor
   (d) generator

24.5 Secondary Induced Voltage

3. The _____ on the secondary winding is a function of the number of secondary wire loops cut by the primary electromagnetic field.

   (a) resistance
   (b) current
   (c) voltage
   (d) power

24.6 Transformer Turns Ratios

4. The relationship of the number of turns of wire on the _____ as compared to the number of turns on the _____ is called the transformer "winding turns ratio."

   (a) primary, secondary
   (b) secondary, primary
   (c) primary, primary
   (d) secondary, secondary

5. A transformer has a primary winding of twenty turns and a secondary of ten turns. The winding turns ratio of this transformer is _____.

   (a) 2:1
   (b) 4:1
   (c) 5:1
   (d) 10:1

6. The relationship between primary voltage and secondary voltage is called the transformer "_____ turns ratio."

   (a) winding
   (b) voltage
   (c) power
   (d) ampere

7. If the primary phase voltage is 480V and the secondary phase voltage is 240V, the voltage turns ratio is _____.

   (a) 1:2
   (b) 1:4
   (c) 2:1
   (d) 4:1

8. The secondary voltage of a 5:1 transformer is _____ if the primary is 240V.

   (a) 6V
   (b) 12V
   (c) 24V
   (d) 48V

9. The secondary voltage of a 4:1 turns ratio transformer is _____ if the primary is 240V.

   (a) 60V
   (b) 210V
   (c) 208V
   (d) 277V

24.7 Isolation Transformers (1:1)

10. If the primary and secondary windings of a transformer have the same number of wire loops (turns), the secondary output voltage will be the same as the primary input voltage. This type of transformer is called a(an) "_____ transformer."

    (a) insulation
    (b) special
    (c) auto
    (d) isolation

24.8 Autotransformers

11. Autotransformers use a _____ winding for both the primary and secondary and are often referred to as "buck-boost transformers."

    (a) different
    (b) special
    (c) separate
    (d) single

24.9 Transformer kVA Rating

12. Transformers are rated in _____.

    (a) Henrys
    (b) kW
    (c) W
    (d) kVA

24.10 Transformer Current Flow

13. The primary electromagnetic field induces a voltage in the secondary. As the secondary current flows, it produces an electromagnetic field that reduces the strength of the primary flux lines. This results in an increase in _____ current.

    (a) primary
    (b) secondary
    (c) tertiary
    (d) none these

14. Current flow in a secondary transformer winding creates an electromagnetic field that opposes the primary electromagnetic field resulting in less primary CEMF. The primary current automatically increases in direct proportion to the _____ current.

    (a) primary
    (b) secondary
    (c) tertiary
    (d) none these

24.11 Transformer Current Rating

15. What is the secondary current for a fully loaded single-phase, 25 kVA, 480V to 240V transformer?

    (a) 52A
    (b) 104A
    (c) 208A
    (d) 250A

16. What is the secondary current for a fully loaded three-phase, 75 kVA, 480V to 208Y/120V transformer?

    (a) 104A
    (b) 140A
    (c) 208A
    (d) 500A

17. The secondary current for a fully loaded single-phase, 37.50 kVA, 480V to 240V transformer is _____.

    (a) 68A
    (b) 78A
    (c) 88A
    (d) 98A

18. What is the primary current for a fully loaded single-phase, 25 kVA, 480V to 240V transformer?

    (a) 52A
    (b) 72A
    (c) 82A
    (d) 614A

19. What is the primary current for a fully loaded three-phase, 75 kVA, 480V to 208Y/120V transformer?

    (a) 10A
    (b) 70A
    (c) 80A
    (d) 90A

20. The primary current for a fully loaded three-phase, 37.50 kVA, 480V to 208Y/120V transformer is _____.

    (a) 45A
    (b) 55A
    (c) 65A
    (d) 75A

24.12 Transformer Configurations

21. _____transformers contain a primary and a secondary mounted on a single laminated iron core.

    (a) Single-phase
    (b) Two-phase
    (c) Three-phase
    (d) none these

22. _____transformers are constructed of three sets of single-phase windings that are connected together to create a three-phase system.

    (a) Single-phase
    (b) Two-phase
    (c) Three-phase
    (d) none these

24.13 Delta/Wye Transformers

23. The _____ windings of a three-phase delta/wye-connected transformer are connected end-to-end with each other.

    (a) primary
    (b) secondary
    (c) low
    (d) high

24. The _____ windings of a three-phase delta/wye-configured transformer have one end of each winding connected to a common point.

    (a) primary
    (b) secondary
    (c) middle
    (d) center

25. The voltage between any two primary wires is called "primary _____ voltage," while the voltage between any two secondary wires is called "secondary _____ voltage."

    (a) line-to-neutral, line-to-neutral
    (b) line-to-line, line-to-line
    (c) minimum, minimum
    (d) maximum, maximum

26. _____ voltage is the voltage between a phase wire and a neutral wire.

    (a) Line-to-neutral
    (b) Line-to-line
    (c) Neutral
    (d) Line

24.14 Delta/Delta (High-Leg) Transformers

27. The _____ circuit wires are connected to each point where the winding leads meet.

    (a) primary
    (b) secondary
    (c) low
    (d) high

28. The load wires are connected to each point where the _____ winding leads meet.

    (a) primary
    (b) secondary
    (c) low
    (d) high

29. The voltage between any two primary wires is known as the "_____ line-to-line voltage," while the voltage between any two secondary wires is referred to as the "_____ line-to-line voltage."

    (a) primary, primary
    (b) secondary, secondary
    (c) primary, secondary
    (d) secondary, primary

30. The line-to-neutral voltage is the voltage between a phase wire and the neutral wire. In a delta/delta high-leg 4-wire system, the Line1- and Line 3-to-neutral voltage is 120V, and the Line2-to-neutral will be _____.

    (a) 120V
    (b) 208V
    (c) 240V
    (d) 277V

PROTECTIVE DEVICES

Chapter 9—Protective Devices

Unit 25—Overcurrent Protection

Overcurrent protection is a complex subject because different types of overcurrent protective devices serve different purposes. In this unit you will learn:

- ▶ the role of circuit overcurrent protection
- ▶ the difference between a circuit breaker and a fuse
- ▶ the fundamentals of time-current curves and selective coordination
- ▶ the difference between interrupting ratings and short-circuit current ratings

Unit 26—GFCIs, GFPEs, AFCIs, and SPDs

In addition to overcurrent protection of electrical circuits, electronic devices with the technology to protect against electric shock and fire are used in the electrical system. In this unit you will learn:

- ▶ what a ground-fault circuit interrupter is
- ▶ what an arc-fault circuit interrupter is
- ▶ what ground-fault protection of equipment is
- ▶ what a surge protective device is

UNIT

25

OVERCURRENT PROTECTION

25.1 Introduction

Overcurrent protection is a complex subject because different types of overcurrent protective devices serve different purposes. In this unit you will learn:

▸ the role of circuit overcurrent protection

▸ the difference between a circuit breaker and a fuse

▸ the fundamentals of time-current curves and selective coordination

▸ the difference between interrupting ratings and short-circuit current ratings ▸Figure 25–1

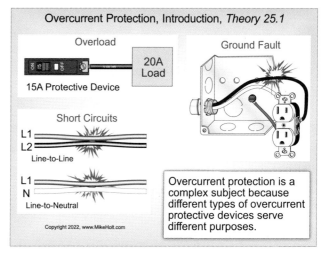

▸Figure 25–1

25.2 Overcurrent Protection

(A) Purpose. The purpose of overcurrent protection is to protect wires and equipment against high temperatures caused by currents that exceed the equipment ampere rating or the ampacity of the wire. Current that exceeds the equipment ampere rating or the ampacity of the wire is known as "overcurrent" and is caused by an overload, short-circuit, or ground-fault event. ▸Figure 25–2

(1) Overload.

(a) Equipment. An equipment overload is a condition where the current exceeds the equipment's ampere rating. Equipment overloads can occur because of undervoltage, undersized equipment for the load, or damages to equipment components such as a faulty motor bearing.

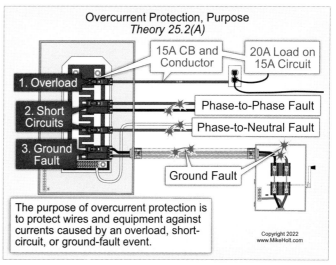

▸Figure 25–2

(b) Wires. An overload on a wire occurs when the load exceeds the ampacity of the wire. ▸Figure 25–3

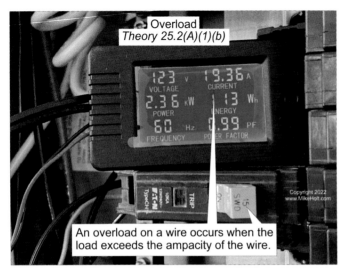

▶Figure 25–3

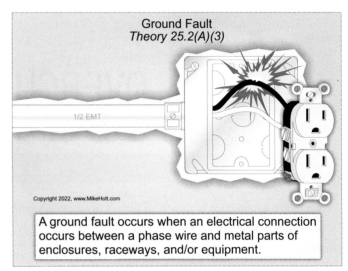

▶Figure 25–5

(2) Short Circuit. A short circuit occurs when there is an electrical connection between two phase wires, or a phase wire and neutral wire. During a short-circuit event, short-circuit current can exceed ten times the ampere rating of the circuit overcurrent protective device. ▶Figure 25–4

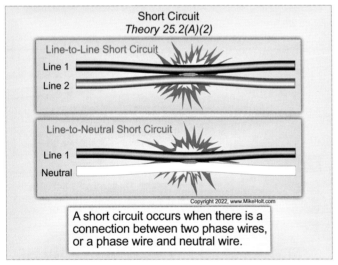

▶Figure 25–4

(3) Ground Fault. A ground fault occurs when an unintentional electrical connection occurs between a phase wire and metal parts of enclosures, raceways, and/or equipment. Ground-fault current can exceed ten times the ampere rating of the circuit overcurrent protective device. ▶Figure 25–5

(B) Overcurrent Protective Devices. Overcurrent protection is typically provided by fuses or circuit breakers. ▶Figure 25–6

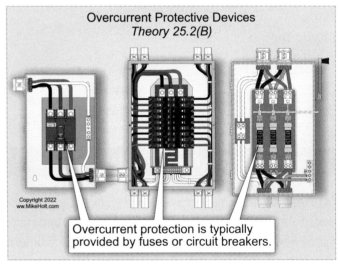

▶Figure 25–6

(C) Standard Sizes. Fuses and circuit breakers are available in a variety of ampere, voltage, and AIC ratings. The standard ampere ratings for overcurrent protective devices for electrical installations are listed in the *National Electrical Code*. ▶Figure 25–7

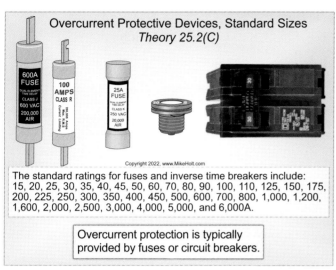

Overcurrent Protective Devices, Standard Sizes
Theory 25.2(C)

The standard ratings for fuses and inverse time breakers include: 15, 20, 25, 30, 35, 40, 45, 50, 60, 70, 80, 90, 100, 110, 125, 150, 175, 200, 225, 250, 300, 350, 400, 450, 500, 600, 700, 800, 1,000, 1,200, 1,600, 2,000, 2,500, 3,000, 4,000, 5,000, and 6,000A.

Overcurrent protection is typically provided by fuses or circuit breakers.

▶Figure 25–7

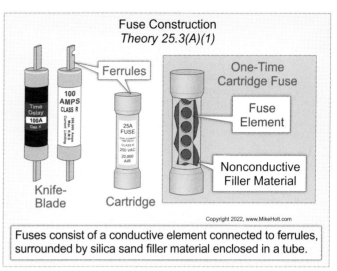

Fuse Construction
Theory 25.3(A)(1)

Fuses consist of a conductive element connected to ferrules, surrounded by silica sand filler material enclosed in a tube.

▶Figure 25–9

25.3 Fuses

(A) Fuse Elements. Fuses have an overload element and a short-circuit element within the fuse body which are designed to melt and open during an overload, short-circuit, or ground-fault event. ▶Figure 25–8

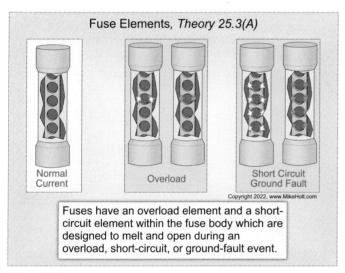

Fuse Elements, *Theory 25.3(A)*

Fuses have an overload element and a short-circuit element within the fuse body which are designed to melt and open during an overload, short-circuit, or ground-fault event.

▶Figure 25–8

(1) Fuse Construction. Fuses consist of a conductive element connected to end blades or caps, surrounded by silica sand filler material enclosed in a tube. ▶Figure 25–9

(B) Clearing Overloads. When current flows through the element of a fuse, it generates heat. During normal operation, the silica sand absorbs this heat. When a sustained overload occurs, the heat is not able to be dissipated and a portion of the fuse element melts which stops the flow of current. The time it takes to melt the fuse element from an overload is dependent on the magnitude of the overload. ▶Figure 25–10

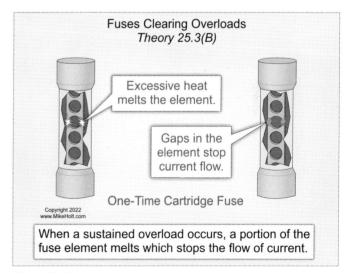

Fuses Clearing Overloads
Theory 25.3(B)

Excessive heat melts the element.

Gaps in the element stop current flow.

One-Time Cartridge Fuse

When a sustained overload occurs, a portion of the fuse element melts which stops the flow of current.

▶Figure 25–10

(C) Clearing Short Circuits and Ground Faults. When a short circuit or ground fault occurs, the fault current can be in the thousands of amperes. The high fault current causes the heat in the element to rise to a point where multiple conductive segments in the fuse melt and stop electrical current flow. ▶Figure 25–11

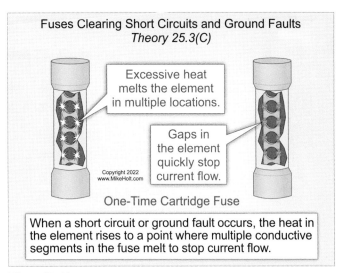

Fuses Clearing Short Circuits and Ground Faults
Theory 25.3(C)

Excessive heat melts the element in multiple locations.

Gaps in the element quickly stop current flow.

Copyright 2022 www.MikeHolt.com

One-Time Cartridge Fuse

When a short circuit or ground fault occurs, the heat in the element rises to a point where multiple conductive segments in the fuse melt to stop current flow.

▶Figure 25–11

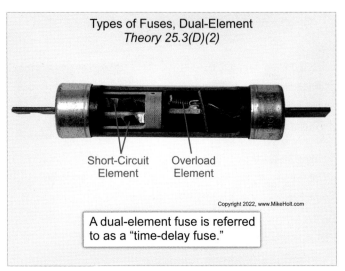

Types of Fuses, Dual-Element
Theory 25.3(D)(2)

Short-Circuit Element   Overload Element

Copyright 2022, www.MikeHolt.com

A dual-element fuse is referred to as a "time-delay fuse."

▶Figure 25–13

(D) Types of Fuses. The three most common types of fuses are single-element, dual-element, and current-limiting.

(1) Single-Element Fuse. A single-element fuse is referred to as a nontime delay fuse and is the least expensive type. ▶Figure 25–12

Author's Comment:

▶ A standard overcurrent protective device will clear in less than two cycles for a fault ten times its rating, and a current-limiting fuse will clear a fault in less than one-half of one cycle for the same fault value. ▶Figure 25–14

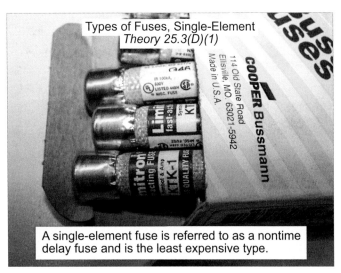

Types of Fuses, Single-Element
Theory 25.3(D)(1)

A single-element fuse is referred to as a nontime delay fuse and is the least expensive type.

▶Figure 25–12

(2) Dual-Element Fuse. A dual-element fuse is often called a "time-delay fuse." ▶Figure 25–13

(3) Current-Limiting Fuses. A current-limiting fuse is designed to clear a short circuit or ground fault in less than one-half a cycle. Current-limiting fuses limit the peak current to a value much less than a most circuit breakers or fuses.

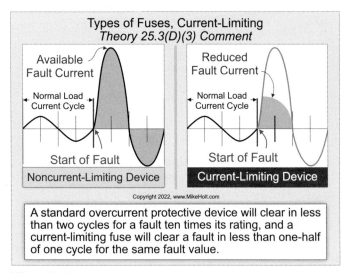

Types of Fuses, Current-Limiting
Theory 25.3(D)(3) Comment

Available Fault Current

Normal Load Current Cycle

Start of Fault

Noncurrent-Limiting Device

Reduced Fault Current

Normal Load Current Cycle

Start of Fault

Current-Limiting Device

Copyright 2022, www.MikeHolt.com

A standard overcurrent protective device will clear in less than two cycles for a fault ten times its rating, and a current-limiting fuse will clear a fault in less than one-half of one cycle for the same fault value.

▶Figure 25–14

25.4 Circuit Breakers

A circuit breaker is capable of being opened and closed manually and automatically opens during an overcurrent condition. Circuit breakers are available in different configurations such as inverse time, instantaneous trip, and adjustable trip.

(A) Inverse Time Circuit Breaker. Inverse time circuit breakers are the most common type used. They operate on the principle that as the current increases, the time it takes for the device to open decreases. They contain a thermal trip element to open during an overload and an electromagnetic trip element to open during a short circuit or ground fault. ▶Figure 25–15

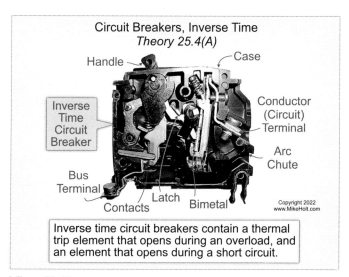

Circuit Breakers, Inverse Time
Theory 25.4(A)

Handle — Case
Inverse Time Circuit Breaker
Conductor (Circuit) Terminal
Arc Chute
Bus Terminal
Contacts — Latch — Bimetal
Copyright 2022 www.MikeHolt.com

Inverse time circuit breakers contain a thermal trip element that opens during an overload, and an element that opens during a short circuit.

▶Figure 25–15

(1) Thermal Trip Element. Inverse time circuit breakers have a mechanical trip mechanism that opens the circuit due to an internal temperature rise from an overload condition. The thermal trip element operates on the time-current principle of being inversely proportional to the magnitude of the current. This means that as the overload current increases, the time it takes for the thermal trip element to open decreases.

(2) Electromagnetic Trip Unit. Inverse time circuit breakers have an electromagnetic trip unit that responds to short-circuit and ground-fault currents. During a short-circuit or ground-fault event, the fault current can be high enough to generate an electromagnetic field within the circuit breaker that is sufficient to electromechanically open the contacts of the circuit breaker almost instantaneously.

(B) Instantaneous Trip Circuit Breaker. Magnetic trip breakers, without thermal elements are commonly referred to as "instantaneous trip circuit breakers" or "motor circuit protectors." Instantaneous trip circuit breakers operate solely on the principle of electromagnetism. The electromagnetic trip unit responds to short-circuit and ground-fault currents. During a short circuit or ground fault, the fault current will be approximately ten times (or more) the ampere rating of the circuit breaker. This high fault current value will generate a substantial electromagnetic field within the circuit breaker to mechanically activate its electromagnetic mechanism and open the circuit almost instantaneously. ▶Figure 25–16

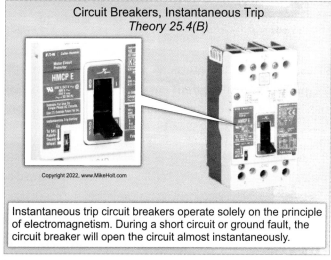

Circuit Breakers, Instantaneous Trip
Theory 25.4(B)

Copyright 2022, www.MikeHolt.com

Instantaneous trip circuit breakers operate solely on the principle of electromagnetism. During a short circuit or ground fault, the circuit breaker will open the circuit almost instantaneously.

▶Figure 25–16

(C) Adjustable (Electronic) Trip Circuit Breaker. Adjustable (electronic) trip circuit breakers use solid-state electronics to provide the ability to adjust the thermal and electromagnetic trip current and/or time settings to provide the user with flexibility for specific applications. ▶Figure 25–17

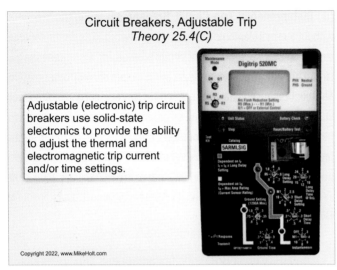

Circuit Breakers, Adjustable Trip
Theory 25.4(C)

Adjustable (electronic) trip circuit breakers use solid-state electronics to provide the ability to adjust the thermal and electromagnetic trip current and/or time settings.

▶Figure 25–17

25.5 Overcurrent Protective Devices, Time-Current Curves

To protect against electric shock or to prevent a fire, a dangerous overload, short circuit, or ground fault must quickly be removed by opening the circuit's overcurrent protective device. The time it takes for an overcurrent protective device to open is plotted on a time-current curve (TCC) chart. This chart has a vertical side that shows the time in seconds it will take the device to open relative to the current in amperes as shown on the bottom of the chart. ▶Figure 25–18

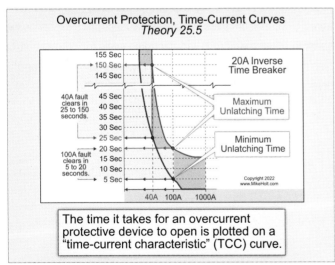

Overcurrent Protection, Time-Current Curves
Theory 25.5

The time it takes for an overcurrent protective device to open is plotted on a "time-current characteristic" (TCC) curve.

▶Figure 25–18

(A) Clearing Overloads. An overcurrent protective device will open and clear an overload. The time it takes for the overcurrent protective device to open is a function of the current of the overload above the ampere rating of the device. As the overload current increases, the time it takes for the thermal trip element to open decreases. ▶Figure 25–19

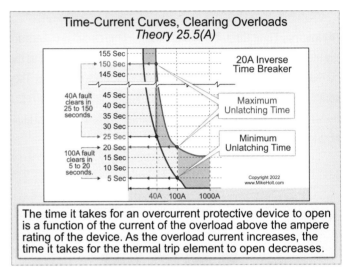

Time-Current Curves, Clearing Overloads
Theory 25.5(A)

The time it takes for an overcurrent protective device to open is a function of the current of the overload above the ampere rating of the device. As the overload current increases, the time it takes for the thermal trip element to open decreases.

▶Figure 25–19

(B) Clearing Short Circuits. To quickly clear a short circuit, the short-circuit current needs to rise to a level between ten and twenty times the rating of the circuit overcurrent protective device. Once the current reaches that level, the short circuit will clear almost immediately. ▶Figure 25–20

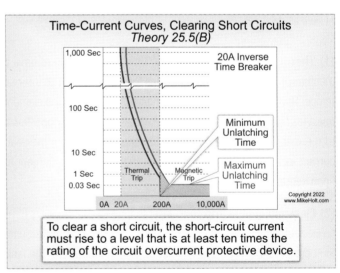

Time-Current Curves, Clearing Short Circuits
Theory 25.5(B)

To clear a short circuit, the short-circuit current must rise to a level that is at least ten times the rating of the circuit overcurrent protective device.

▶Figure 25–20

(C) Clearing Ground-Faults.

(1) General. To quickly clear a ground fault, the ground-fault current needs to rise to a level between ten and twenty times the rating of the circuit overcurrent protective device. ▶Figure 25–21

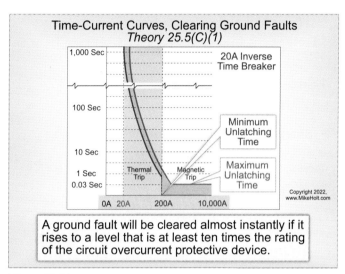

Time-Current Curves, Clearing Ground Faults
Theory 25.5(C)(1)

A ground fault will be cleared almost instantly if it rises to a level that is at least ten times the rating of the circuit overcurrent protective device.

▶Figure 25–21

(2) Low-Impedance Ground-Fault Current Path. To remove dangerous touch voltage on metal parts produced by a ground fault, the fault-current path must have low enough impedance to allow the fault current to quickly rise to facilitate the opening of the protection device. ▶Figure 25–22

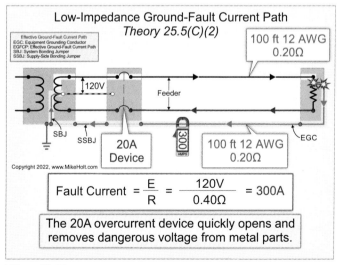

Low-Impedance Ground-Fault Current Path
Theory 25.5(C)(2)

$$\text{Fault Current} = \frac{E}{R} = \frac{120V}{0.40\Omega} = 300A$$

The 20A overcurrent device quickly opens and removes dangerous voltage from metal parts.

▶Figure 25–22

25.6 Available Short-Circuit Current

The available short-circuit current is the largest short-circuit current capable of being delivered at a given point on the electrical system. The available short-circuit current is calculated at the line terminals of the service disconnect, panelboards, and equipment disconnects. ▶Figure 25–23

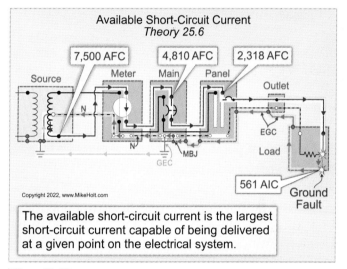

Available Short-Circuit Current
Theory 25.6

The available short-circuit current is the largest short-circuit current capable of being delivered at a given point on the electrical system.

▶Figure 25–23

(A) At Utility Transformer. The available short-circuit current is first determined at the secondary terminals of the utility transformer and is provided by the electric utility—no calculation is required. The available short-circuit current is highest at the utility transformer and lowest at the branch-circuit load because of circuit wire impedance. ▶Figure 25–24

(B) At Electrical Equipment. Calculating the available short-circuit fault current at the terminals of the service equipment, branch-circuit panelboards, branch-circuit disconnects, and electrical equipment considers the following factors:

(1) Transformer kVA, secondary system voltage, and transformer impedance.

(2) Wire material and circuit length.

(3) Steel or PVC raceway.

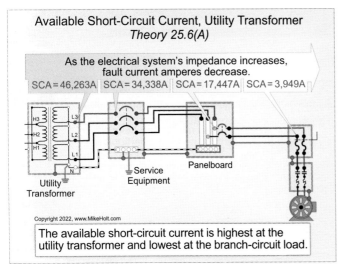

Available Short-Circuit Current, Utility Transformer
Theory 25.6(A)

As the electrical system's impedance increases, fault current amperes decrease.

SCA = 46,263A   SCA = 34,338A   SCA = 17,447A   SCA = 3,949A

Utility Transformer

Service Equipment

Panelboard

Copyright 2022, www.MikeHolt.com

The available short-circuit current is highest at the utility transformer and lowest at the branch-circuit load.

▶Figure 25–24

(C) Load-Side of Transformer. Factors that determine the available short-circuit current at the secondary terminals of a transformer include the kVA rating, impedance, and system voltage. The available short-circuit fault current at the secondary terminals of a transformer is calculated by the formula:

Short-Circuit Current = Transformer Secondary Amperes/
Transformer Impedance %

▶ Short-Circuit Current—Single-Phase Example

Question: What is the approximate available short-circuit current on the secondary of a single-phase, 50 kVA, 480V to 240V transformer having an impedance rating of 1.50 percent?

(a) 11,000A   (b) 12,000A   (c) 13,000A   (d) 14,000A

Solution:

There are two steps required to solve this problem.

Step 1: Determine the transformer secondary amperes:
    Transformer Secondary Amperes = VA/Volts
    Transformer Secondary Amperes = 50,000 VA/240V
    Transformer Secondary Amperes = 208A

Step 2: Determine the available short-circuit fault current at the transformer secondary terminals:
    Short-Circuit Current = Transformer Secondary Amperes/Transformer Impedance %
    Transformer Impedance = 1.50%
    Short-Circuit Current = 208A/1.50%
    Short-Circuit Current = 13,866A

Answer: (d) 14,000A

▶ Short-Circuit Current—Three-Phase Example

Question: What is the approximate available short-circuit current on the secondary of a three-phase, 112.50 kVA, 480V to 208Y/120V transformer having an impedance rating of three percent?

(a) 10,500A   (b) 11,500A   (c) 12,500A   (d) 13,500A

Solution:

There are two steps required to solve this problem.

Step 1: Determine the transformer secondary amperes:
    Transformer Secondary Amperes = VA/(Volts × 1.732)
    Transformer Secondary Amperes = 112,500 VA/(208V × 1.732)
    Transformer Secondary Amperes = 112,500 VA/360
    Transformer Secondary Amperes = 313A

Step 2: Determine the available short-circuit fault current at the transformer secondary terminals:
    Short-Circuit Current = Transformer Secondary Amperes/Transformer Impedance %
    Transformer Impedance = 3%
    Short-Circuit Current = 313A/3%
    Short-Circuit Current = 10,433A

Answer: (a) 10,500A

25.7 Overcurrent Protective Devices, Interrupting Rating

(A) General. Overcurrent protective devices are intended to interrupt a circuit during an overload, short circuit, and/or ground fault. The interrupting rating marked on circuit breakers and fuses such as 10K, 22K, and 65K, must be sufficient for the available short-circuit current at the line terminals of the overcurrent protective device. ▶Figure 25–25

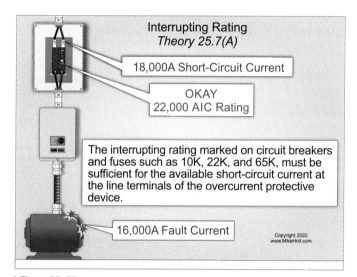

Interrupting Rating
Theory 25.7(A)

18,000A Short-Circuit Current

OKAY
22,000 AIC Rating

The interrupting rating marked on circuit breakers and fuses such as 10K, 22K, and 65K, must be sufficient for the available short-circuit current at the line terminals of the overcurrent protective device.

16,000A Fault Current

Copyright 2022
www.MikeHolt.com

▶Figure 25–25

(B) Hazard. Short-circuit currents can produce tremendously destructive thermal and electromagnetic forces. If the circuit overcurrent protective device is not rated to interrupt the available short-circuit current, it can explode while attempting to clear the fault. ▶Figure 25–26

25.8 Equipment Short-Circuit Current Rating (SCCR)

(A) General. Electrical equipment must have a short-circuit current rating (SCCR) that prevents extensive damage to the electrical components of the equipment during a short circuit or ground fault. ▶Figure 25–27

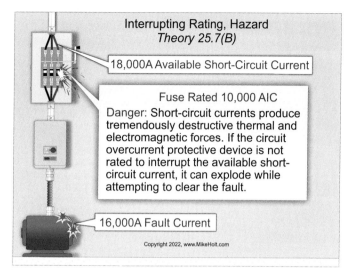

Interrupting Rating, Hazard
Theory 25.7(B)

18,000A Available Short-Circuit Current

Fuse Rated 10,000 AIC
Danger: Short-circuit currents produce tremendously destructive thermal and electromagnetic forces. If the circuit overcurrent protective device is not rated to interrupt the available short-circuit current, it can explode while attempting to clear the fault.

16,000A Fault Current

Copyright 2022, www.MikeHolt.com

▶Figure 25–26

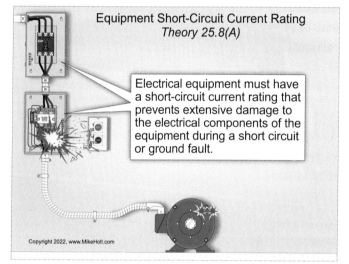

Equipment Short-Circuit Current Rating
Theory 25.8(A)

Electrical equipment must have a short-circuit current rating that prevents extensive damage to the electrical components of the equipment during a short circuit or ground fault.

Copyright 2022, www.MikeHolt.com

▶Figure 25–27

(B) Hazard. If the equipment is not rated to withstand the available short-circuit current, it can explode while waiting for the circuit protective device to clear the fault. ▶Figure 25–28

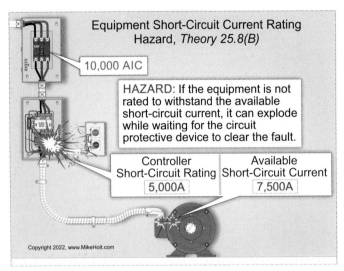

▶Figure 25-28

25.9 Coordination of Overcurrent Protective Devices

(A) General. "Selective coordination" is when overcurrent protective devices are designed to clear a short circuit or ground fault in a manner that localizes the short circuit or ground fault to that given circuit. ▶Figure 25-29

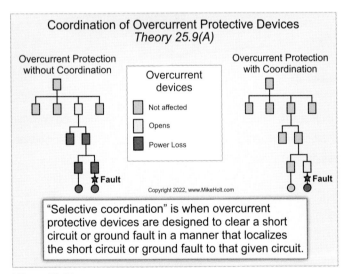

▶Figure 25-29

Author's Comment:

▸ Selectively coordinating overcurrent devices requires a computer program and someone who is skilled in understanding the information required.

(B) Avoiding Power Losses. When overcurrent protective devices are selectively coordinated, a short circuit or ground fault will be isolated by the protective device(s) for that circuit. This selective coordination of overcurrent protective devices prevents unintended power losses to loads not part of the faulted circuit. ▶Figure 25-30

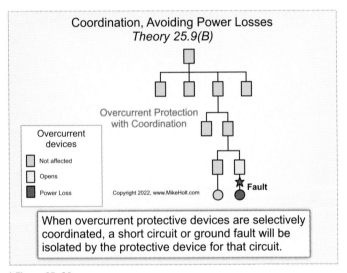

▶Figure 25-30

(C) Power Losses. When overcurrent protective devices are not selectively coordinated, a short circuit or ground fault may cause a device other than the one closest to the fault to open. This lack of selectively coordinating overcurrent protective devices can result in unintended power losses to loads that are not part of the faulted circuit. ▶Figure 25-31

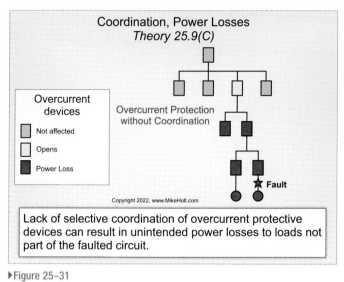

Coordination, Power Losses
Theory 25.9(C)

Overcurrent devices

- Not affected
- Opens
- Power Loss

Overcurrent Protection without Coordination

★ Fault

Copyright 2022, www.MikeHolt.com

Lack of selective coordination of overcurrent protective devices can result in unintended power losses to loads not part of the faulted circuit.

▶Figure 25–31

1st Printing

UNIT

26

GFCIs, GFPEs, AFCIs, AND SPDs

26.1 Introduction

In addition to overcurrent protection of electrical circuits, electronic devices with the technology to protect against electric shock and fire are used in the electrical system. In this unit you will learn:

▸ what a ground-fault circuit interrupter is

▸ what an arc-fault circuit interrupter is

▸ what ground-fault protection of equipment is

▸ what a surge protective device is

26.2 Ground-Fault Circuit Interrupters (GFCIs)

Ground-fault circuit interrupter (GFCI) protective devices detect the imbalance of current between circuit wires. During normal operation, the current returning to the power source through the GFCI is equal to the current leaving the power source. When the difference between the current leaving and returning through the GFCI exceeds 5 mA (± 1 mA), the solid-state circuitry in the GFCI will open the circuit. ▸Figure 26–1

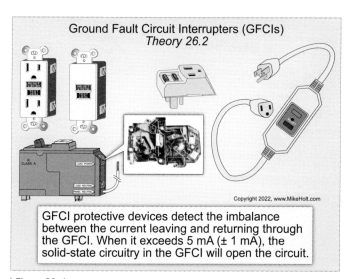

Ground Fault Circuit Interrupters (GFCIs)
Theory 26.2

GFCI protective devices detect the imbalance between the current leaving and returning through the GFCI. When it exceeds 5 mA (± 1 mA), the solid-state circuitry in the GFCI will open the circuit.

Copyright 2022, www.MikeHolt.com

▸Figure 26–1

Author's Comment:

▸ The abbreviation "mA" stands for one one-thousandth (1/1,000) of an ampere, so 5 mA is equal to 5/1,000 of an ampere or 0.005A. ▸Figure 26–2

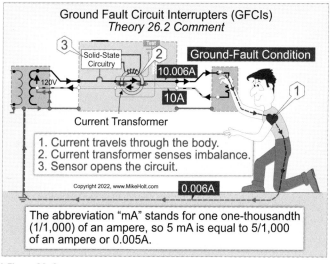

Ground Fault Circuit Interrupters (GFCIs)
Theory 26.2 Comment

Ground-Fault Condition

Solid-State Circuitry

10.006A

10A

Current Transformer

1. Current travels through the body.
2. Current transformer senses imbalance.
3. Sensor opens the circuit.

Copyright 2022, www.MikeHolt.com

0.006A

The abbreviation "mA" stands for one one-thousandth (1/1,000) of an ampere, so 5 mA is equal to 5/1,000 of an ampere or 0.005A.

▸Figure 26–2

(A) Equipment Grounding Wire Not Required. An equipment grounding wire is not necessary for the proper function of a GFCI device. ▶Figure 26–3

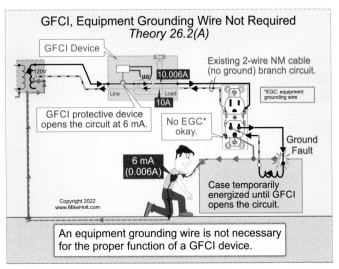

▶Figure 26–3

(B) Neutral-to-Case Detection. GFCIs detect connections between the neutral wire and the metal part(s) of the electrical system (case). If a neutral connection to a metal part(s) occurs, the GFCI protective device will open. ▶Figure 26–4

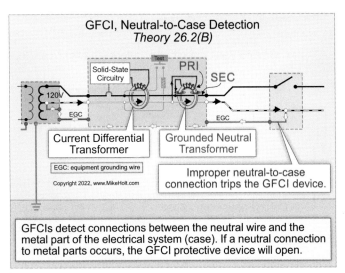

▶Figure 26–4

(C) Line-to-Neutral Shock Hazard. Severe electric shock or death can occur if someone touches the phase and neutral wires at the same time, even if the circuit is GFCI protected. This is because the GFCI does not sense an imbalance between the departing and returning current. ▶Figure 26–5

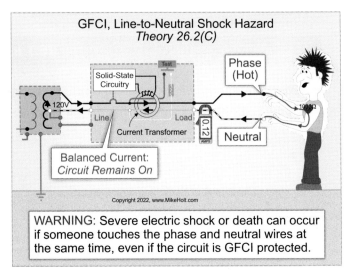

▶Figure 26–5

(D) GFCI Failure—Circuit Remains Energized. A hazard can exist if the electronics within the GFCI fail. The circuit will remain energized without GFCI protection. ▶Figure 26–6

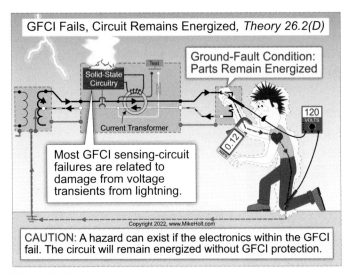

▶Figure 26–6

(E) GFCI Test Button. GFCIs can only be properly tested by pressing the GFCI test button. When the GFCI test button on a 120V circuit is pressed, current will flow inside the current sensor of the GFCI to the test button at a value of 6 mA or more and return the neutral outside the current sensor. Since the GFCI "sees" a 6-mA imbalance, it will open the contacts of the GFCI device. ▶Figure 26–7

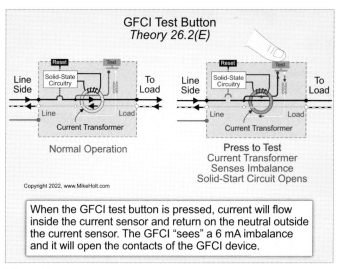

GFCI Test Button
Theory 26.2(E)

Line Side | To Load

Solid-State Circuitry

Line | Load

Current Transformer

Normal Operation

Press to Test
Current Transformer
Senses Imbalance
Solid-Start Circuit Opens

Copyright 2022, www.MikeHolt.com

When the GFCI test button is pressed, current will flow inside the current sensor and return on the neutral outside the current sensor. The GFCI "sees" a 6 mA imbalance and it will open the contacts of the GFCI device.

▶Figure 26–7

26.3 Special-Purpose Ground-Fault Circuit Interrupters (SPGFCIs)

A special-purpose GFCI device is used in circuits where the voltage-to-ground is greater than 150V. A special-purpose GFCI device functions just like a GFCI device but the difference is that its tripping threshold opens when the difference between the current leaving and returning through the SPGFCI is in the range of 15 mA to 20 mA. When that is the case, it de-energizes the circuit. ▶Figure 26–8

Special-Purpose Ground-Fault Interrupter
Theory 26.3

A special-purpose GFCI functions like a GFCI by de-energizing the circuit when there is a difference between the current leaving and returning through the SPGFCI, but it has a higher tripping range of 15 through 20 mA.

▶Figure 26–8

26.4 Ground-Fault Protection of Equipment (GFPEs)

Ground-fault protection of equipment (GFPE) devices detect the imbalance of current between circuit wires. During normal operation, the current returning to the power source through the GFPE is equal to the current leaving the power source. If the difference between the two wires through the GFPE protective device exceeds 30 mA, the solid-state circuitry in the device will open the circuit. This type of protective device is not intended to protect persons because its opening ground-fault trip setting is 30 mA—not 6 mA as with a GFCI. ▶Figure 26–9

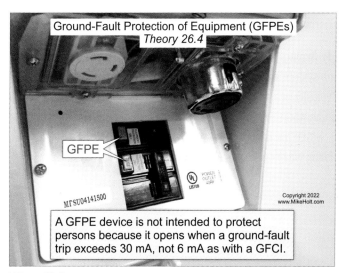

Ground-Fault Protection of Equipment (GFPEs)
Theory 26.4

GFPE

Copyright 2022
www.MikeHolt.com

A GFPE device is not intended to protect persons because it opens when a ground-fault trip exceeds 30 mA, not 6 mA as with a GFCI.

▶Figure 26–9

26.5 Arc-Fault Circuit Interrupters (AFCIs)

An arc-fault circuit interrupter (AFCI) is a device intended to de-energize a circuit when it detects the current waveform characteristics unique to an arcing fault. ▸Figure 26–10

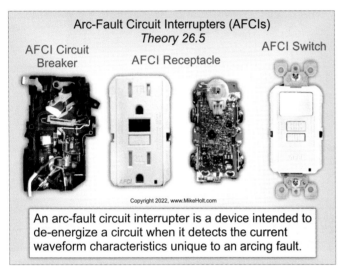

Arc-Fault Circuit Interrupters (AFCIs)
Theory 26.5

AFCI Circuit Breaker   AFCI Receptacle   AFCI Switch

Copyright 2022, www.MikeHolt.com

An arc-fault circuit interrupter is a device intended to de-energize a circuit when it detects the current waveform characteristics unique to an arcing fault.

▸Figure 26–10

26.6 Clearing Arcing Faults

(A) Parallel Arcing Fault. A parallel arcing fault can occur when the insulation between two wires degrades to a level where arcing can take place across the insulation between the wires. An arc fault between wires can create heat at the point of the arc, which can ignite nearby combustible material such as wood framing. ▸Figure 26–11

(1) Arcing Waveform. The current in an arcing fault is limited by the system impedance and the impedance of the arcing fault itself. Typically, at a receptacle, fault current will be above 75A, but not likely above 450A. The electronic circuit within the AFCI will open the circuit if, within the last 30 half-cycle waveforms, it detects eight or more arcing waveforms of over 75A peak. ▸Figure 26–12

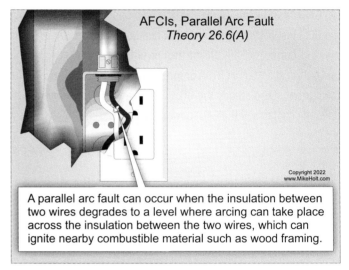

AFCIs, Parallel Arc Fault
Theory 26.6(A)

Copyright 2022
www.MikeHolt.com

A parallel arc fault can occur when the insulation between two wires degrades to a level where arcing can take place across the insulation between the two wires, which can ignite nearby combustible material such as wood framing.

▸Figure 26–11

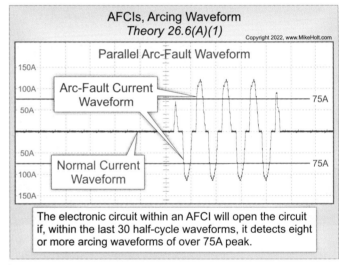

AFCIs, Arcing Waveform
Theory 26.6(A)(1)

Copyright 2022, www.MikeHolt.com

Parallel Arc-Fault Waveform

150A
100A
50A
50A
100A
150A

Arc-Fault Current Waveform

75A

Normal Current Waveform

75A

The electronic circuit within an AFCI will open the circuit if, within the last 30 half-cycle waveforms, it detects eight or more arcing waveforms of over 75A peak.

▸Figure 26–12

(B) Series Arcing Fault Current. A series arcing fault occurs when the wire within a cord is unintentionally broken, causing the current to arc across the gap in the wire. Series arc-fault current is load limited and the electronic circuit within the AFCI will open the circuit if the device detects a series arcing current of 5A or more.

26.7 Surge Protective Devices (SPDs)

(A) General. Surge protective devices (SPDs) protect equipment by preventing damaging transient voltage from reaching the equipment. Upon sensing a transient voltage, an SPD diverts damaging impulse current away from the load while simultaneously reducing transient voltage at the load to a value that does not damage the equipment. ▶Figure 26–13

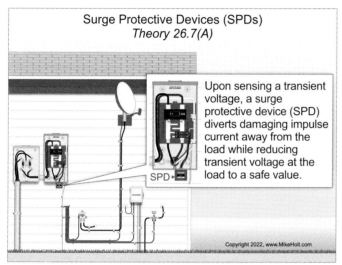

Surge Protective Devices (SPDs)
Theory 26.7(A)

Upon sensing a transient voltage, a surge protective device (SPD) diverts damaging impulse current away from the load while reducing transient voltage at the load to a safe value.

SPD

Copyright 2022, www.MikeHolt.com

▶Figure 26–13

Author's Comment:

▶ If surge protection is not provided, electrical equipment can be damaged by transient voltages. ▶Figure 26–14

(B) Sources of Transient Voltages.

(1) Interior Sources. Transient voltages inside a building can originate from high current loads that are switched on and off, such as those for copiers, laser printers, motors, and air-conditioning. ▶Figure 26–15

(2) Exterior Sources. Exterior sources of transient voltage include the switching of utility power factor correction capacitors or lightning strikes. ▶Figure 26–16

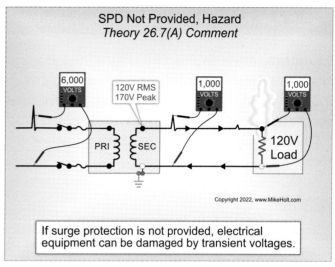

SPD Not Provided, Hazard
Theory 26.7(A) Comment

6,000 VOLTS | 120V RMS 170V Peak | 1,000 VOLTS | 1,000 VOLTS

PRI SEC | 120V Load

Copyright 2022, www.MikeHolt.com

If surge protection is not provided, electrical equipment can be damaged by transient voltages.

▶Figure 26–14

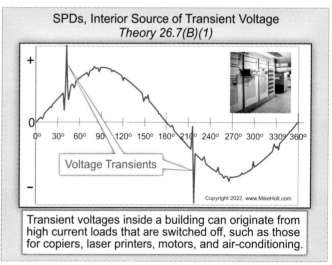

SPDs, Interior Source of Transient Voltage
Theory 26.7(B)(1)

Voltage Transients

Copyright 2022, www.MikeHolt.com

Transient voltages inside a building can originate from high current loads that are switched off, such as those for copiers, laser printers, motors, and air-conditioning.

▶Figure 26–15

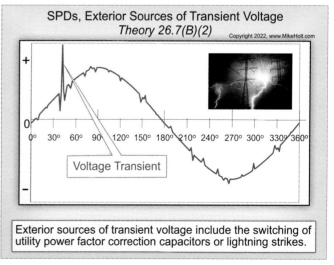

SPDs, Exterior Sources of Transient Voltage
Theory 26.7(B)(2)   Copyright 2022, www.MikeHolt.com

Voltage Transient

Exterior sources of transient voltage include the switching of utility power factor correction capacitors or lightning strikes.

▶Figure 26–16

26.8 How Surge Protective Devices Function

Surge protective devices are connected in parallel with the load and typically use "metal-oxide varistors" (MOVs) to divert transient current and limit the voltage from a surge to the connected load. MOVs function by changing the impedance from open to closed to clamp transient voltage and current pulses to protected equipment from transient voltages.
▶Figure 26–17

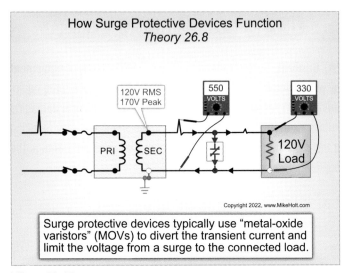

How Surge Protective Devices Function
Theory 26.8

Surge protective devices typically use "metal-oxide varistors" (MOVs) to divert the transient current and limit the voltage from a surge to the connected load.

▶Figure 26–17

CHAPTER 9

PRACTICE QUESTIONS

CHAPTER 9—PRACTICE QUESTIONS

Unit 25—Overcurrent Protection

25.2 Overcurrent Protection

1. Overcurrent is current in excess of the equipment ampere rating or ampacity of the wires. It may result from a(an) _____.

   (a) overload
   (b) short circuit
   (c) ground fault
   (d) any of these

2. A(An) _____ is the operation of equipment or wires in excess of their rated ampacity.

   (a) overload
   (b) short circuit
   (c) ground fault
   (d) all of these

3. A(An) _____ is an electrical connection between any two phase wires, or a phase wire and neutral wire.

   (a) overload
   (b) short circuit
   (c) ground fault
   (d) all of these

4. A(An) _____ occurs when an unintentional electrical connection occurs between a phase wire and metal parts of enclosures, raceways, and/or equipment.

   (a) overload
   (b) short circuit
   (c) ground fault
   (d) all of these

5. Overcurrent protection is typically provided by _____.

   (a) fuses
   (b) circuit breakers
   (c) fuses or circuit breakers
   (d) none of these

25.3 Fuses

6. Fuses consist of a _____ element connected to end blades or caps, surrounded by silica sand filler material enclosed in a tube.

   (a) conductive
   (b) foam
   (c) light
   (d) nonconductive

7. When a sustained overload occurs through the element(s) of a fuse, the heat melts _____, stopping the flow of current.

   (a) several elements
   (b) all of the elements
   (c) a portion of the element
   (d) none of these

8. When a short circuit or ground fault occurs through the element of a fuse, the heat in the element rises to a point where _____ in the fuse melt to stop electrical current flow.

   (a) multiple conductive segments
   (b) a small portion of the segment
   (c) all of the segments
   (d) none of these

9. A _____ fuse is referred to as a nontime-delay fuse and is the least expensive type.

    (a) single-element
    (b) dual-element
    (c) current-limiting
    (d) all of these

10. A _____ fuse is often called a "time-delay fuse."

    (a) single-element
    (b) dual-element
    (c) current-limiting
    (d) all of these

11. A _____ fuse is designed to clear a short circuit or ground fault in less than one-half a cycle.

    (a) one-time fuses
    (b) dual-element fuses
    (c) special trip fuses
    (d) current-limiting

25.4 Circuit Breakers

12. A _____ is capable of being opened and closed manually and automatically opens during an overcurrent condition.

    (a) fuse
    (b) circuit breaker
    (c) motor starter
    (d) disconnect

13. _____ circuit breakers operate on the principle that as the current increases, the time it takes for the device to open decreases.

    (a) Inverse time
    (b) Adjustable trip
    (c) Instantaneous trip
    (d) all of these

14. The _____ trip element of a circuit breaker operates on the time-current principle of being inversely proportional to the magnitude of the current, which means that as the overload current increases, the time it takes for the trip element to open decreases.

    (a) magnetic
    (b) electronic
    (c) thermal
    (d) none of these

15. Inverse time circuit breakers have a(an) _____ trip unit that responds to short-circuit and ground-fault currents.

    (a) adjustable
    (b) instantaneous
    (c) electromagnetic
    (d) none of these

16. _____ circuit breakers operate on the principle of electromagnetism only and are commonly known as motor circuit protectors.

    (a) Inverse time
    (b) Adjustable trip
    (c) Instantaneous trip
    (d) all of these

17. _____ circuit breakers permit the thermal and electromagnetic trip current and/or time settings to be adjusted to provide the user with flexibility for specific applications.

    (a) Inverse time
    (b) Adjustable trip
    (c) Instantaneous trip
    (d) all of these

25.5 Overcurrent Protective Devices, Time-Current Curves

18. The time it takes for an overcurrent protective device to open is plotted on a _____ curve chart.

    (a) time-current characteristics
    (b) bar graph
    (c) pie chart
    (d) none of these

19. As the overload current _____, the time it takes for the thermal trip element to open decreases.

    (a) increases
    (b) decreases
    (c) remains the same
    (d) none of these

20. To quickly clear a short circuit, the short-circuit _____ must rise to a level that is between ten and twenty times the rating of the circuit overcurrent protective device.

    (a) voltage
    (b) current
    (c) resistance
    (d) power

21. To quickly clear a(an) _____, the ground-fault current needs to rise to a level between ten and twenty times the rating of the circuit overcurrent protective device.

    (a) overload
    (b) arcing fault
    (c) ground fault
    (d) none of these

22. To remove dangerous touch voltage on metal parts produced by a ground fault, the fault-current path must have _____ to allow the fault current to quickly rise to facilitate the opening of the protection device.

    (a) high impedance
    (b) low impedance
    (c) high voltage
    (d) low voltage

25.6 Available Short-Circuit Current

23. Available short-circuit current is the _____ current in amperes that is available at a given point in the electrical system.

    (a) phase
    (b) line
    (c) largest
    (d) smallest

24. The available short-circuit current is highest at the utility transformer and lowest at the _____ load because of the impedance of the circuit.

    (a) branch-circuit
    (b) feeder
    (c) service
    (d) utility transformer

25. The available short-circuit current is different at each point of the electrical system; it is highest at the _____.

    (a) branch circuit
    (b) feeder
    (c) service
    (d) utility transformer

26. The available short-circuit current at the _____ transformer is provided by the electric utility; no calculation is required.

    (a) occupancy
    (b) building
    (c) premises
    (d) utility

27. The factor(s) that impact the available short-circuit current on the load side of a transformer is(are) _____.

    (a) system voltage
    (b) kVA rating
    (c) impedance
    (d) all of these

28. What is the approximate available short-circuit current on the secondary of a 50 kVA, 480V to 240V transformer having an impedance rating of 1.20 percent?

    (a) 10,000A
    (b) 12,000A
    (c) 14,000A
    (d) 17,000A

29. What is the approximate available short-circuit current on the secondary of a three-phase, 112.50 kVA, 480V to 208Y/120V transformer having an impedance rating of 2.40 percent?

    (a) 10,500A
    (b) 11,000A
    (c) 12,500A
    (d) 13,000A

25.7 Overcurrent Protective Devices, Interrupting Rating

30. Circuit breakers and fuses are intended to interrupt the circuit, and they must have an ampere interrupting rating (AIR) _____ for the available short-circuit current.

    (a) inadequate
    (b) sufficient
    (c) sustainable
    (d) none of these

31. If the protective device is not rated to _____ the available fault current at its listed voltage rating, it can explode while attempting to clear the fault.

    (a) interrupt
    (b) withstand
    (c) hold
    (d) break

25.8 Equipment Short-Circuit Current Rating (SCCR)

32. Equipment must have a(an) _____ current rating that permits the protection device to clear a short circuit or ground fault without extensive damage to the equipment components.

    (a) overload
    (b) short-circuit
    (c) ground-fault
    (d) none of these

33. If the equipment is not rated to _____ the available short-circuit current, it can explode while waiting for the circuit protective device to clear the fault.

    (a) interrupt
    (b) withstand
    (c) hold
    (d) break

25.9 Coordination of Overcurrent Protective Devices

34. "_____" of overcurrent protective devices is when the devices are designed to clear a short circuit or ground fault in a manner that localizes the short circuit or ground fault to that given circuit.

    (a) Plotting
    (b) Sequencing
    (c) Selective coordination
    (d) none of these

35. Selective coordination of overcurrent protective devices prevents _____ power losses to loads not part of the faulted circuit.

    (a) intended
    (b) unintended
    (c) excessive
    (d) none of these

36. Lack of selective coordination of overcurrent protective devices can result in unintended _____ to loads not part of the faulted circuit.

    (a) surges
    (b) power losses
    (c) blackouts
    (d) shutdowns

Unit 26—GFCIs, GFPEs, AFCIs, and SPDs

26.2 Ground-Fault Circuit Interrupters (GFCIs)

1. GFCI protective devices detect the _____ current between circuit wires.

    (a) grounded
    (b) neutral
    (c) imbalance of
    (d) phase

2. If the difference between the current leaving and returning through the current transformer of the GFCI protective device exceeds _____ (± 1 mA), the solid-state circuitry de-energizes the circuit.

    (a) 1 mA
    (b) 3 mA
    (c) 5 mA
    (d) 10 mA

3. A(An) _____ wire is not necessary for the proper function of a GFCI device.

    (a) phase
    (b) grounded
    (c) neutral
    (d) equipment grounding

4. GFCIs detect connections between the neutral wire and the metal parts of the electrical system (case). If a neutral connection to metal parts occurs, the GFCI protective device will _____.

    (a) open
    (b) explode
    (c) overload
    (d) none of these

5. Severe electric shock or death can occur if a person touches the _____ and neutral wires at the same time, even if the circuit is GFCI protected.

    (a) phase
    (b) service
    (c) equipment grounding
    (d) none of these

6. A hazard can exist if the electronics within a GFCI fail because the circuit remains _____ without GFCI protection.

    (a) de-energized
    (b) energized
    (c) off
    (d) any of these

7. GFCIs can only be properly tested by pressing the GFCI _____ button.

    (a) disconnect
    (b) reset
    (c) test
    (d) any of these

26.3 Special Purpose Ground-Fault Circuit Interrupters (SPGFCIs)

8. A special purpose GFCI device is used in circuits where the voltage-to-ground is greater than _____.

    (a) 30V
    (b) 50V
    (c) 120V
    (d) 150V

26.5 Arc-Fault Circuit-Interrupters (AFCIs)

9. An arc-fault circuit interrupter is a device intended to de-energize a circuit when it detects the current waveform characteristics unique to a(an) _____ fault.

    (a) ground
    (b) neutral
    (c) arcing
    (d) any of these

26.6 Clearing Arcing Faults

10. A _____ arcing fault can occur when the insulation between two wires degrades to a level where arcing can take place across the insulation between the two wires.

    (a) series
    (b) parallel
    (c) ground
    (d) neutral

11. The current in an arcing fault is limited by the system impedance and the impedance of the arcing fault itself. Typically, at a receptacle, fault current will be above 75A, but not likely above _____.

    (a) 100A
    (b) 220A
    (c) 330A
    (d) 450A

12. A _____ arcing fault occurs when the wire within a cord is unintentionally broken, causing the current to arc across the gap in the wire.

    (a) series
    (b) parallel
    (c) ground
    (d) neutral

26.7 Surge Protective Devices (SPDs)

13. _____ protective devices protect equipment by preventing damaging transient voltage from reaching the equipment.

    (a) Short-circuit
    (b) Overload
    (c) Overcurrent
    (d) Surge

14. _____ voltages inside a building can originate from high current loads that are switched on and off, such as those for copiers, laser printers, motors, and air-conditioning.

    (a) Actual
    (b) Sag
    (c) Transient
    (d) Nominal

15. _____ sources of transient voltage include the switching of utility power factor correction capacitors or lightning strikes.

    (a) Special
    (b) Interior
    (c) Exterior
    (d) any of these

26.8 How Surge Protective Devices Function

16. Surge protective devices are connected in _____ with the load.

    (a) parallel
    (b) series
    (c) series-parallel
    (d) none of these

CHAPTER 10

GENERAL KNOWLEDGE

Chapter 10—General Knowledge

Unit 27—Wire Resistance and Voltage Drop

In this unit you will learn:

- ▸ what is included in direct-current wire resistance
- ▸ what is included in alternating-current wire resistance
- ▸ how to calculate wire voltage drop using Ohm's Law

Unit 28—Multiwire Circuits

Understanding series, parallel, and series-parallel circuits is the foundation for understanding multiwire branch circuits. A multiwire circuit is a circuit consisting of two or more phase wires that have a voltage between them, and an equal voltage between each phase wire and the neutral wire. A typical 3-wire, 120/240V, single-phase circuit is an example.

Unit 29—The Formula Wheel

The formula wheel combines the Ohm's Law Formula Circle and Power Formula Circle (Watt's Law). In this unit you will learn how to perform calculations using the formula wheel.

UNIT 27

WIRE RESISTANCE AND VOLTAGE DROP

27.1 Introduction

In this unit you will learn:

▸ what is included in direct-current wire resistance

▸ what is included in alternating-current wire resistance

▸ how to calculate wire voltage drop using Ohm's Law

27.2 Wire Sizes

Wires are sized according to the American Wire Gage (AWG) or circular mils (cmil). ▸Figure 27–1

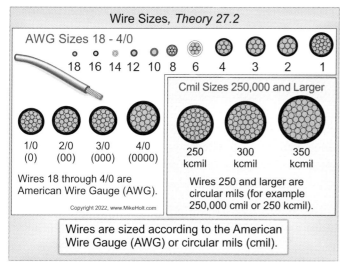

Wire Sizes, *Theory 27.2*

AWG Sizes 18 - 4/0

18 16 14 12 10 8 6 4 3 2 1

1/0 (0)   2/0 (00)   3/0 (000)   4/0 (0000)

Cmil Sizes 250,000 and Larger

250 kcmil   300 kcmil   350 kcmil

Wires 18 through 4/0 are American Wire Gauge (AWG).

Wires 250 and larger are circular mils (for example 250,000 cmil or 250 kcmil).

Copyright 2022, www.MikeHolt.com

Wires are sized according to the American Wire Gauge (AWG) or circular mils (cmil).

▸Figure 27–1

27.3 Direct-Current Wire Resistance

Metals intended to carry electrical current are called "conductors" or "wires" and, by their nature, they oppose the flow of electrons. Wires for applications covered by the *NEC* can be solid or stranded and are most often made from copper or aluminum. All materials oppose the flow of electrons. This opposition to electron movement is known as "resistance." All wires offer some degree of resistance to electron movement.

A wire's opposition to the flow of direct current depends on the wire's physical resistance which includes the following:

▸ material (copper or aluminum)

▸ cross-sectional area (wire size)

▸ length

▸ operating temperature

(A) Material. Wire resistance varies with the material from which it is made. A copper wire has a lower resistance compared to an equivalent size aluminum wire. ▸Figure 27–2

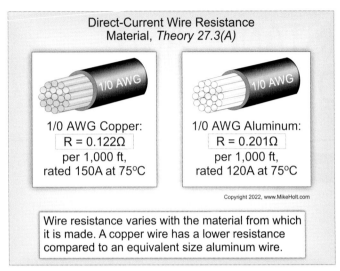

▶Figure 27–2

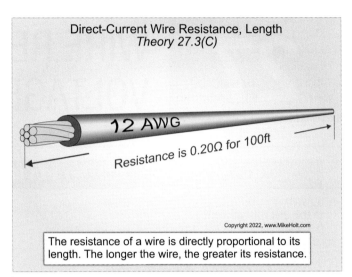

▶Figure 27–4

Aluminum is often used when weight or cost are important considerations, but copper is the most common type of metal used for electrical wires.

(B) Cross-Sectional Area. The larger the wire's cross-sectional area, the greater the number of available electron paths and the lower the wire's resistance. Wire resistance varies inversely with the wire's size, the smaller the wire, the greater its resistance. The larger the wire, the lower its resistance.   ▶Figure 27–3

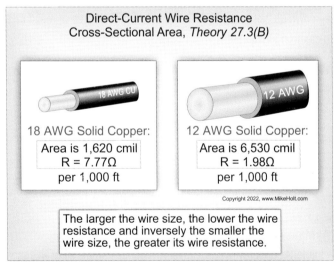

▶Figure 27–3

(C) Wire Length. The resistance of a wire is directly proportional to its length. The longer the wire, the greater its resistance. ▶Figure 27–4

Chapter 9, Table 8 of the *National Electrical Code* provides examples of wire resistances for direct-current circuits and circular mil areas for wires 1,000 ft long. Longer or shorter lengths will naturally have different wire resistances.

(D) Temperature. The resistance of a wire changes with temperature. The amount of change per degree is called the "temperature coefficient." A positive temperature coefficient indicates that as the temperature rises, the wire resistance also rises. Copper and aluminum wires have a positive temperature coefficient.

27.4 *NEC* Wire Direct-Current Resistance

The *NEC* lists the resistance and area in circular mils for both direct-current and alternating-current circuit wires. Direct-current circuit wire resistances are listed in Chapter 9, Table 8, and alternating-current circuit wire resistances (and reactance) are listed in Chapter 9, Table 9. The tables include both solid and stranded wires. Table 8 lists both coated and uncoated copper. Uncoated copper is the most commonly used wire. Unless specifically stated that the wire is a coated wire, use uncoated (for most resistance calculations, there's very little difference between the two).

The following formula can be used to determine the wire resistance for wire lengths other than 1,000 ft:

**Direct-Current Wire Resistance =
(Wire Resistance Ohms/1,000 ft) × Wire Length.**

Chapter 9, Table 8, Wire Properties			
Wire Size American Wire Gage	Wire dc Resistance Per 1,000 Feet at 75°C	Wire Diameter Inches	Wire Area Circular Mils
14 AWG	3.140Ω (stranded)	0.073	4,110
12 AWG	1.980Ω (stranded)	0.092	6,530
10 AWG	1.240Ω (stranded)	0.116	10,380
8 AWG	0.778Ω (stranded)	0.146	16,510
6 AWG	0.491Ω (stranded)	0.184	26,240

▶ Chapter 9, Table 8 Example 1

Question: *According to Chapter 9, Table 8, what is the direct-current resistance of 200 ft of a 12 AWG stranded wire?* ▶Figure 27–5

(a) 0.21Ω   *(b) 0.29Ω*   *(c) 0.396Ω*   *(d) 0.72Ω*

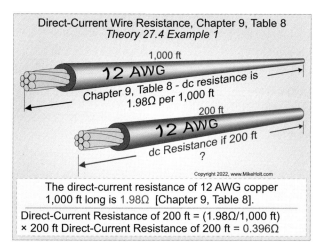

Direct-Current Wire Resistance, Chapter 9, Table 8
Theory 27.4 Example 1

The direct-current resistance of 12 AWG copper 1,000 ft long is 1.98Ω [Chapter 9, Table 8].
Direct-Current Resistance of 200 ft = (1.98Ω/1,000 ft) × 200 ft Direct-Current Resistance of 200 ft = 0.396Ω

▶Figure 27–5

Solution:

The direct-current resistance of 12 AWG copper 1,000 ft long is 1.98Ω [Chapter 9, Table 8].

Direct-Current Resistance of 200 ft = (1.98Ω/1,000 ft) × 200 ft
Direct-Current Resistance of 200 ft = 0.396Ω

Answer: *(c) 0.396Ω*

▶ Chapter 9, Table 8 Example 2

Question: *According to Chapter 9, Table 8, what is the direct-current resistance of 200 ft of a 6 AWG wire?* ▶Figure 27–6

(a) 0.021Ω   *(b) 0.029Ω*   *(c) 0.049Ω*   *(d) 0.098Ω*

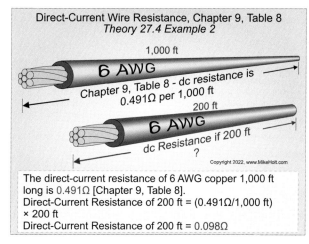

Direct-Current Wire Resistance, Chapter 9, Table 8
Theory 27.4 Example 2

The direct-current resistance of 6 AWG copper 1,000 ft long is 0.491Ω [Chapter 9, Table 8].
Direct-Current Resistance of 200 ft = (0.491Ω/1,000 ft) × 200 ft
Direct-Current Resistance of 200 ft = 0.098Ω

▶Figure 27–6

Solution:

The direct-current resistance of 6 AWG copper 1,000 ft long is 0.491Ω [Chapter 9, Table 8].

Direct-Current Resistance of 200 ft = (0.491Ω/1,000 ft) × 200 ft
Direct-Current Resistance of 200 ft = 0.0982Ω

Answer: *(d) 0.098Ω*

27.5 Alternating-Current Wire Resistance

In direct-current circuits, the only property that opposes the flow of electrons is resistance. The opposition to current flow is greater for alternating-current circuits compared to the resistance of direct-current circuits because of eddy currents and skin effect, in addition to the resistance of the wire.

(A) Eddy Currents. The expanding and collapsing magnetic field of alternating current flowing through a wire generates small, erratic, independent currents called "eddy currents." Eddy currents consume power and increase the opposition to the current flow of the circuit. ▶Figure 27–7

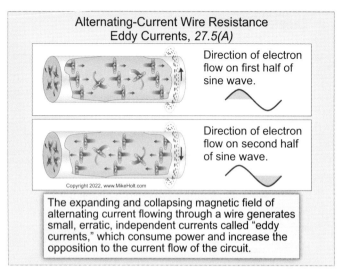

Alternating-Current Wire Resistance
Eddy Currents, 27.5(A)

Direction of electron flow on first half of sine wave.

Direction of electron flow on second half of sine wave.

The expanding and collapsing magnetic field of alternating current flowing through a wire generates small, erratic, independent currents called "eddy currents," which consume power and increase the opposition to the current flow of the circuit.

▶Figure 27–7

(B) Skin Effect. Eddy currents are strongest in the center of the wires and repel the flowing electrons toward the wire surface. This is known as "skin effect." Because of skin effect, the effective cross-sectional area of an alternating-current wire is reduced, which results in an increased opposition to current flow. ▶Figure 27–8

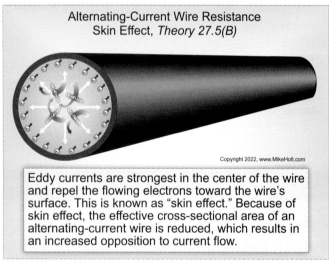

Alternating-Current Wire Resistance
Skin Effect, *Theory 27.5(B)*

Eddy currents are strongest in the center of the wire and repel the flowing electrons toward the wire's surface. This is known as "skin effect." Because of skin effect, the effective cross-sectional area of an alternating-current wire is reduced, which results in an increased opposition to current flow.

▶Figure 27–8

Skin effect is greatly impacted by the frequency of alternating current. Using a stranded wire reduces skin effect losses because the individual strands provide more surface area than does a solid wire.

27.6 Alternating-Current Resistance versus Direct-Current Resistance

The opposition to current flow is greater for alternating-current circuits compared to the resistance of direct-current circuits because of eddy currents and skin effect in addition to the resistance of the wire. Our "Alternating-Current versus Direct-Current Resistance" table provides some comparisons between alternating-current resistance and direct-current resistance. Note that for wires smaller than 1/0 AWG, the two values are essentially equal. ▶Figure 27–9

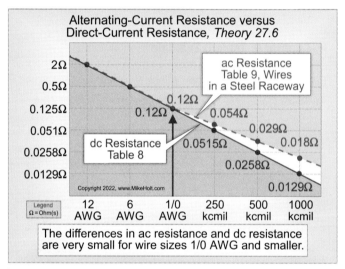

Alternating-Current Resistance versus Direct-Current Resistance, *Theory 27.6*

The differences in ac resistance and dc resistance are very small for wire sizes 1/0 AWG and smaller.

▶Figure 27–9

27.7 Wire Voltage Drop—Ohm's Law Method

(A) Voltage Drop. When electrical current flows through a wire, there is a certain amount of voltage drop in the wire due to its inherent resistance. Excessive voltage drop can deliver a voltage to the load that is less than the rated voltage of the equipment. When resistance causes the voltage to be dropped below an acceptable point, the wire size should be increased, the supply voltage should be increased, the length of the circuit should be decreased, or the circuit current should be decreased.

(B) Ohm's Law. The voltage drop of a circuit wire is in direct proportion to the wire's resistance and magnitude (amount) of current. A longer wire results in greater wire resistance and greater wire voltage drop. Increased current flow will also result in greater wire voltage drop. The voltage drop of the circuit wires for single-phase systems can be determined by the Ohm's Law method: $E_{VD} = I \times R$.

E_{VD} = Wire voltage drop expressed in volts.

I = The load in amperes at 100 percent (not at 125 percent for motors or continuous loads).

R = Wire resistance: see the *National Electrical Code*, Chapter 9, Table 8 for direct-current resistance.

▶ Ohm's Law Wire Voltage Drop Example

Question: What is the voltage drop of two 12 AWG wires (total of 0.40Ω for both wires) supplying a 16A load, located 100 ft from the power supply? Formula: $E_{VD} = I \times R$

(a) 3.60V   (b) 5.20V   (c) 6.40V   (d) 10.80V

Solution:

$E_{VD} = I \times R$
I = 16A
R = 0.40Ω

E_{VD} = 16A × 0.40Ω
E_{VD} = 6.40V

Answer: (c) 6.40V

▶ Ohm's Law Voltage Drop, 120V Example

Question: What is the operating voltage of a single-phase, 16A, 115V rated load wired with 12 AWG if it is located 150 ft from the power supply and has a nominal circuit voltage of 120V? ▶Figure 27–10

(a) 110.40V   (b) 116.40V   (c) 117.60V   (d) 118.80V

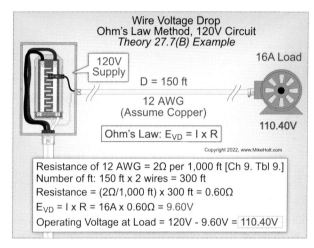

▶Figure 27–10

Solution:

$E_{VD} = I \times R$

I = 16A Load
R of 12 AWG = 2Ω per 1,000 ft [Chapter 9, Table 8]

R = (2Ω per 1,000 ft/1,000 ft) × 300 ft (150 ft × two wires)
R = 0.60Ω

Circuit Voltage Drop (VD) = I × R
E_{VD} = 16A × 0.60Ω
E_{VD} = 9.60V

Equipment Operating Voltage = Nominal Voltage –
Circuit Voltage Drop
Equipment Operating Voltage = 120V – 9.60V
Equipment Operating Voltage = 110.40V

Answer: (a) 110.40V

▶ Ohm's Law Voltage Drop, 240V Example

Question: What is the operating voltage of a single-phase, 24A, 240V rated load wired with 10 AWG if it is located 200 ft from the power supply and has a nominal circuit voltage of 240V? ▶**Figure 27–11**

(a) 228.48V   *(b) 229.80V*   *(c) 230.30V*   *(d) 231.80V*

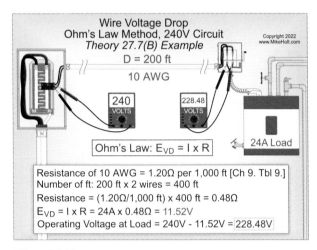

Wire Voltage Drop
Ohm's Law Method, 240V Circuit
Theory 27.7(B) Example
D = 200 ft
10 AWG

Copyright 2022
www.MikeHolt.com

240 VOLTS   228.48 VOLTS   24A Load

Ohm's Law: $E_{VD} = I \times R$

Resistance of 10 AWG = 1.20Ω per 1,000 ft [Ch 9. Tbl 9.]
Number of ft: 200 ft x 2 wires = 400 ft
Resistance = (1.20Ω/1,000 ft) x 400 ft = 0.48Ω
E_{VD} = I x R = 24A x 0.48Ω = 11.52V
Operating Voltage at Load = 240V - 11.52V = 228.48V

▶Figure 27–11

Solution:

I = 24A Load

R of 10 AWG = 1.20Ω per 1,000 ft [Chapter 9, Table 8]

R = (1.20Ω per 1,000 ft/1,000 ft) × 400 ft (200 ft × two wires)
R = 0.48Ω

Circuit Voltage Drop (VD) = I × R
$E_{VD} = 24A \times 0.48Ω$
$E_{VD} = 11.52V$

Equipment Operating Voltage =
Nominal Voltage – Circuit Voltage Drop
Equipment Operating Voltage = 240V – 11.52V
Equipment Operating Voltage = 228.48V

Answer: (a) 228.48V

UNIT
28

MULTIWIRE CIRCUITS

28.1 Introduction

Understanding series, parallel, and series-parallel circuits is the foundation for understanding multiwire branch circuits. A multiwire circuit is a circuit consisting of two or more phase wires that have a voltage between them, and an equal voltage between each phase wire and the neutral wire. A typical 3-wire, 120/240V, single-phase circuit is an example. ▶Figure 28–1

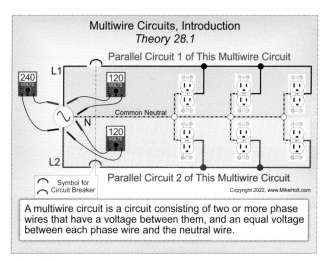

Multiwire Circuits, Introduction
Theory 28.1

A multiwire circuit is a circuit consisting of two or more phase wires that have a voltage between them, and an equal voltage between each phase wire and the neutral wire.

▶Figure 28–1

28.2 Neutral Wire

(A) Neutral Wire. The neutral wire is connected to the neutral point of a system and is intended to carry neutral current under normal conditions. ▶Figure 28–2

Author's Comment:

▶ The neutral wire of a solidly grounded system is required to be grounded (connected to the Earth), therefore this wire is also called a "grounded wire."

(B) Neutral Point. The neutral point of a system is the common point of a 4-wire, three-phase, wye-connected system; the midpoint of a 3-wire, single-phase system; or the midpoint of the single-phase portion of a three-phase, delta-connected system. ▶Figure 28–3

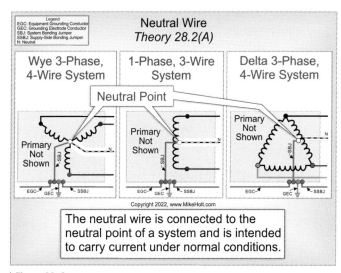

Neutral Wire
Theory 28.2(A)

Legend
EGC: Equipment Grounding Conductor
GEC: Grounding Electrode Conductor
SBJ: System Bonding Jumper
SSBJ: Supply-Side Bonding Jumper
N: Neutral

| Wye 3-Phase, 4-Wire System | 1-Phase, 3-Wire System | Delta 3-Phase, 4-Wire System |

Neutral Point

The neutral wire is connected to the neutral point of a system and is intended to carry current under normal conditions.

▶Figure 28–2

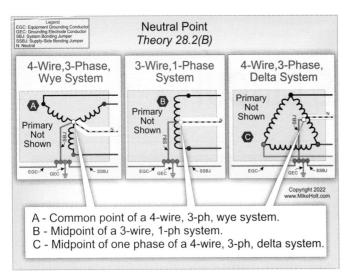

A - Common point of a 4-wire, 3-ph, wye system.
B - Midpoint of a 3-wire, 1-ph system.
C - Midpoint of one phase of a 4-wire, 3-ph, delta system.

▶Figure 28–3

28.3 Grounded Wire

The grounded wire is the wire that is intentionally grounded to the Earth from a point of a transformer secondary winding.

When the grounded conductor is connected to the neutral point of a 4-wire, three-phase, wye-connected system; the midpoint of a 3-wire, single-phase system; or the midpoint of the single-phase portion of a three-phase, delta-connected system, this wire is known as the "neutral wire." ▶Figure 28–4

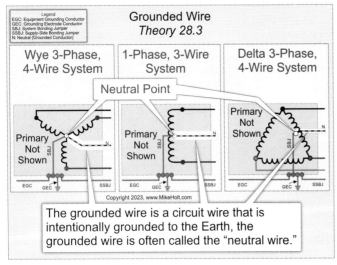

The grounded wire is a circuit wire that is intentionally grounded to the Earth, the grounded wire is often called the "neutral wire."

▶Figure 28–4

Author's Comment:

▶ For convenience, I will refer to the neutral and the grounded wire as the neutral wire.

28.4 Current Flow on the Neutral Wire

To understand the current flow on the neutral wire, review the following circuits.

(A) 2-Wire Circuit. The current flowing in the neutral wire of a 2-wire circuit is the same as the current flowing in the phase wire. ▶Figure 28–5

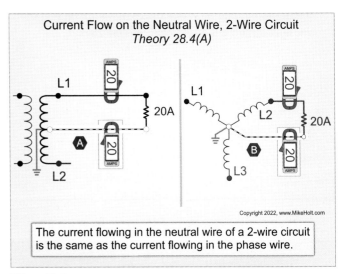

The current flowing in the neutral wire of a 2-wire circuit is the same as the current flowing in the phase wire.

▶Figure 28–5

(B) 3-Wire, 120/240V, Single-Phase Circuit, Balanced Current. The current flowing in the neutral wire of a 3-wire, 120/240V, single-phase circuit equals the difference in current flowing in the phase wires $I_N = (L1 - L2)$. ▶Figure 28–6

(C) 3-Wire, 120/240V, Single-Phase Circuit, Unbalanced Current. The current on the neutral wire is equal to the difference in phase wire current because at any instant the currents on the two phase wires oppose each other $I_N = (L1 - L2)$. ▶Figure 28–7

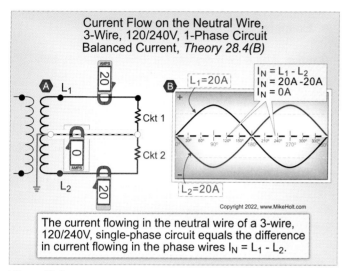

▶Figure 28–6

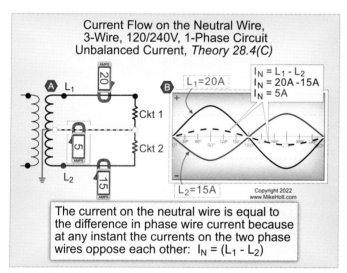

▶Figure 28–7

Caution

CAUTION: If the phase wires of a 3-wire, 120/240V, single-phase circuit are not terminated to different phases, the currents on the phase wires will not cancel, but will add on the neutral wire. This can cause the neutral current to be in excess of the neutral wire's ampacity rating. ▶Figure 28–8

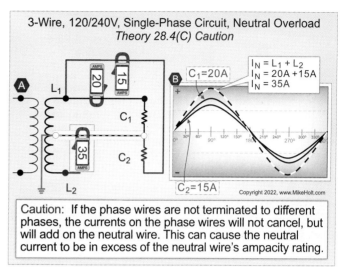

▶Figure 28–8

Author's Comment:

▶ This is one reason white neutral wires sometimes turn brown or black.

28.5 Multiwire Branch Circuits

Multiwire branch circuits are more cost effective than 2-wire circuits in that they have fewer wires for a given number of circuits, which enables the use of a smaller raceway. In addition, the use of multiwire branch circuits results in lower circuit voltage drop.

(A) Reduced Number of Wires. Normally it requires four wires to install two 120V single-phase circuits. By using a multiwire branch circuit, which allows the neutral between the two circuits to be shared, the installation can be made using three wires. Likewise, the six wires required for three 120V circuits on a three-phase system can be replaced by a multiwire branch circuit of four wires: three hot wires sharing a neutral wire between them. ▶Figure 28–9

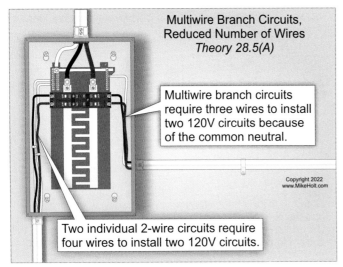

▶Figure 28–9

(B) Reduced Raceway Size. If the number of wires is reduced for a multiwire circuit, the size of the raceway can often be reduced. Reducing the number of wires and installing a smaller raceway is very cost effective. The cost savings include the material and labor, as well as overhead. ▶Figure 28–10

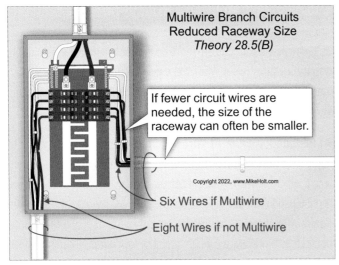

▶Figure 28–10

(C) Reduced Circuit Voltage Drop. The voltage drop of the circuit wires is dependent upon the magnitude of current and wire resistance: $E_{VD} = I \times R$.

(1) 2-Wire Circuit, Voltage Drop. A typical 2-wire circuit has current flow over both the phase and neutral wires. Therefore, the circuit voltage drop includes the voltage drop of both wires.

▶ **Example**

Question: What is the voltage drop of two 12 AWG wires, each 75 ft long, supplying a 2-wire, 20A load? ▶**Figure 28–11**

(a) 2V   (b) 3V   (c) 4V   (d) 6V

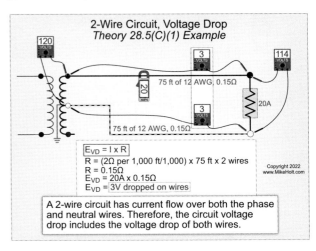

▶Figure 28–11

Solution:

$E_{VD} = I \times R$

$I = 20A$

$R = (2\Omega$ per 1,000 ft/1,000) $\times$ 75 ft $\times$ 2 wires
$R = 0.30\Omega$

$E_{VD} = 20A \times 0.30\Omega$
$E_{VD} = 6V$

Answer: (d) 6V

(2) Multiwire Branch Circuit, Voltage Drop. A balanced 3-wire, single-phase or 4-wire, three-phase multiwire branch circuit has current flowing only on the phase circuit wires. Therefore, the circuit voltage drop only includes the voltage drop of one wire.

▶ Example

Question: What is the voltage drop of two 12 AWG wires, each 75 ft long, supplying a 2-wire, 20A load? ▶Figure 28–12

(a) 2V   (b) 3V   (c) 4V   (d) 6V

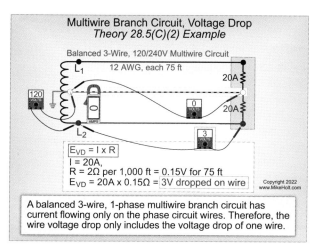

▶Figure 28–12

Solution:

$E_{VD} = I \times R$

I = 20A

R = (2Ω per 1,000 ft/1,000) × 75 ft × 2 wires
R = 0.15Ω

$E_{VD} = 20A \times 0.15Ω$
$E_{VD} = 3V$

Answer: (b) 3V

28.6 Dangers of Multiwire Circuits

Multiwire branch circuits offer fewer wires, and reduced raceway size and voltage drop. However, improper wiring or mishandling of multiwire circuits can cause a fire hazard and/or equipment failure.

(A) Fire Hazard. Failure to terminate the phase wires to separate phases may cause the neutral wire to become overloaded from excessive neutral current, and the insulation may be damaged or destroyed. Overheating is known to decrease insulating material service life, potentially resulting in a fire from arcing faults in hidden locations. It is difficult to predict just how long wire insulation will last under normal operating conditions, but heat does decrease its life span. ▶Figure 28–13

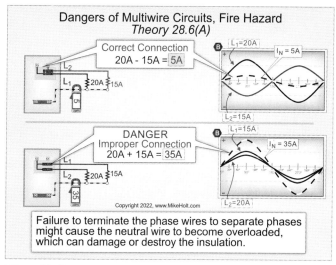

▶Figure 28–13

(B) Equipment Failure. If the continuity of the neutral wire of a multiwire circuit is interrupted (opened), there could be a fire and/or destruction of electrical equipment resulting from overvoltage or undervoltage.

▶ **Example**

Example: A 3-wire, 120/240V circuit supplies a 1,200W, 120V hair dryer and a 600W, 120V television. If the neutral wire is interrupted, it will cause the 120V television to operate at 160V and consume 1,067W of power (instead of 600W) for only a few seconds before it burns up. ▶**Figure 28–14**

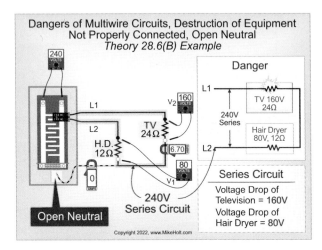

▶Figure 28–14

Solution:

Step 1: *Determine the resistance of each appliance:*

$R = E^2/P$

Hair Dryer

$R = 120V^2/1,200W$

$R = 12\Omega$

Television

$R = 120V^2/600W$

$R = 24\Omega$

Step 2: *Determine the current of the circuit:*

$I = E/R$

$I = 240V/(12\Omega + 24\Omega)$

$I = 6.70A$

Step 3: *Determine the operating voltage for each appliance:*

$E = I \times R$

Hair Dryer Operates at = 6.70A × 12Ω

Hair Dryer Operates at = 80V

Television Operates at = 6.70A × 24Ω

Television Operates at = 160V

28.7 *NEC* Requirements

Because of the dangers associated with an open neutral wire, the *NEC* specifies that the continuity of the neutral wire of a multiwire branch circuit cannot be dependent upon any wiring device [300.13(B)]. In other words, the neutral wires of a multiwire circuit should be spliced together, and a wire (pigtail) brought out to the device. This way, if the receptacle is removed, it does not result in an open neutral wire. ▶Figure 28–15

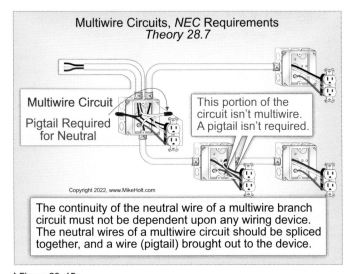

▶Figure 28–15

UNIT
29

THE FORMULA WHEEL

29.1 Introduction

The formula wheel combines the Ohm's Law Formula Circle and Power Formula Circle (Watt's Law). In this unit you will learn how to perform calculations using the formula wheel. ▶Figure 29–1

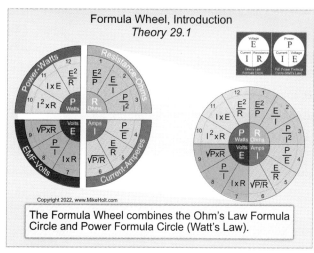

Formula Wheel, Introduction
Theory 29.1

The Formula Wheel combines the Ohm's Law Formula Circle and Power Formula Circle (Watt's Law).

▶Figure 29–1

29.2 Formula Wheel Quadrants

The formula wheel is divided into four sections with three formulas in each section. The sections include: ▶Figure 29–2

- ▶ "P" for power measured in watts
- ▶ "R" for resistance measured in ohms
- ▶ "I" for intensity or current measured in amperes
- ▶ "E" for electromotive force measured in volts

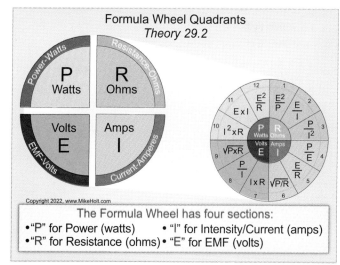

Formula Wheel Quadrants
Theory 29.2

The Formula Wheel has four sections:
- "P" for Power (watts)   • "I" for Intensity/Current (amps)
- "R" for Resistance (ohms)• "E" for EMF (volts)

▶Figure 29–2

29.3 Using the Formula Wheel

When working with the formula wheel, the key to finding the correct answer is to follow these steps:

Step 1: What is the question? Amperes, voltage, resistance, or power?

Step 2: What do you know? Amperes, voltage, resistance, or power?

Step 3: Select the formula from the wheel.

Step 4: Work out the formula calculation.

▶ Resistance Example

Question: *What is the resistance of two wires where each wire has a voltage drop of 1.50V and the current flowing in the circuit is 100A?*
▶Figure 29–3

(a) 0.03Ω   (b) 2Ω   (c) 30Ω   (d) 300Ω

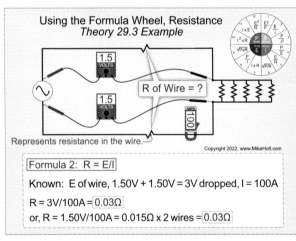

▶Figure 29–3

Solution:

Step 1: *What is the question? What is "R"?*

Step 2: *What do you know?*
    Voltage Drop = 3V
    Circuit Current = 100A

Step 3: *The formula to use is **R = E/I**.*

Step 4: *Calculate the answer:*
    R = 3V/100A
    R = 0.03Ω

Answer: (a) 0.03Ω

▶ Current Example

Question: *What is the current flow in amperes through a 7.50 kW heat strip rated 230V when connected to a 230V power source?*
▶Figure 29–4

(a) 25A   (b) 33A   (c) 39A   (d) 230A

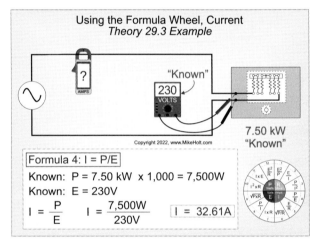

▶Figure 29–4

Solution:

Step 1: *What is the question? What is "I"?*

Step 2: *What do you know?*
    Heat Strip Power Rating, P = 7.50 kW × 1,000
    Heat Strip Power Rating, P = 7,500W
    Heat Strip Voltage Rating, E = 230V

Step 3: *The formula to use is **I = P/E**.*

Step 4: *Calculate the answer:*
    I = 7,500W/230V
    I = 32.61A

Answer: (b) 33A

▶ Voltage Example

Question: *What is the voltage of a circuit carrying 1.20A supplying a 100Ω resistor?* ▶**Figure 29–5**

(a) 110V   *(b) 120V*   *(c) 160V*   *(d) 320V*

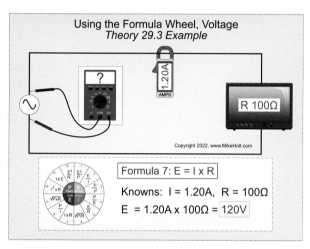

▶Figure 29–5

Solution:

Step 1:   *What is the question? What is "E"?*

Step 2:   *What do you know?*

   Current (I) = 1.20A
   Resistance (R) = 100Ω

Step 3:   *The formula to use is* **E = I × R**.

Step 4:   *Calculate the answer:*

   E = 1.20A × 100Ω
   E = 120V

Answer: *(b) 120V*

▶ Power Example

Question: *What is the power loss of a 2-wire circuit carrying 16A having a length of 75 ft with two 12 AWG wires each having a resistance of 0.15Ω?* ▶**Figure 29–6**

(a) 67.20W   *(b) 76.80W*   *(c) 83.50W*   *(d) 96.30W*

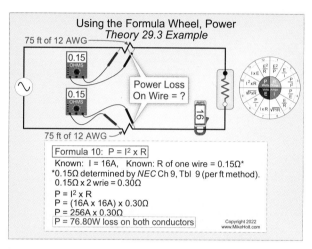

▶Figure 29–6

Solution:

Step 1:   *What is the question? What is the power loss of the wires in watts ("P")?*

Step 2:   *What do you know about the circuit?*

   I = 16A
   R = 0.15Ω per wire × 2 wires
   R = 0.30Ω

Step 3:   *What is the formula?* $P = I^2 × R$.

Step 4:   *Calculate the answer:*

   $P = 16A^2 × 0.30Ω$
   P = (16A × 16A) × 0.30Ω
   P = 256A × 0.30Ω
   P = 76.80W

Answer: *(b) 76.80W*

CHAPTER 10

PRACTICE QUESTIONS

CHAPTER 10—PRACTICE QUESTIONS

Unit 27—Wire Resistance and Voltage Drop

27.2 Wire Sizes

1. The cross-sectional area of a wire is commonly expressed in _____.

   (a) square inches
   (b) mils
   (c) circular mils
   (d) none of these

27.3 Direct-Current Wire Resistance

2. In dc circuits, the only property that affects current flow is _____.

   (a) impedance
   (b) reactance
   (c) resistance
   (d) none of these

3. Wire dc resistance is determined by the _____.

   (a) material type
   (b) cross-sectional area
   (c) wire length and operating temperature
   (d) all of these

4. Aluminum has _____ resistance to the flow of electrons than does copper.

   (a) higher
   (b) lower
   (c) equal
   (d) none of these

5. Smaller wires have _____ resistance and larger wires have lower resistance.

   (a) lesser
   (b) greater
   (c) the same
   (d) all of these

6. The dc resistance of a wire is directly proportional to its _____.

   (a) color
   (b) length
   (c) weight
   (d) insulation

7. The resistance of a wire is affected by temperature change. This is called the "_____."

   (a) temperature correction factor
   (b) temperature coefficient
   (c) ambient temperature factor
   (d) none of these

27.4 NEC Wire Direct-Current Resistance

8. The _____ lists the resistance and area in circular mils for both direct-current and alternating-current circuit wires.

   (a) *NEC*
   (b) CEC
   (c) IEC
   (d) none of these

9. What is the direct-current resistance of a 6 AWG copper wire that is 400 ft long?

   (a) 0.20Ω
   (b) 0.30Ω
   (c) 0.40Ω
   (d) 0.50Ω

10. What is the direct-current resistance of a 1 AWG copper wire that is 200 ft long?

    (a) 0.0308Ω
    (b) 0.0311Ω
    (c) 0.0423Ω
    (d) 0.0564Ω

11. What is the direct-current resistance of a 3 AWG aluminum wire that is 1,000 ft long?

    (a) 0.231Ω
    (b) 0.313Ω
    (c) 0.403Ω
    (d) 0.422Ω

12. What is the direct-current resistance of a 1/0 AWG aluminum wire that is 800 ft long?

    (a) 0.08Ω
    (b) 0.16Ω
    (c) 0.23Ω
    (d) 0.56Ω

13. What is the direct-current resistance of a 1 AWG copper wire that is 100 ft long?

    (a) 0.0154Ω
    (b) 0.1620Ω
    (c) 0.2330Ω
    (d) 0.5610Ω

14. What is the direct-current resistance of a 3 AWG aluminum wire that is 500 ft long?

    (a) 0.0231Ω
    (b) 0.1614Ω
    (c) 0.2015Ω
    (d) 0.2330Ω

15. According to Chapter 9, Table 8, what is the cross-sectional area in circular mils for a 4 AWG wire?

    (a) 41,740 cmil
    (b) 63,360 cmil
    (c) 70,380 cmil
    (d) 96,510 cmil

16. According to Chapter 9, Table 8, what is the cross-sectional area in circular mils for a 2 AWG wire?

    (a) 41,740 cmil
    (b) 66,360 cmil
    (c) 70,380 cmil
    (d) 83,690 cmil

17. According to Chapter 9, Table 8, what is the cross-sectional area in circular mils for a 1 AWG wire?

    (a) 41,740 cmil
    (b) 63,360 cmil
    (c) 70,380 cmil
    (d) 83,690 cmil

18. According to Chapter 9, Table 8, what is the cross-sectional area in circular mils for a 1/0 AWG wire?

    (a) 83,690 cmil
    (b) 105,600 cmil
    (c) 167,800 cmil
    (d) 211,600 cmil

19. According to Chapter 9, Table 8, what is the cross-sectional area in circular mils for a 3/0 AWG aluminum wire?

    (a) 83,690 cmil
    (b) 105,600 cmil
    (c) 167,800 cmil
    (d) 211,600 cmil

27.5 Alternating-Current Wire Resistance

20. For ac circuits, the ac _____ of a wire is greater than the dc resistance because of eddy currents and skin effect.

    (a) voltage
    (b) current
    (c) resistance
    (d) power

21. _____ currents are small independent currents that are produced as a result of the expanding and collapsing magnetic field. They flow erratically within the wire opposing current flow and consuming power.

    (a) Lenz
    (b) Ohm's
    (c) Eddy
    (d) Kirchhoff's

22. Eddy currents are strongest in the center of the wires and repel the flowing electrons toward the wire surface. This is known as "_____ effect."

    (a) inductive
    (b) skin
    (c) surface
    (d) watt

27.6 Alternating-Current Resistance versus Direct-Current Resistance

23. The opposition to current flow is greater for alternating-current circuits than for direct-current circuits because of _____.

    (a) eddy currents
    (b) skin effect
    (c) eddy currents and skin effect
    (d) none of these

27.7 Wire Voltage Drop—Ohm's Law Method

24. A _____ wire results in greater wire resistance and greater wire voltage drop.

    (a) wider
    (b) shorter
    (c) longer
    (d) none of these

25. Increased _____ flow will result in greater wire voltage drop.

    (a) resistance
    (b) voltage
    (c) current
    (d) none of these

Unit 28—Multiwire Circuits

28.1 Introduction

1. A _____ circuit is a circuit consisting of two or more phase wires that have a voltage between them, and an equal voltage between each phase wire and the neutral wire.

    (a) series
    (b) parallel
    (c) multiwire
    (d) series-parallel

28.2 Neutral Wire

2. The _____ wire is connected to the neutral point of a system and is intended to carry current under normal conditions.

   (a) neutral
   (b) phase
   (c) copper
   (d) none of these

3. The common point of a 4-wire, three-phase, wye-connected system; the midpoint of a 3-wire, single-phase system; or the midpoint of the single-phase portion of a three-phase, delta-connected system is referred to as the "_____ point."

   (a) neutral
   (b) phase
   (c) copper
   (d) none of these

28.3 Grounded Wire

4. The grounded wire is a wire that is intentionally _____ to the Earth.

   (a) grounded
   (b) bolted
   (c) earthed
   (d) bonded

28.4 Current Flow on the Neutral Wire

5. The current on the neutral wire of a 2-wire circuit is the _____ the current on the phase wire.

   (a) same as
   (b) different than
   (c) opposite that of
   (d) all of these

6. The current flowing in the neutral wire of a 3-wire, 120/240V, single-phase circuit equals the _____ current flowing in the phase wires.

   (a) minimum
   (b) difference in
   (c) opposition to
   (d) maximum

7. The current on the neutral wire is equal to the difference in phase wire current because at any instant the currents on the two phase wires _____ each other.

   (a) attract
   (b) oppose
   (c) equal
   (d) rely

28.5 Multiwire Branch Circuits

8. Multiwire branch circuits are more _____ than 2-wire circuits in that they have fewer wires for a given number of circuits, which enables the use of a smaller raceway, and result in lower circuit voltage drop.

   (a) cost effective
   (b) conductive
   (c) nicer
   (d) easier

9. Multiwire branch circuits have _____ wires for a given number of circuits, which requires the use of a smaller raceway.

   (a) fewer
   (b) more
   (c) bigger
   (d) smaller

10. If the number of wires is reduced for a multiwire circuit, the size of the raceway can often be _____.

    (a) reduced
    (b) copper
    (c) increased
    (d) aluminum

11. A typical 2-wire circuit has current flow over both the phase and neutral wires and the circuit voltage drop includes the voltage drop of _____ wire(s).

    (a) zero
    (b) one
    (c) both
    (d) three

12. What is the voltage drop of two 12 AWG wires, each 150 ft long, supplying a 2-wire, 20A load?

    (a) 6V
    (b) 10V
    (c) 12V
    (d) 16V

13. A balanced 3-wire, single-phase or 4-wire, three-phase multi-wire branch circuit has current flowing only on the phase circuit wires and the circuit voltage drop includes the voltage drop of _____ wire(s).

    (a) one
    (b) two
    (c) three
    (d) four

14. What is the circuit voltage drop over each line wire of a balanced 3-wire multiwire circuit? Each wire is 12 AWG, 150 ft long, supplying a 20A load.

    (a) 2V
    (b) 3V
    (c) 4V
    (d) 6V

28.6 Dangers of Multiwire Circuits

15. Improper wiring or mishandling of multiwire circuits can cause _____.

    (a) better power quality
    (b) a fire hazard
    (c) equipment failure
    (d) a fire hazard and/or equipment failure

16. Failure to terminate the phase wires to separate phases may cause the neutral wire to become _____ from excessive neutral current, and the insulation may be damaged or destroyed.

    (a) short circuit
    (b) grounded
    (c) overloaded
    (d) all of these

17. If the continuity of the _____ wire of a multiwire circuit is interrupted (opened), there could be a fire and/or destruction of electrical equipment resulting from overvoltage or undervoltage.

    (a) grounding
    (b) neutral
    (c) phase
    (d) all of these

28.7 NEC *Requirements*

18. Because of the dangers associated with an _____ neutral wire, the continuity of the neutral wire(s) in a multiwire branch circuit cannot depend upon the receptacle.

    (a) closed
    (b) open
    (c) ungrounded
    (d) grounded

Unit 29—The Formula Wheel

29.2 Formula Wheel Quadrants

1. The Formula Wheel is divided into _____ sections with three formulas in each section.

    (a) two
    (b) three
    (c) four
    (d) five

29.3 Using the Formula Wheel

2. What is the resistance of the circuit wires when the wire voltage drop is 7.20V and the current flow is 50A?

    (a) 0.14Ω
    (b) 0.30Ω
    (c) 3Ω
    (d) 14Ω

3. What is the resistance of the circuit wires when the wire voltage drop is 3.60V and the current flow is 20A?

    (a) 0.15Ω
    (b) 0.18Ω
    (c) 3.0Ω
    (d) 5.55Ω

4. What is the resistance of the circuit wires when the wire voltage drop is 6.24V and the current flow is 40A?

    (a) 0.145Ω
    (b) 0.156Ω
    (c) 0.60Ω
    (d) 6.41Ω

5. What is the resistance of the circuit wires when the wire voltage drop is 14.40V and the current flow is 60A?

    (a) 0.24Ω
    (b) 0.30Ω
    (c) 3.14Ω
    (d) 4.20Ω

6. What is the current flow in amperes through a 9.50 kW heat strip rated 230V when connected to a 230V power source?

    (a) 25A
    (b) 39A
    (c) 41A
    (d) 230A

7. What is the current flow in amperes through a 9.50 kW heat strip rated 208V when connected to a 208V power source?

    (a) 35A
    (b) 39A
    (c) 46A
    (d) 55A

8. What is the current flow in amperes through a 6.50 kW heat strip rated 460V when connected to a 460V power source?

    (a) 14A
    (b) 21A
    (c) 27A
    (d) 30A

9. What is the current flow in amperes through a 6.50 kW heat strip rated 480V when connected to a 480V power source?

    (a) 13.50A
    (b) 19.40A
    (c) 21.30A
    (d) 23.20A

10. What is the voltage of a circuit carrying 4.80A supplying a 100Ω resistor?

    (a) 110V
    (b) 220V
    (c) 360V
    (d) 480V

11. What is the voltage of a circuit carrying 20.80A supplying a 10Ω resistor?

    (a) 110V
    (b) 208V
    (c) 460V
    (d) 500V

12. What is the voltage of a circuit carrying 7.50A supplying a 37Ω resistor?

    (a) 120V
    (b) 277V
    (c) 360V
    (d) 520V

13. What is the voltage of a circuit carrying 4.60A supplying a 52Ω resistor?

    (a) 110V
    (b) 120V
    (c) 230V
    (d) 240V

14. What is the power loss at a terminal having a resistance of 0.20Ω when carrying 40A?

    (a) 100W
    (b) 210W
    (c) 320W
    (d) 430W

15. What is the power loss at a terminal having a resistance of 0.40Ω when carrying 20A?

    (a) 100W
    (b) 160W
    (c) 250W
    (d) 300W

16. What is the power loss at a terminal having a resistance of 0.50Ω when carrying 15A?

    (a) 112.50W
    (b) 200.40W
    (c) 230.20W
    (d) 340.30W

17. What is the power loss at a terminal having a resistance of 0.70Ω when carrying 10A?

    (a) 10W
    (b) 40W
    (c) 70W
    (d) 100W

ELECTRICAL THEORY FINAL EXAM

CHAPTER 1—ELECTRICAL FUNDAMENTALS

Unit 1—Atomic Structure

1. Because of their light weight, _____ actively participate in the transfer of energy and have lines of force going inward in all directions.

    (a) electrons
    (b) protons
    (c) neutrons
    (d) nuclei

2. Coulomb's Law states that, "Particles with _____ electrostatic charges repel each other."

    (a) balanced
    (b) charged
    (c) unlike
    (d) like

3. Coulomb's Law states that, "Particles with _____ electrostatic charges attract each other."

    (a) balanced
    (b) charged
    (c) unlike
    (d) like

4. If an atom contains more electrons than protons, the atom has a _____ atomic charge.

    (a) balanced
    (b) positive
    (c) negative
    (d) none of these

5. If an atom contains more protons than electrons, the atom has a _____ atomic charge.

    (a) balanced
    (b) positive
    (c) negative
    (d) none of these

6. When objects are quickly separated, both materials display a charge because one material has an excess of electrons while the other has _____ electrons.

    (a) no
    (b) fewer
    (c) more
    (d) extra

7. Lightning is the _____ of high-voltage cells within clouds to, and from, the Earth and sometimes to space.

    (a) buildup
    (b) charging
    (c) discharging
    (d) neutralizing

8. The lightning protection system intercepts the lightning strike and provides a safe path for it to _____ the Earth.

    (a) discharge to
    (b) neutralize within
    (c) dissipate to
    (d) charge particles in

Unit 3—Electrical Circuits and Power Sources

9. According to the Conventional Current Flow Theory, Benjamin Franklin theorized that electric current flowed out of the _____ terminal, through the circuit and into the _____ terminal of the source.

   (a) positive, negative
   (b) negative, positive
   (c) negative, negative
   (d) positive, positive

10. According to the _____ Current Flow Theory, Joseph J. Thompson discovered that electrons flowed from the negative terminal of the source toward the positive terminal of the source.

    (a) Conventional
    (b) Electron
    (c) Maxwell
    (d) Tesla

11. Chemical activity in the _____ causes a buildup of electrons at the negative terminal, creating the energy necessary to move electrons within a circuit.

    (a) battery
    (b) generator
    (c) solar cell
    (d) wind turbine

CHAPTER 2—USES AND DANGERS OF ELECTRICITY

Unit 5—Uses of Electricity

12. A solar _____ system combines all components and subsystems that convert solar energy into electric energy.

    (a) pluton
    (b) photovoltaic (PV)
    (c) electron
    (d) none of these

13. When a high-voltage arc between the electrodes occurs in a _____ bulb, ultraviolet radiation is emitted causing the phosphor coating to glow.

    (a) incandescent
    (b) fluorescent
    (c) LED
    (d) none of these

14. When direct current passes through a semiconductor device known as a(an) "_____," light is produced.

    (a) incandescent circuit
    (b) light-emitting diode
    (c) fluorescent tube
    (d) none of these

Unit 6—Dangers of Electricity

15. The primary causes of an electrical _____ is excessive heat when wires are not terminated correctly, not properly sized, and the loads exceed the circuit wires' ampacity rating.

    (a) fire
    (b) overload
    (c) short circuit
    (d) fault

16. The severity of an electric shock is dependent on the amount of current flowing through the body, which is impacted by circuit voltage and _____ resistance.

    (a) contact
    (b) the Earth's
    (c) the body's
    (d) circuit

17. An electric arc flash can cause temperatures approaching _____ to vaporize anything within its immediate vicinity.

    (a) 10,000°F
    (b) 15,000°F
    (c) 25,000°F
    (d) 35,000°F

18. The strength of an arc _____ creates an explosive pressure wave that can eject shrapnel, molten metal, plastic, and paint across a room and cause severe injuries or death.

    (a) flash
    (b) blast
    (c) fault
    (d) fire

19. _____ energy is the amount of thermal energy measured in cal/cm² at a given working distance during an electric arc-flash event.

    (a) Flash
    (b) Blast
    (c) Fault
    (d) Incident

20. Personal protective equipment (PPE) is intended to _____ the severity of an injury so it is survivable.

    (a) eliminate
    (b) maximize
    (c) minimize
    (d) deflect

CHAPTER 3—MAGNETISM AND ELECTROMAGNETISM

Unit 7—Basics of Magnetism

21. The magnetic molecules in iron can align themselves so their magnetic poles point in the _____ direction.

    (a) same
    (b) opposite
    (c) Earth's
    (d) magnet's

Unit 8—Electromagnetism

22. Hans Oersted discovered that when he applied power from a battery to a section of wire, the electrons flowing in the wire produced a(an) _____ field that influenced the direction in which a nearby compass pointed.

    (a) magnetic
    (b) electromagnetic
    (c) current
    (d) voltage

23. When two wires with current flowing in opposite directions are next to each other, the electromagnetic fields generated by the current flowing in each wire will _____ each other.

    (a) repel
    (b) attract
    (c) combine with
    (d) none of these

24. When two wires with current flowing in the same direction are next to each other, the electromagnetic fields of the wires will _____.

    (a) repel each other
    (b) oppose each other
    (c) combine
    (d) none of these

CHAPTER 4—MATHEMATICS

Unit 10—Basic Math

25. The decimal equivalent for "225 percent" is _____.

    (a) 0.225
    (b) 2.25
    (c) 22.50
    (d) 225

26. What is the sum of 5 and 10 added to the product of 5 and 10?

    (a) 26
    (b) 32
    (c) 46
    (d) 65

27. The numeric equivalent of 12^2 is _____.

    (a) 3.46
    (b) 24
    (c) 144
    (d) 1,728

28. What is the approximate square root ($\sqrt{}$) of 1,000?

    (a) 3
    (b) 32
    (c) 100
    (d) 500

29. What is the reciprocal of 1.25?

    (a) 0.80
    (b) 1.10
    (c) 1.25
    (d) 1.50

CHAPTER 5—OHM'S LAW AND WATT'S LAW

Unit 12—Ohm's Law

30. All electrical circuits contain a _____ necessary to produce pressure to move electrons through the circuit wire to supply the load.

    (a) power source
    (b) wire
    (c) load
    (d) all of these

31. Electrical pressure is called "_____," and it is measured in a unit called volts.

    (a) EMF
    (b) potential
    (c) voltage
    (d) none of these

32. Every component of an electrical circuit contains _____, which includes the power source, the circuit wiring, and the load.

    (a) resistance
    (b) voltage
    (c) current
    (d) power

33. In an electrical circuit, the intensity of the current flow is measured in the unit called an "ampere," which is represented by the letter "I" for _____.

    (a) resistance
    (b) power
    (c) pressure
    (d) intensity

34. The intensity of the circuit is measured in a unit called "_____."

    (a) voltage
    (b) ohms
    (c) watts
    (d) amperes

35. Ohm's Law states that current is _____ proportional to the voltage, this means that current will increase in direct proportion to the voltage increase if the resistance of the circuit remains the same.

    (a) indirectly
    (b) inversely
    (c) aversely
    (d) directly

36. Ohm's Law states that current is _____proportional to the resistance, this means that current will decrease in direct proportion to the increase in resistance if the voltage remains the same.

    (a) indirectly
    (b) inversely
    (c) aversely
    (d) directly

37. The voltage to a 12Ω resistor carrying 10A is _____.

    (a) 1V
    (b) 110V
    (c) 120V
    (d) 125V

38. If a 120V source supplies a 12Ω resistor, the current flow in the circuit will be _____.

    (a) 5A
    (b) 10A
    (c) 13A
    (d) 25A

39. The resistance of a circuit rated 120V drawing 10A is _____.

    (a) 12Ω
    (b) 17Ω
    (c) 19Ω
    (d) 20Ω

Unit 13—Watt's Law

40. What is the power loss of a circuit carrying 20A having a voltage drop of 10.20V?

    (a) 122W
    (b) 174W
    (c) 204W
    (d) 354W

41. What is the approximate power consumed by a 4.32Ω heat strip rated 208V?

    (a) 8 kW
    (b) 9 kW
    (c) 10 kW
    (d) 11 kW

CHAPTER 6—ELECTRICAL CIRCUIT TYPES

Unit 14—Series Circuits

42. What is the total resistance of three resistors where R_1 is 15Ω, R_2 is 20Ω, and R_3 is 35Ω?

    (a) 50Ω
    (b) 70Ω
    (c) 100Ω
    (d) 150Ω

43. The current for a 240V circuit that has three resistors in series where R_1 is 15Ω, R_2 is 20Ω, and R_3 is 25Ω is _____.

    (a) 4A
    (b) 7A
    (c) 9A
    (d) 12A

44. A 120V circuit has three resistors in series where R_1 is 10Ω, R_2 is 15Ω, and R_3 is 25Ω. The voltage across R_1 is _____.

    (a) 24V
    (b) 30V
    (c) 104V
    (d) 110V

45. A series circuit has which of the following characteristics?

    (a) Circuit resistance is equal to the sum of the resistances.
    (b) Current is the same through all the resistors.
    (c) The total voltage across all resistors is equal to the voltage source.
    (d) all of these

Unit 15—Parallel Circuits

46. A 12V circuit has two 5Ω resistors connected in parallel. The voltage across any one of these resistors is _____.

    (a) 12V
    (b) 24V
    (c) 48V
    (d) 120V

47. A circuit has three 25A resistors connected in parallel. The current of this circuit is _____.

    (a) 35A
    (b) 45A
    (c) 65A
    (d) 75A

48. A parallel circuit has which of the following characteristics?

    (a) The total circuit resistance is always less than the smallest component.
    (b) Current is equal to the sum of the current of all branches.
    (c) Voltage is the same across each parallel branch.
    (d) all of these

CHAPTER 7—ALTERNATING CURRENT

Unit 17—Alternating Current Fundamentals

49. A simple ac generator consists of a loop of wire rotating between the _____ fields between the opposite poles of a magnet.

    (a) magnetic
    (b) static
    (c) gravity
    (d) all of these

50. A _____ waveform is symmetrical with positive values above and negative values below the zero-reference level.

    (a) nonsinusoidal
    (b) nonsymmetrical
    (c) sinusoidal
    (d) any of these

51. A nonsinusoidal waveform is produced when _____ loads distort the voltage and current sinusoidal waveform.

    (a) linear
    (b) resistive
    (c) inductive
    (d) nonlinear

52. The full rotation of an alternating-current generator is equal to 360° and its frequency output is expressed as "cycles per second" measured in "_____."

    (a) degrees
    (b) sine waves
    (c) phases
    (d) Hertz

53. If the voltage and current waveforms begin and end simultaneously, then the two waveforms are "_____" with each other.

    (a) in-phase
    (b) out-of-phase
    (c) coupled
    (d) any of these

54. When the voltage and current waveforms reach their zero and peak values at different times, the waveforms are said to be "_____" with each other.

    (a) in-phase
    (b) out-of-phase
    (c) in-phase or out-of-phase
    (d) none of these

55. The peak voltage of an alternating-current circuit having an effective RMS voltage of 240V is _____.

    (a) 170V
    (b) 339V
    (c) 392V
    (d) 480V

56. What is the effective RMS voltage of a circuit with a peak value of 392V?

(a) 120V
(b) 208V
(c) 277V
(d) 300V

Unit 18—Inductance

57. When alternating current flows in wire, the expanding and collapsing electromagnetic field from the center to the outside of the wire self-_____ an opposing voltage in the wire.

(a) applies
(b) induces
(c) distorts
(d) any of these

58. _____induction occurs when one coil of wire induces a voltage onto another coil of wire because of the expanding and collapsing electromagnetic fields of adjacent windings.

(a) Mutual
(b) Self-
(c) Voltage
(d) Current

Unit 20—True Power, Power Factor, and Apparent Power

59. What is the approximate power consumed by a 30A resistive heater rated 240V?

(a) 2,350W
(b) 3,500W
(c) 5,000W
(d) 7,200W

60. What is the approximate power loss of a circuit carrying 6A having a total wire resistance of 0.60Ω?

(a) 22W
(b) 75W
(c) 150W
(d) 320W

61. The power loss of a terminal carrying 25A with a contact resistance of 0.20Ω is _____.

(a) 100W
(b) 125W
(c) 140W
(d) 150W

62. If the output power is 1,320W and the input power is 1,800W, what is the efficiency of the equipment?

(a) 62 percent
(b) 73 percent
(c) 80 percent
(d) 100 percent

63. Electric bills are based on the energy consumed during a month, multiplied by the cost of the energy in _____ hours.

(a) kilowatt
(b) voltage
(c) ohm
(d) amp

64. What is the power factor percentage for a ballast at 120V rated 0.85A supplying two bulbs, each rated 40W?

(a) 78 percent
(b) 89 percent
(c) 93 percent
(d) 95 percent

65. When an ac circuit supplies power to a purely resistive load, the circuit voltage and current are in-phase with each other. This condition is called "_____power factor."

(a) capacitive
(b) inductive
(c) unity
(d) any of these

66. What is the apparent power of a 120V load rated 18A?

(a) 1,632 VA
(b) 1,800 VA
(c) 1,920 VA
(d) 2,160 VA

67. What is the true power of a 120V load rated 18A with a power factor of 95 percent?

   (a) 1,632W
   (b) 1,800W
   (c) 2,052W
   (d) 2,400W

68. How many 120V, 20A circuits are required for forty-two, 300W luminaires (assume this is a noncontinuous inductive load) that have a power factor of 85 percent?

   (a) 5 circuits
   (b) 6 circuits
   (c) 7 circuits
   (d) 8 circuits

CHAPTER 8—MOTORS, GENERATORS, RELAYS, AND TRANSFORMERS

Unit 21—Motors

69. A motor uses opposing electromagnetic fields in order to rotate the motor shaft. The stationary electromagnetic field is created by the _____, and the rotating electromagnetic field is created by the _____.

   (a) stator, rotor
   (b) rotor, stator
   (c) winding A, winding B
   (d) none of these

70. What size motor in horsepower is required to produce approximately 30 kW of output watts?

   (a) 20 hp
   (b) 30 hp
   (c) 40 hp
   (d) 50 hp

71. What are the approximate output in watts of a 15 hp motor?

   (a) 11 kW
   (b) 15 kW
   (c) 22 kW
   (d) 31 kW

72. When a motor starts, the current drawn is between six and ten times the motor's nameplate _____ amperes.

   (a) starting
   (b) lock-rotor
   (c) running
   (d) load

73. Once a motor begins turning, the rotor windings are increasingly cut by the stationary magnetic field, resulting in an increasing counter-electromotive force in the _____.

   (a) stator
   (b) rotor
   (c) shaft
   (d) any of these

74. What is the nameplate FLA for a 5 hp, 230V, single-phase motor with 93 percent power factor and 87 percent efficiency?

   (a) 10A
   (b) 20A
   (c) 28A
   (d) 35A

75. Dual-voltage ac motors are made with two field windings. The field windings are connected in _____ for low-voltage operation and in _____ for high-voltage operation.

   (a) series, parallel
   (b) parallel, series
   (c) series, series
   (d) parallel, parallel

76. Swapping _____ of the line wires can reverse a three-phase ac motor's rotation.

   (a) one
   (b) two
   (c) three
   (d) four

Unit 22—Generators

77. Three-phase alternating-current generators have three sets of equally spaced windings, each winding is _____ out-of-phase with each other.

    (a) 90°
    (b) 120°
    (c) 180°
    (d) 240°

78. The approximate output current for a single-phase, 22 kVA, 240V generator is _____.

    (a) 50A
    (b) 70A
    (c) 90A
    (d) 100A

Unit 23—Relays

79. An electromagnetic _____ uses electromagnetism to open or close a contact.

    (a) motor
    (b) generator
    (c) transformer
    (d) relay

Unit 24—Transformers

80. The transformer winding that is connected to the source is called the "_____" winding and the transformer winding that is connected to the load is called the "_____" winding.

    (a) secondary, primary
    (b) primary, secondary
    (c) high-leg, low-leg
    (d) none of these

81. Both the primary and secondary windings are wound on the same iron core, so the electromagnetic field from the primary winding cuts the secondary winding, which induces a voltage on the _____.

    (a) primary
    (b) secondary
    (c) motor
    (d) generator

82. A transformer has a primary winding of twenty turns and a secondary of ten turns. The winding turns ratio of this transformer is _____.

    (a) 2:1
    (b) 4:1
    (c) 5:1
    (d) 10:1

83. If the primary phase voltage is 480V and the secondary phase voltage is 240V, the voltage turns ratio is _____.

    (a) 1:2
    (b) 1:4
    (c) 2:1
    (d) 4:1

84. What is the secondary current for a fully loaded three-phase, 75 kVA, 480V to 208Y/120V transformer?

    (a) 104A
    (b) 140A
    (c) 208A
    (d) 500A

85. What is the primary current for a fully loaded three-phase, 75 kVA, 480V to 208Y/120V transformer?

    (a) 10A
    (b) 70A
    (c) 80A
    (d) 90A

CHAPTER 9—PROTECTIVE DEVICES

Unit 25—Overcurrent Protection

86. A(An)_____ is the operation of equipment or wires in excess of their rated ampacity.

    (a) overload
    (b) short circuit
    (c) ground fault
    (d) all of these

87. A(An) _____is an electrical connection between any two phase wires, or a phase wire and neutral wire.

    (a) overload
    (b) short circuit
    (c) ground fault
    (d) all of these

88. A(An) _____occurs when an unintentional electrical connection occurs between a phase wire and metal parts of enclosures, raceways, and/or equipment.

    (a) overload
    (b) short circuit
    (c) ground fault
    (d) all of these

89. Fuses consist of a _____ element connected to end blades or caps, surrounded by silica sand filler material enclosed in a tube.

    (a) conductive
    (b) foam
    (c) light
    (d) nonconductive

90. _____circuit breakers operate on the principle that as the current increases, the time it takes for the device to open decreases.

    (a) Inverse time
    (b) Adjustable trip
    (c) Instantaneous trip
    (d) all of these

Unit 26—GFCIs, GFPEs, AFCIs, and SPDs

91. If the difference between the current leaving and returning through the current transformer of the GFCI protective device exceeds _____ (± 1 mA), the solid-state circuitry de-energizes the circuit.

    (a) 1 mA
    (b) 3 mA
    (c) 5 mA
    (d) 10 mA

92. A special-purpose GFCI device is used in circuits where the voltage-to-ground is greater than _____.

    (a) 30V
    (b) 50V
    (c) 120V
    (d) 150V

93. Ground-fault protection of equipment is not intended to protect _____ because its opening ground-fault trip setting is 30 mA—not 6 mA as with a GFCI.

    (a) property
    (b) persons
    (c) equipment
    (d) any of these

94. An arc-fault circuit interrupter is a device intended to de-energize a circuit when it detects the current waveform characteristics unique to a(an) _____fault.

    (a) ground
    (b) neutral
    (c) arcing
    (d) any of these

95. _____ protective devices protect equipment by preventing damaging transient voltage from reaching the equipment.

    (a) Short-circuit
    (b) Overload
    (c) Overcurrent
    (d) Surge

CHAPTER 10—GENERAL KNOWLEDGE

Unit 27—Wire Resistance and Voltage Drop

96. The cross-sectional area of a wire is commonly expressed in _____.

    (a) square inches
    (b) mils
    (c) circular mils
    (d) none of these

97. Wire dc resistance is determined by the _____.

    (a) material type
    (b) cross-sectional area
    (c) wire length and operating temperature
    (d) all of these

Unit 28—Multiwire Circuits

98. The _____ wire is connected to the neutral point of a system and is intended to carry current under normal conditions.

    (a) neutral
    (b) phase
    (c) copper
    (d) none of these

99. The current flowing in the neutral wire of a 3-wire, 120/240V, single-phase circuit equals the _____ current flowing in the phase wires.

    (a) minimum
    (b) difference in
    (c) opposition to
    (d) maximum

100. If the continuity of the _____ wire of a multiwire circuit is interrupted (opened), there could be a fire and/or destruction of electrical equipment resulting from overvoltage or undervoltage.

    (a) grounding
    (b) neutral
    (c) phase
    (d) all of these

INDEX

ABOUT THE AUTHOR

Mike Holt

Founder and President

Mike Holt Enterprises

Groveland, Florida

Mike Holt is an author, businessman, educator, speaker, publisher and *National Electrical Code* expert. He has written hundreds of electrical training books and articles, founded three successful businesses, and has taught thousands of electrical *Code* seminars across the U.S. and internationally. His dynamic presentation style, deep understanding of the trade, and ability to connect with students are some of the reasons that he is one of the most sought-after speakers in the industry.

His company, Mike Holt Enterprises, has been serving the electrical industry for almost 50 years, with a commitment to creating and publishing books, videos, online training, and curriculum support for electrical trainers, students, organizations, and electrical professionals. His devotion to the trade, coupled with the lessons he learned at the University of Miami's MBA program, have helped him build one of the largest electrical training and publishing companies in the United States.

Mike is committed to changing lives and helping people take their careers to the next level. He has always felt a responsibility to provide education beyond the scope of just passing an exam. He draws on his previous experience as an electrician, inspector, contractor and instructor, to guide him in developing powerful training solutions that electricians understand and enjoy. He is always mindful of how hard learning can be for students who are intimidated by school, by their feelings towards learning, or by the complexity of the *NEC*. He's mastered the art of simplifying and clarifying complicated technical concepts and his extensive use of illustrations helps students apply the content and relate the material to their work in the field. His ability to take the intimidation out of learning is reflected in the successful careers of his students.

Mike's commitment to pushing boundaries and setting high standards extends into his personal life as well. He's an eight-time Overall National Barefoot Waterski Champion. Mike has more than 20 gold medals, many national records, and has competed in three World Barefoot Tournaments. In 2015, at the tender age of 64, he started a new adventure—competitive mountain bike racing. Every day he continues to find ways to motivate himself, both mentally and physically.

Mike and his wife, Linda, reside in New Mexico and Florida, and are the parents of seven children and seven grandchildren. As his life has changed over the years, a few things have remained constant: his commitment to God, his love for his family, and doing what he can to change the lives of others through his products and seminars.

Special Acknowledgments

My Family. First, I want to thank God for my godly wife who's always by my side and for my children.

My Staff. A personal thank you goes to my team at Mike Holt Enterprises for all the work they do to help me with my mission of changing peoples' lives through education. They work tirelessly to ensure that, in addition to our products meeting and exceeding the educational needs of our customers, we stay committed to building life-long relationships throughout their electrical careers.

The National Fire Protection Association. A special thank you must be given to the staff at the National Fire Protection Association (NFPA), publishers of the *NEC*—in particular, Jeff Sargent for his assistance in answering my many *Code* questions over the years. Jeff, you're a "first class" guy, and I admire your dedication and commitment to helping others understand the *NEC*.

ABOUT THE ILLUSTRATOR

Mike Culbreath—Illustrator

Mike Culbreath
Graphic Illustrator
Alden, Michigan

Mike Culbreath has devoted his career to the electrical industry and worked his way up from apprentice electrician to master electrician. He started working in the electrical field doing residential and light commercial construction, and later did service work and custom electrical installations. While working as a journeyman electrician, he suffered a serious on-the-job knee injury. As part of his rehabilitation, Mike completed courses at Mike Holt Enterprises, and then passed the exam to receive his Master Electrician's license. In 1986, with a keen interest in continuing education for electricians, he joined the staff to update material and began illustrating Mike Holt's textbooks and magazine articles.

Mike started with simple hand-drawn diagrams and cut-and-paste graphics. Frustrated by the limitations of that style of illustrating, he took a company computer home to learn how to operate some basic computer graphics software. Realizing that computer graphics offered a lot of flexibility for creating illustrations, Mike took every computer graphics class and seminar he could to help develop his skills. He's worked as an illustrator and editor with the company for over 30 years and, as Mike Holt has proudly acknowledged, has helped to transform his words and visions into lifelike graphics.

Originally from South Florida, Mike now lives in northern lower Michigan where he enjoys hiking, kayaking, photography, gardening, and cooking; but his real passion is his horses. He also loves spending time with his children Dawn and Mac and his grandchildren Jonah, Kieley, and Scarlet.

ABOUT THE MIKE HOLT TEAM

There are many people who played a role in the production of this textbook. Their efforts are reflected in the quality and organization of the information contained in this textbook, and in its technical accuracy, completeness, and usability.

Technical Writing

Mario Valdes is Technical Content Editor and works directly with Mike to ensure the content is technically accurate, relatable, and valuable to all electrical professionals. He played an important role in gathering research, analyzing data, and assisting Mike in the writing of this book. He reworked content into different formats to improve the flow of information and assure the expectations were being met in terms of message, tone, and quality. He edited illustrations and proofread content to 'fact-check' each sentence, title, and image structure. Mario enjoys working in collaboration with Mike and Brian to enhance the company's brand image, training products, and technical publications.

Editorial and Production

Brian House is part of the content team that reviews our material to make sure it's ready for our customers. He also coordinates the team that constructs and reviews this textbook and its supporting resources to ensure its accuracy, clarity, and quality.

Toni Culbreath worked tirelessly to proofread and edit this publication. Her attention to detail and her dedication is irreplaceable. A very special thank you goes out to Toni (Mary Poppins) Culbreath for her many years of dedicated service.

Cathleen Kwas handled the design, layout, and typesetting of this book. Her desire to create the best possible product for our customers is greatly appreciated, and she constantly pushes the design envelope to make the product experience just a little bit better.

Vinny Perez and **Eddie Anacleto** have been a dynamic team. They have taken the best instructional graphics in the industry to the next level. Both Eddie and Vinny bring years of graphic art experience to the pages of this book and have been a huge help updating our graphics.

Dan Haruch is an integral part of the livestream process and spends much of his time making sure that the instructor resources for this product are the best in the business. His dedication to the instructor and student experience is much appreciated.

Video Team

The following special people provided technical advice in the development of this textbook as they served on the video team along with author **Mike Holt**.

Thomas Domitrovich

Electrical Engineer
Ellisville, Missouri

Thomas Domitrovich is an electrical engineer with Eaton Corporation's Bussmann series solutions in the Circuit Protection Division. He has experience in power systems engineering, sales and marketing, business development, and product management. Thomas is actively involved with the electrical industry through industry organizations including NFPA, NEMA, IEC, NECA, IBEW, the electrical training ALLIANCE, and more.

He's the principle representative for NEMA on NFPA Code-Making Panel 2 for the continued development of the *National Electrical Code (NFPA 70)*. Thomas also represents NEMA on the NFPA committee for the continued development of NFPA 73, Standard for Electrical Inspections for Existing Dwellings. In addition, he's a LEED® Accredited Professional, a licensed Professional Engineer, and holds a Bachelor of Electrical Engineering from Gannon University.

Thomas is passionate about saving lives through the continued growth of electrical safety and is an author with a wide range of trade magazine articles and technical white papers.

Daniel Brian House

Master Electrician, Instructor, Vice President of
   Digital and Technical Training
Mike Holt Enterprises
Ocala, Florida

Brian House is Vice President of Digital and Technical Training at Mike Holt Enterprises, and a Certified Mike Holt Instructor. He is a permanent member of the video teams, on which he has served since the 2011 *Code* cycle. Brian has worked in the trade since the 1990s in residential, commercial and industrial settings. He opened a contracting firm in 2003 that designed energy-efficient lighting retrofits, explored "green" biomass generators, and partnered with residential PV companies in addition to traditional electrical installation and service.

In 2007, Brian was personally selected by Mike for development and began teaching seminars for Mike Holt Enterprises after being named a "Top Gun Presenter" in Mike's Train the Trainer boot camp. Brian travels around the country teaching electricians, instructors, the military personnel, and engineers. His experience in the trenches as an electrical contractor, along with Mike Holt's instructor training, gives him a teaching style that is practical, straightforward, and refreshing.

Today, as Vice President of Digital and Technical Training at Mike Holt Enterprises, Brian leads the apprenticeship and digital product teams. They create cutting-edge training tools, and partner with in-house and apprenticeship training programs nationwide to help them reach the next level. He is also part of the content team that helps Mike bring his products to market, assisting in the editing of the textbooks, coordinating the content and illustrations, and assuring the technical accuracy and flow of the information.

Brian is high energy, with a passion for doing business the right way. He expresses his commitment to the industry and his love for its people in his teaching, working on books, and developing instructional programs and software tools.

Brian and his wife Carissa have shared the joy of their four children and many foster children during 25 years of marriage. When not mentoring youth at work or church, he can be found racing mountain bikes or SCUBA diving with his kids. He's passionate about helping others and regularly engages with the youth of his community to motivate them into exploring their future.

Eric Stromberg, P.E.

Electrical Engineer/Instructor
Los Alamos, New Mexico

Eric Stromberg has a bachelor's degree in Electrical Engineering and is a professional engineer. He started in the electrical industry when he was a teenager helping the neighborhood electrician. After high school, and a year of college, Eric worked for a couple of different audio companies, installing sound systems in a variety of locations from small buildings to baseball stadiums. After returning to college he worked as a journeyman wireman for an electrical contractor.

After graduating from the University of Houston, Eric took a job as an electronic technician and installed and serviced life safety systems in high-rise buildings. After seven years he went to work for Dow Chemical as a power distribution engineer. His work with audio systems had made him very sensitive to grounding issues and he took this experience with him into power distribution. Because of this expertise, Eric became one of Dow's grounding subject matter experts. This is also how Eric met Mike Holt, as Mike was looking for grounding experts for his 2002 Grounding vs. Bonding video.

Eric taught the *National Electrical Code* for professional engineering exam preparation for over 20 years, and has held continuing education teacher certificates for the states of Texas and New Mexico. He was on the electrical licensing and advisory board for the State of Texas, as well as on their electrician licensing exam board. Eric now consults for a Department of Energy research laboratory in New Mexico, where he's responsible for the electrical standards as well as assisting the laboratory's AHJ.

Eric's oldest daughter lives with her husband in Zurich, Switzerland, where she teaches for an international school. His son served in the Air Force, has a degree in Aviation logistics, and is a pilot and owner of an aerial photography business. His youngest daughter is a singer/songwriter in Los Angeles.

Mario Valdes, Jr.
Master Electrician, Electrical Inspector, Electrical
  Plans Examiner, Technical Content Editor
Mike Holt Enterprises
Ocala, Florida

Mario Valdes, Jr. is a member of the technical team at Mike Holt Enterprises, working directly with Mike Holt in researching, re-writing, and coordinating content, to assure the technical accuracy of the information in the products. He is a permanent member of the video teams, on which he has served since the 2017 *Code* cycle.

Mario is licensed as an electrical contractor, most recently having worked as an electrical inspector and plans examiner for an engineering firm in South Florida. Additionally, he was an electrical instructor for a technical college, teaching students pursuing an associate degree in electricity. He taught subjects such as ac/dc fundamentals, residential and commercial wiring, blueprint reading, and electrical estimating. He brings to the Mike Holt team a wealth of knowledge and devotion for the *NEC*.

He started his career at 16 years old in his father's electrical contracting company. Once he got his Florida State contractor's license, he ran the company as project manager and estimator. Mario's passion for the *NEC* prompted him to get his inspector and plans review certifications and embark on a new journey in electrical *Code* compliance. He's worked on complex projects such as hospitals, casinos, hotels and multi-family high rise buildings. Mario is very passionate on educating electrical professionals about electrical safety and the *National Electrical Code*.

Mario's a member of the IAEI, NFPA, and ICC, and enjoys participating in the meetings; he believes that by staying active in these organizations he'll be ahead of the game, with cutting-edge knowledge pertaining to safety codes.

When not immersed in the electrical world Mario enjoys fitness training. He resides in Pembroke Pines, Florida with his beautiful family, which includes his wife and his two sons. They enjoy family trip getaways to Disney World and other amusement parks.

Save 25% On These Best-Selling Libraries

Understanding the NEC® Complete Video Library

This library makes it easy to learn the Code and includes the following best-selling textbooks and videos:

Understanding the National Electrical Code® Volume 1 textbook
Understanding the National Electrical Code® Volume 2 textbook
Bonding and Grounding textbook
Understanding the National Electrical Code® Workbook

General Requirements videos
Wiring and Protection videos
Bonding and Grounding videos
Wiring Methods and Materials videos
Equipment for General Use videos
Special Occupancies videos
Special Equipment videos
Special Conditions and Communications Systems videos

Plus! A digital version of each book!

" *Excellent material that makes it easy to understand the Code.* - Josue G.

Product Code: [UNDLIBMM]

Electrical Estimating Video Program

Mike Holt's Electrical Estimating Training Program will give you the skills and the knowledge to get more jobs and to make sure that those jobs are profitable. This program gives you a comprehensive understanding of estimating and will also help you understand how electrical estimating software can improve your process.

Program includes:
Electrical Estimating textbook
Electrical Estimating videos

Plus! A digital version of the book!

" *This product is a must for electricians starting their own business. Avoiding the mistakes that cause most startups to fail is critical to success.* - Keith H.

Product Code: [EST2MM]

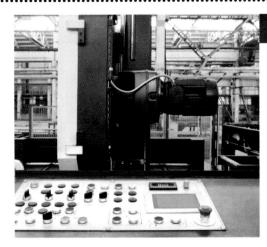

Motor Controls Video Program

Mike Holt's Motor Controls Training Program provides you with the tools necessary to understand common basic motor control circuits. This program is designed to provide a foundation for students who are just beginning to learn about motor controls. It can also be helpful for Journeyman and Master Exam Preparation.

Program includes:
Motor Controls textbook
Motor Controls videos

Plus! A digital version of the book!

" *Mike's graphics and illustrations are second only to working on actual equipment. The subjects are not glossed over but fully explained.* - William C.

Product Code: [MC2MM]

Call Now 888.NEC.CODE (632.2633)
& mention discount code: ET25

Mike Holt Enterprises